The Marshall Cavendish
ILLUSTRATED ENCYCLOPEDIA OF
PLANTS
AND
EARTH SCIENCES

VOLUME TEN

EDITOR-IN-CHIEF
Professor David M. Moore

SPECIALIST SUBJECT EDITORS
Professor V. H. Heywood
Botany
Professor A. Hallam
Earth Sciences
Dr S. R. Chant
Botany

ADVISORY EDITORS
Professor W. T. Stearn
Flowering Plants
Dr I. B. K. Richardson
Flowering Plants
Dr Peter Raven
Plant Ecology
Professor Lincoln Constance
Special Consultant

EDITORIAL DIRECTOR
Dr Graham Bateman

Marshall Cavendish
New York · London · Sydney

CONTENTS

Reference Edition Published 1988

Published by:
Marshall Cavendish Corporation
147 West Merrick Road
Freeport N.Y. 11520

AN EQUINOX BOOK

Planned and produced by:
Equinox (Oxford) Ltd
Littlegate House
St Ebbe's Street
Oxford OX1 1SQ
England

Copyright © Equinox (Oxford) Ltd 1988

Library of Congress Cataloging-in-Publication Data
The Encyclopedia of plants and earth sciences.
   Bibliography: p.
   Includes index.
   1. Botany—Dictionaries. 2. Botany, Economic—Dictionaries.
3. Crops—Dictionaries. 4. Angiosperms-Dictionaries. 5. Earth
sciences—Dictionaries. 6. Ecology—Dictionaries. I. Marshall
Cavendish Corporation.
QK7.E53 1988   580'.3'21   87-23927

ISBN 0-86307-901-6 (Set)
ISBN 0-86307-911-3 (Vol 10)

Alphabetical Index

Within each entry or sub-entry, volume numbers are given in **bold** (followed by a colon) before the first page number within each volume; volume numbers are not repeated when successive page numbers belong to the same volume.

A **bold** page number indicates a major entry. An *italic* number indicates an illustration, and an *italic* number in parentheses indicates that the illustration caption also contains relevant information.

aa 8:1058
Aaron's beard 2:184
Aaron's rod 2:233
abaca 5:646, 647
abaca fiber 1:6, 6, 2:145, 173, 236, 3:316
Abelia 1:6, 5:610
Abeliophyllum 5:576, 577
Abelmoschus 2:176, 248
Abies 1:6, 3:346, 6:749, 7:838, 867, 895, 902, 941;
  alba 7:904;
  balsamea 7:903;
  concolor 7:866;
  fraseri 7:904;
  grandis 6:683, 7:866;
  lasiocarpa 7:867, 904, 942;
  mariesii 6:685;
  sibirica 7:903;
  venusta 6:683
abiotic environment 6:710
abir 2:171, 5:648
ablation 8:986, 989
abrin 1:6
Abroma 1:6, 4:442
Abronia 4:419, 420
Abrontanella 7:905
Abrus 1:6, 2:203
absinthe 1:16, 31, 41, 58
absolute age 7:914
absolute dating 6:735
abstract community 6:709
abundance 6:715-6
Abutileae 4:445
Abutilon 1:7, 87, 2:216, 4:444, 445
abyssal hills 8:1060, 1061-2
abyssal plains 8:1059, 1060, 1062, 1064
Abyssinian banana 5:647
Acacia 1:7, 78, 112, 2:187, 3:357, 4:499, 502, 502, 6:721, 770, 791, 7:842, 856, 862;
  aneura 6:721;
  craspedocarpa 6:791;
  dealbata 7:837;
  oswaldii 6:719
acacia 1:8;
  bull-horn 1:7;
  false 3:295;
  sweet 1:7, 78
Acaena 1:7, 4:491, 494, 6:816, 7:905, 919;
  magellanica 7:911
acajou 1:8, 2:167
acajou gum 1:28
Acalypha 1:8, 4:535, 537, 537
Acalypheae 4:537
Acanthaceae 4:506, 5:593, 600, 600-1
Acanthocarpus 5:666
acanthodians (spiny sharks) 9:1163-4, 1232
Acantholimon 1:8, 4:428, 429
Acanthopanax 5:568, 568
Acanthosicyos 4:465, 467
Acanthospermum 5:617, 618
Acanthosyris 1:8, 4:521, 522
Acanthus 1:8, 5:600, 600, 601
accidentals 6:729
aceituno 3:315
Acer 1:8, 3:329, 330, 5:545, 546, 546, 6:747, 749, 817, 826, 7:838, 841;
  grandidentatum 7:912;
  monspessulanum 6:749;
  rubrum 6:706;
  saccharum 7:912
Aceraceae 5:545-6, 546, 548
Aceras 1:8, 5:675
Acetabularia 1:9
3-acetyl-6-
  methoxybenzaldehyde 6:822

Acharia 4:462, 463
Achariaceae 4:462, 462-3, 465
Achatocarpaceae 4:422
Achatocarpeoideae 4:421, 422
Achatocarpus 4:421
Achillea 1:9, 5:618;
  borealis 6:705;
  millefolium 6:769
Achimenes 1:9, 5:596, 598
Achlyeae 3:396
Achlyphila 5:628
Achlys 3:395
achocha 4:467
achondrites 8:987, 988
Achras 4:482, 483
Achyranthes 2:186, 4:420
Aciachne 5:635
Acicarpha 5:613, 613
Aciculilignosa formation-type 7:838
Acidanthera 1:9, 5:662
acidity:
  of soils 6:805-6;
  of water 7:944
Acioa 4:498
Aciphylla 1:9, 5:569
Acmena 4:512
Acokanthera 1:9, 5:575
aconite 1:9, 2:227, 3:399;
  Indian 1:9;
  winter 2:132
aconitine 1:26, 2:227
Aconitum 1:9, 3:396, 396, 399
Acorus 1:9, 5:659
acquired characters 6:760, 764
Acridocarpus 5:563, 563, 564
acritarchs 9:1162, 1215, 1216
Acrostichum 1:10, 6:747
Actaea 1:10, 3:396, 399
Actinidia 1:10, 6:748
actinolite 8:1083, 1084, 1085, 1095, 1100
actinopterygians 9:1184, 1206-7, 1211, 1212, 1232, 1234-5
active epibionty 7:915-6
Adam's apple 3:331
Adam's flannel 2:233
Adam's needle 3:361
adamellite 9:1127
adamite 8:1095
Adanson, Michel 6:683
Adansonia 1:10, 4:443;
  digitata 6:719
adaptability 6:769
adaptation 6:766-75;
  to alpine zone 7:868-9;
  for climbing 6:771-2, 772;
  in crops 7:932;
  to deserts 7:848-50;
  to salty habitats 7:890, 891;
  to temperature differences 6:770-1
adaptive evolution 6:768, 769
adaptive radiation 6:773-4, 774, 7:908
adder's meat 3:324
adder's tongue 2:252;
  yellow 2:135
Adenia 4:452
Adenocarpus 1:10
Adenophora 5:604, 606
Adenostoma:
  fasciularis 7:843;
  fasciculatum 6:822-3
adiabatical warming 7:844
Adiantites 6:743
Adiantum 1:10;
  reniforme 6:778
Adinandra 4:432
Adonis 1:10, 3:399
adonis:
  autumn 1:10;
  spring 1:10, 11;
  summer 1:10
Adoxa 5:609
Adoxaceae 5:609
Adromischus liebenbergii 6:700
advanced cultivars 7:956, 957-8

Aechmea 1:10, 5:644, 644, 646
Aegialitis 4:429
Aegiceras 4:486, 486
Aegilops 1:11, 5:638;
  umbellulata 7:958
Aeginetia 5:598
aegirine 9:1126
Aegle 1:11, 5:554
Aegopodium 1:11, 5:571;
  podagraria 7:948
Aegyptopithecus 9:1250
Aeollanthus 5:589
Aeonium 1:11, 4:495, 6:774;
  simsii 7:954
aeration:
  of mangrove root system 7:891;
  of soil 6:803, 804-5
aerenchyma of rush 6:770
aerial mangrove roots 7:891
aerial-root epiphytes 6:721
Aërides 3:267, 5:675
Aeschynanthus 1:11, 5:596, 596, 6:817
Aeschynomene 1:11
Aesculus 1:12, 5:544, 545, 545, 7:838;
  hippocastanum 7:959
Aestilignosa formation-type 7:838
Aethionema 1:12, 4:472
Aextoxicaceae 7:896
Aextoxicon 1:12, 4:537
afara 3:334, 341, 4:515
afforestation 7:938;
  of peat bog 7:879-80
Aframomum 1:75, 3:265, 5:648, 648
African exploration 6:682, 683-4
African marigold 5:618
African oak 4:433, 537
African region 7:897
African violet 5:596, 598
African walnut 4:523, 524
afriemengras 2:135
Afrocrania 4:517
Afrormosia 1:12, 3:341
afrormosia 1:12, 3:341
Afrothismia 5:671
Afrostyrax 4:483
Aftonian interglacial 6:749
Afzelia 1:12, 2:187
agamospermy 6:777
Agapanthus 1:12, 5:664, 665
agapanthus, blue 1:13
Agapetes 4:477, 477
agar 1:18, 2:160
agaric, fly 2:158, 226
Agaricus 1:13
Agassiz, J. 9:1263
Agastache 2:184
Agathis 2:192, 7:837;
  australis 7:837
Agathosma 5:554
Agavaceae 5:664, 665, 666, 667
Agave 1:13, 2:173, 187, 3:316, 5:665, 666, 7:843, 849, 896;
  palmeri 6:786
agave-form succulents 6:721
Agdestidaceae 4:421
Agdestideae 4:421
Agdestis 4:421, 422
age:
  absolute or relative 7:914;
  and area 7:906;
  and isolation 7:916, 917-9
Agelaea 5:542, 542, 543
Ageratum 1:13, 5:617, 618
agglomerate 9:1122
aggregates in soil 6:803, 803-4, 804-5, 809
agriculture:
  ancient Egyptian 7:924;
  and bogs 7:879-80;
  and breeding 7:931-4, 956-9;
  and fens 7:882;

and forest destruction 6:751, 7:838, 938;
  future 7:935;
  and grasslands 7:862, 938-41;
  and pollution 7:946;
  prehistoric 6:751, 7:925-9, 928;
  tropical 7:842, 880, 935, 935, 952;
  and weeds 7:948-50
Agriculture, US Department of 6:686
Agrimonia 1:13, 4:494, 494
agrimony 1:13, 14;
  hemp 6:723
Agropyron 1:13, 5:638, 7:860;
  junceiforme 6:825, 825, 7:886, 887;
  repens 7:948
Agrostemma 1:14, 4:417, 419
Agrostideae 5:638
Agrostis 1:14, 5:638, 7:862, 863;
  curtisii 6:800;
  stolonifera 6:705, 723, 769, 815-6;
  tenuis 6:776
aguacate 1:47, 2:151, 3:266
aguardiente 1:31
aigialosaurs 9:1239
Ailanthus 1:14, 5:549, 549
air at leaf surface 6:789
air plant 2:192
air movements 6:787, 788;
  in soil 6:803, 804-5
airborne solubles 7:943-4
Aizoaceae 4:415-7, 416, 419, 425, 495, 7:908
ajowan oil 1:77
Ajuga 1:14, 5:574, 589
Akania 5:544
Akaniaceae 5:544
akavit 1:16
Akebia 1:14, 3:399, 400, 400
akee 1:16, 2:151, 5:543, 544
akoloa 1:61
akye 5:544
al 2:232
alabaster 8:1091
alan 3:341
Alangiaceae 4:516-7, 517, 518
Alangium 4:516, 517, 517
albedo 7:835, 866
Albermarle, Duke of 6:682
Albertus Magnus 9:1257, 1263, 1264
albite 8:996, 1080, 1094, 1096, 1103, 9:1138
Albizia 1:14, 4:502
albizia 1:14
Alcea 2:178
Alchemilla 1:15, 4:491, 494
Alcimandra 3:378
alcohol 1:16
alder 1:15, 2:126, 4:409, 473;
  black 1:15, 2:177;
  common 1:15;
  European 1:15;
  gray 1:15;
  red 1:15;
  white 1:15;
  yellow 3:346;
  see also Alnus
alder bark 1:15
alder buckthorn 1:15, 2:148, 227
alder-carr 7:884
aldrin 7:946
Aldrovanda 4:489, 490
ale 1:16
alecost 2:174
alehoof 2:162
Aleuria 2:156
Aleurites 1:15, 3:346, 4:535, 537
Alexander the Great 6:680
alexanders 2:174, 3:316, 317
alfa 2:135;
  false 2:135
alfalfa 2:149, 211, 211, 221, 7:932;
  common 2:211;

yellow-flowered 2:211
Alfaroa 5:555
alfilaria 2:134
alga, frog-spawn 1:53
algae 1:18, 8:997, 1044, 1117,
9:*1131*, 1134, 1152, 1153,
1154, 1162, 1163, 1165,
1170, 1185, 1189, 1209,
1214-6, 1221;
blue-green 1:50, 9:1151, 1185,
1201, 1202, 1208, 1215;
brown 1:66, 9:1214;
golden-brown 9:1215, 1216;
green 2:164, 9:1213, 1215;
red 3:289, 9:1215
algae in evolution 6:*739*
algal blooms 7:945
algarroba 1:15, 76
algarrobo bean 3:281
algarrobo blanca 3:281
alginates 1:8, 2:196, 214
Alhagi 2:219
aliens 7:947, 950-2;
and colonization 6:819;
in New Zealand, on Tristan da
Cunha 7:921;
on South Georgia 7:936
Alisma 1:15, 5:*620*, 620
Alismataceae 5:619-20, *620*, 623,
627, 631, 654
Alismatales 3:399, 5:619-20, 622,
624, 644
Alismatidae 5:619-27
alizarin 2:214
alkaline soils 6:805-6, 809
alkaloids 1:26
alkanet 2:126, 5:585;
dyer's 1:15
Alkanna 1:15, 2:126, 5:586
all-good 1:86
all-heal 1:17, 3:282
Allamanda 1:15, 5:574, 575
Allanblackia 4:436, 437
alleles 6:(*761*), 774
allelopathy 6:821-3, *822*
Allerød interstadial 6:750
Alliaceae 5:664, 665
alliances 6:*728*
Alliaria 2:174, 4:470
alligator pear 1:47, 2:151, 3:350
Allium 1:17, 87, 2:155, 199, 249,
3:*314*, 5:*662*, 662, 664, 665;
vineale 7:949
Allomyces 1:17
allopatric species 6:776, 778
Allophyllum 5:583
Alloplectus 5:596
Allosaurus 9:1181
allspice 1:17, 2:146, 147, 4:511;
Carolina 1:17, 76;
Japanese 1:17
Alluaudia 4:*424*, 424;
humbertii 7:*897*
Alluaudiopsis 4:*424*, 424
alluvial fans 8:1047, 1048,
9:1133
alluvial soils 6:810
almandine 8:1090, 1091
almond 1:17, *17*, 2:245, *245*,
3:282, 4:494;
bitter 1:24, 2:245;
country 1:24;
ground 1:113;
Indian 1:24, 3:334;
Java 1:24, 2:245;
oil 1:24;
sweet 1:24, 2:245;
tropical 1:24, 3:334
Alnus 1:15, 4:409, *409*, 410, 473,
6:745, 748, 817, 826, 7:838,
873, 881, 882, 884, 885,
903;
glutinosa 6:*826*, 7:*883*;
incarna 7:*894*
Alocasia 1:24, 3:333, 5:659
Aloe 1:24, 5:*662*, 662, 664, 6:720
aloe 2:227;
American 1:13;

Barbados 1:24;
Cape 1:24;
Curaçao 1:24;
green 2:154;
partridge breast 1:24;
water 3:325, *325*
Alona 5:577
Alonsoa 1:24
Alopecurus 1:24, 5:638, 7:854,
901;
alpinus 7:861;
geniculatus 7:885;
pratensis 7:861
Aloysia 2:174, 208, 3:353
alpine meadows 7:*830*, 860, 868,
869
alpine poppy 4:403
alpine tundra 7:850, 851, 854,
868, 937
alpine zone 7:*830*, 866, 868-70,
869, 910
Alpinia 2:154, 5:*648*, 648
Alps 8:1001, 1035, 1036, 1037,
9:1151, 1180, 1263, 1272
Alseuosmia 5:610
Alseuosmiaceae 5:610
Alsinoideae 4:417, 419
Alsodeia 4:451
Alsomitra 4:465, 6:817
Alsophila 1:112, 3:342
Alstonia 5:574
Alstroemeria 1:25, 5:666
Alstroemeriaceae 5:666
Alternanthera 1:25, 4:420
Althaea 1:25, 2:216, 4:444, 445
Athenia 5:625, 625
Altingia 3:*288*, 4:407
altitude:
and ecotypes 6:*705*;
and exposure 6:800-1;
and light 7:869;
and precipitation 7:866;
and zonation 7:832
alum root 2:161, 173
alumina 8:1102, *1103*, 9:1123
aluminosilicates *see* clay minerals
aluminum 8:972, 973, 980, 995,
996, 1021, 1045, 1074,
1089, 1103, 1106, 9:1122,
1128, 1130, *1135*, 1141
aluminum plant 3:271
alundum 8:1088
alveolinids 9:1219
Alysseae 4:470
Alyssum 1:25, 4:470, 472
Amanita 1:25
amaranth, grain 1:83
Amaranthaceae 4:420, *421*, 427
Amarantheae 4:420
Amaranthoideae 4:420
Amaranthus 1:25, 2:163, 4:420,
421
amarillo 2:128
Amarolea 5:576, 577
Amaryllidaceae 5:662, 664-6,
665, 675
Amaryllis 1:27, 5:664, 666
amaryllis (*Hippeastrum*) 2:177,
5:666
amazonite 8:1094
ambarella 3:322
amber 3:290, 8:1083, 1102
amberbell 2:135
amblypods 9:1195
Amborella 3:384
Amborellaceae 3:384
amboyna 3:283, 341
Ambrosia 1:27, 5:617, 618
Amburana 1:27
amchur 2:218
Amelanchier 1:27, 4:494
Amentiferae 4:407
American ash 5:577
American hog plum 4:523
American mastic 5:548
Americas, explorations in 6:682-3
amethyst 8:*1083*, 1083-4, 1097
Amherst, Countess Sarah 6:(*749*)

Amherstia 1:27, 6:686;
nobilis 6:686
Ammi 1:27
Ammieae 5:571
Ammobroma 5:582
ammonites 9:1176, 1177, 1184-5,
1186, 1189, 1191, 1211,
1223, 1224, 1225, 1261
ammonoids 9:1163, 1164, 1177,
1178, 1189, 1224-5
Ammophila 1:27, 2:2201, 5:638,
6:825, 7:886, 888;
arenaria 6:724, 7:*886-7*
Amomum 1:75
Amomyrtus 2:237
Amomum 1:75
Amoreuxia 4:457, 457
Amorpha 2:185
Amorphophallus 1:27, 5:659
Ampelodesma 5:640
Ampelopsis 1:28, 4:539
amphibians 9:*1211*, 1232, 1234,
1235-6;
Carboniferous 9:1170, 1173,
1206;
Permian 9:1176;
Triassic 9:1178
amphiboles 8:972, 1083, 1084,
1086, 1088, 1089, 1091,
1092, 1097, 9:1126, 1136,
1137, *1138*, 1139, 1140
Amphibolis 5:627
amphibolites 8:1092, 9:1137,
1140
Amphiphyllum 5:629
Amphipterygium 5:544
amplitude, sociological 6:710
Amsonia 5:575
amygdales 8:1101
Amygdalus 1:17, 2:239, 262,
3:282, 4:494
Amyris 2:129, 5:554
Anabaena 1:28
anabasine 1:26
Anabasis 1:26, 4:423
Anacampseros 4:424, 425
Anacamptis 1:28, 5:675
Anacardiaceae 4:499, 5:547-8,
548, 552, 555
Anacardieae 5:548
Anacardium 1:8, 28, 5:547, 548,
548
Anacyclus 1:28, 5:618
Anadenanthera 2:232
Anaectochilus 5:675
Anagallis 1:28, 4:484
analcite 8:1101
Anamirta 3:401
Ananas 2:126, 3:272, 5:644, 644;
comosus 7:*926*
Anaphalis 1:29, 5:617
anaphase in meiosis 6:*763*
Anaptychia fusca 6:*829*
Anarthria 5:634
Anarthriaceae 5:634
Anastatica 3:290, 4:470
Anaxagora 3:380
Anchietea 4:450, 451
Anchusa 1:15, 29, 5:586, 586
Ancistrocladaceae 4:*460*, 460-1
Ancistrocladus 4:460, 460, 461
andalusite 8:1084, 1093, 1099,
9:1138
Andean region 7:*897*
Anders, Edward 6:758
Andes 8:1005, *1036*, 1041, 1073,
9:1126, 1127, 1151, 1172,
1190, 1198
Andesia 5:641
andesine 8:1096, 9:1126
andesites 8:1034, 1085, 1092,
1111, 9:1127, 1150, 1162,
1180
andiroba 2:250
andradite 8:1090, 1091
Andreaea 1:29
Andromeda 1:29, 4:477;
polifolia 7:876, 885
andromeda, marsh 1:29, 7:876,
885

Andropogon 1:29, 5:638, *638*,
7:860;
gerardii 7:863;
greenwayi 7:863;
scoparius 7:863
Andropogoneae 5:638
Androsace 1:29, 4:484;
helvetica 6:722
Androstachys 4:537
Andruris 5:627
Aneilema 5:631
Anemia 1:29
Anemone 1:29, 3:396, 399, *399*,
6:680;
nemorosa 7:908;
quinquefolia 7:908
anemone 1:29, *30*;
crown 1:30;
Japanese 1:30;
poppy 1:30;
scarlet 1:30;
wood 1:30
Anemoneae 3:399
Anemopsis 3:389, *389*
Anethum 1:121, 5:571
Aneulophus 5:560
Angara (Angaraland) 9:1166,
1173, 1175, 1176, 1179
Angaran province 6:*741*, 743
Angelica 1:30, 5:569, 571;
archangelica 7:921
angelica 1:39, 2:147, 174;
Japanese 1:39;
lovage 2:211;
purple 1:30;
wild 1:30, *30*, 2:174
angelica tree, Chinese 1:38
angel's fishing rod 1:120
angel's tears 2:238, 3:318
angel's trumpet 1:117, 2:226
Angiopteris 1:30
angiosperms (flowering plants)
1:32;
in evolution 6:*739*, 766,
9:1185, 1188-9, 1209, 1216,
1218-9, *1219*, 1229, 1242
Anglian glaciation 6:749
angostura 1:30, 112, 2:147
Angraecum 1:31, 5:675
anhydrite 8:1016, 1083, 1084,
1091, 1104, 9:1135
Anigozanthos 1:31, 5:668
animals:
and grasslands 6:689, 785, 821,
see also grazing;
and island disruptions 7:921;
and seed dispersal 6:816-7;
and weed control 7:950
Anisadenia 5:557
anise 1:31, 2:185, *146*, 147, 174,
5:569, 571;
Japanese star 2:185;
purple 2:185;
star 1:31, 2:185;
yellow star 2:185
anise tree 2:185
aniseed 2:136, 227
anisette 1:31
Anisomeria 4:421
Anisophyllea 4:508
ankerite 8:*1091*
annatto 1:31, 4:455, 456
Annelida 9:1209
Annesleya 4:432
Annona 1:31, 3:380, *380*, 381
annona blanca 1:31
Annonaceae 3:378, 379, *380*,
380-1, 382, 383, 385, 6:744
Annonales 3:378
Annoniflorae 3:381
Annonoideae 3:381
annuals:
breeding of 7:932, 933;
desert 7:850;
stem-herb, summer, winter
6:724;
and therophytes 6:727
Annularia 6:765, 765

Anoectochilus 1:31, 5:675
Anomalesia 5:662
Anomospermeae 3:401
Anomospermum 3:401
anorthite 8:996, 1096, 9:1151
anorthosite 8:979, 9:1150, 1151
Anredera 4:426, *426*
Antarctic dominion 7:898, *904-5*, **904-5**;
 tundra of 7:*851*, 852, *853*, 855
Antennaria 1:31, 5:617
Anthemideae 5:617-8
Anthemis 1:36, 5:618
Anthericum 1:36, 5:662
Anthistiria imberbis 7:863
Anthoboleae 4:521
Anthobolus 4:*521*, 521
Anthobryum 4:461, *462*
Anthoceros 1:36
Antholyza 5:662
Antholyzeae 5:662
Anthoxanthum 1:36, 5:638, 7:863;
 odoratum 7:862
anthozoans *see* corals
anthracite 8:1117
anthracosaurs 9:1235
anthracotheres 9:1248
Anthracotherium 9:1195
anthraquinone 2:227
anthrax 1:49
Anthriscus 1:36, 5:571
anthropoids 9:1249
Anthurium 1:36, 5:659, *659*
anthurium, white 3:320
Anthyllis 2:149, 3:354;
 vulneraria 6:779
Antian phase 6:748
antiarchs 9:1232
Antiaris 3:347
Anticlea 3:362
anticlines 8:*1113*
Antidesma 4:537
antidunes 8:1017
Antigonon 4:427, *428*
antigorite 8:1099
antimony 8:1099, **1109**
Antirrhinoideae 5:593
Antirrhinum 1:36, 5:593, *595*
Antoniaceae 5:572
Antonieae 5:572
anu 3:*299*, 345, *350*
Anurosperma 3:393
anyu 3:345, 350
aonori 1:19
Apache beads 3:389
Apama 3:391
apamate 3:331
apatite 8:*1078*, 1080, 1082, 1088, 1104, 9:1135, 1140
Apatzingania 4:465
ape, blue 3:359
Aphananthe 4:446
Aphelandra 1:36, 5:600, *601*
Apiaceae 5:569
Apidium 9:1250
Apieae 5:571
Apinagia 4:503
apio 1:41
Apioideae 5:569, 571
Apium 1:37, *80*, 5:571, 7:905
Apocynaceae 5:573, *574*, **574-5**, 576
Apocynoideae 5:575
Apocynum 1:37, 5:575
Apodantheae 4:528
Apodanthes 4:*527*, 528
Apodemus sylvaticus and land bridges 7:909
Apodytes 4:530, 531
apoendemics 7:915, 917
Apollonias 3:387
apomixis 6:**777-8**
Aponogeton 1:37, 5:620, *622*, 622-3
Aponogetonaceae 5:619, 620, *622*, **622-3**, 624
Apostasia 5:675, *675*
Apostasiaceae 5:675

Apostasioideae 5:675
Appalachian province 7:*898*
appearance, description by 6:*717-27*, *718*
apple 1:37, *38*, 58, 2:151, *152*, 4:491, 494;
 Adam's 3:331;
 balsam 2:232;
 beef 2:219;
 bitter 1:91, 110;
 cashew 2:151, *244*;
 chess 3:319;
 conch 2:*261*;
 crab 1:*108*;
 custard 2:151;
 downy thorn 2:226;
 golden 3:279, 322;
 Himalayan may 3:276;
 Indian 1:117;
 Jew's 1:46, 3:317;
 kangaroo 3:317;
 love 3:317;
 mad 1:46, 3:317;
 mammee 2:151, 217;
 may 3:276;
 melon 2:222;
 pond 1:31;
 sugar 1:31;
 thorn 2:226, 227;
 yellow rose 2:137
apple berry 4:489
apple of Peru 2:241
apple of Sodom 3:317
appleberry 1:59
applejack 1:16
apricot 1:38, 2:151, *152*, 3:282, 4:*494*;
 St Domingo 2:217
apsidospondyls *see* labyrinthodonts
aquamarine 8:1080, **1084**, 1086
aquatic cryptogams 6:*725*, **725**
aquatic weeds 6:*820*, 7:*948*, 948, *950*
aqueous habitats 6:769-70
aquifers 8:1070
Aquifoliaceae 4:529, 531, *532*, **532**
Aquilarioideae 4:510
Aquilegia 1:38, 3:396, *396*, 399;
 vulgaris 6:779
Arabian jasmine 5:577
Arabideae 4:470
Arabidopsis 4:470
Arabis 1:38, 4:470, *472*
Araceae 5:644, 654, 655, 656, **657-9**, *659*
Arachis 1:38, 4:499, 502
arachnids 9:1229
Arachnites 5:671
aragonite 8:1015, 1021, 1084, 1102, 1104, 9:1134, 1213, 1220, 1225
araguaney 3:331, 5:600
Arales 5:656-9
Aralia 1:38, 3:308, 5:*568*, 568
aralia:
 Chinese 1:38;
 false 1:122
Araliaceae 4:518, 5:**567-8**, *568*, 571, 609, 618
Araliales 4:494
Aramina 1:39
aramina 1:39, 2:144, 4:444, *445*
Araucaria 1:39, 2:242, 7:837, 919;
 bidwillii 7:837;
 cunninghamii 7:837
Araucariaceae 6:743
arbor-vitae 3:335;
 American 3:335, 341;
 false 3:336;
 giant 3:335, *335*, 341;
 hiba 3:336;
 Japanese 3:336;
 Oriental 3:336;
 Western 3:335
arboreta 6:680, 685, 7:963
arbutin 6:823
Arbutus 1:39, 4:477, 7:843;

unedo 7:894, 898, 909
Arcangelisia 3:401
Arceuthobieae 4:525
Arceuthobium 2:231
Archaean system 6:*738*, 756, **9:1150-1**, 1152
archaeocetes 9:1249
archaeocyathids 9:1152, 1154, 1155, **1221**
archaeology of crop plants 7:928-9
Archaeopteryx 9:1181, **1244**, 1272
Archaeosperma 6:*766*, 766
archangel, yellow 2:196
Archangelica 1:39, 2:147, 5:571, 7:*921*
archegosaurs 9:1235
archer plant 1:99
arches 8:1056
archosaurs 9:1206, 1236, 1239, 1243
Arctic provinces 7:*898*, 898
Arctic region 7:897, **898-900**, *901*, 910-1;
 tundra of 7:851-2, *852-4*, 854-5
Arctium 5:617
Arctostaphylos 1:39, 4:477, *477*, 6:722, 7:843;
 glandulosum 6:823;
 uva-ursi 6:800
Arctotideae 5:615, 617
Arctotis 1:40, 5:617, *618*
Ardisia 1:40, 4:486, *486*
Ardiseae 4:486
area:
 age and 7:906;
 basal 6:716;
 minimal 6:727
Areca 1:57, 5:654, 7:896
Arecaceae 5:651
Arecales 5:651-4
Arecidae 5:651-9
arecife 7:862
arecoid palms 5:653-4
arecoline 1:26, 2:227
Aregalia 5:646
arenaceous rocks 9:*1123*, 1130, **1131-2**, *see also* sandstones (quartz), arkoses, graywackes
Arenaria 1:40, 4:417, *419*
Arenga 1:40, 5:653, 654
arêtes 8:1037, 1048
arfvedsonite 9:1126
Argand, E. 9:**1263-4**
Argemone 1:40, 3:*279*, 4:402, 403
Argentinian region 7:897, 904
argentite 8:1108
argillaceous rocks 9:**1130-1**, *1138*, *see also* clays, marls, mudstones, shales
argon 8:982, 988, 997
Argyranthemum 1:89, 5:*617*, 618, 6:774, 7:915
Argyroxiphium 5:617
arid landscapes 8:**1045-8**, *1046*, *1047*
Ariocarpus 4:415, *415*
Arisaema 1:40, 5:659;
 griffithii 6:687;
 utile 6:687
Aristida 5:*636*, 638, 6:723, 7:862
Aristideae 5:638
Aristolochia 1:40, 3:391, *391*, 392, 5:574
Aristolochiaceae 3:391, **391-2**, 4:528
Aristolochiales 3:378, 391-3, 4:405
Aristolochieae 3:391
Aristotelia 4:439, *440*, 440
Aristotle 6:680, 9:1255, 1263, **1264**
Arjona 4:521
arkoses 9:1131, **1132**
armagnac 1:16
armalcolite 8:979
Armeniaca 4:494
Armeria 1:40, 4:428, 429, *429*, 5:662, 6:*815*;

maritima 6:*711*, 722, *750*, 750, 7:*889*, 889
Armillaria 1:40
Armoracia 2:147, *179*, 4:470
Armorican geosyncline 9:1165
Arnebia 1:40, 5:586
Arnica 1:41, 5:617
arnicine 1:41
Arnold Arboretum 6:685
aroids 5:657
Aromadendron 3:378
Aronia 4:494;
 asiatica 6:685
arracacha 1:41, 3:350
Arracacia 1:41
arrack 1:16, 41, 5:654
Arrhenatherum 2:149, 6:*690*, 7:*861*;
 elatius 7:862
Arrhenius, S. 9:**1264**
arrow leaf 3:302
arrowgrass 5:623
arrowhead:
 common European 3:302, *305*;
 giant 3:302
arrowroot 1:41, 2:219, 3:298, *299*, 328, 5:648, *649*, 650, 668;
 African 1:41;
 Bermuda 1:41;
 Bombay 1:41;
 Brazilian 1:77;
 Brazilian Para 1:41;
 East Indian 1:41, 111, 3:328, 331;
 Fijian 3:328, 331;
 Florida 3:361;
 Guinea 1:70;
 Indian 1:111;
 Polynesian 3:331, *331*;
 Portland 1:41, *42*;
 Queensland 1:41, *73*, 73, 3:328;
 Rio 1:41;
 St Vincent 1:41;
 tacca 1:41;
 Tahitian 3:328, 331;
 tous-les-mois 1:41;
 Tulema 1:41;
 West Indian 1:41
arroyos 8:1048
arsenic 8:1084, 1098, 1106, **1107-8**
arsenopyrite 8:*1084*, 1087, 1107
Artabotrys 3:361, 381
Artedia 5:569, *571*
Artemisia 1:41, 2:219, 3:319, 333, 5:618, 6:721, 751, 7:843;
 absinthium 7:940;
 californica 6:*822*, 822;
 tridentata 7:843
artesian flow 8:1044, 1070
Arthrocnemum 3:305, 4:423
arthrodires 9:*1163-4*, 1232
arthropyrites 9:1175
arthropods 9:1189, 1209, 1224, **1227-9**
artichoke 1:42, 3:350, 5:613, 615, 618;
 Chinese 1:42, 3:323, 350;
 French 1:42;
 globe 1:42, *42*, 85, 113, 3:350, *351*;
 Japanese 1:42, 3:323;
 Jerusalem 1:42, 3:298, 329, 350
artificial classification 6:695
artillery gunpowder 3:271
artillery plant 4:448
artiodactyls 9:1195, 1197, 1247, **1248**
Artocarpus 1:42, 4:447, *447*;
 communis 7:926
Arum 1:42, 5:659, *659*;
 maculatum 6:723
arum:
 bog 1:*70*, 70;
 dragon 1:*124*;
 water 1:70;

whitespot giant **1:**27
arum lily **1:42**, *42*, **3:**361, **5:**659
Aruncus **1:**42, **4:**491, 498
Arundinaria **1:**43, **5:**636, *636*, **7:**861
Arundineae **5:**636-8
Arundinella **5:**638
Arundinelleae **5:**638
Arundinoideae **5:**636-8, 640
Arundo **1:**43, **3:**289, **5:**638, 640
asafoetida **2:139**, *227*, **5:**571
Asarum **3:**391, *391, 392*
Ascarina **3:**386, *386*
asbestos **8:**1081, 1083, **1084-5**, 1087, 1099, 1100, *see also* crocidolite (blue asbestos)
Ascarinopsis **3:**386
Asclepiadaceae **5:**574, *575*, **575-6**
Asclepiadeae **5:**576
Asclepias **1:**43, **5:**575, *575, 576*
Ascobolus **1:**43
Ascophyllum **1:**43;
  nodosum **6:**828-9, *829*
Ascroe **3:**324
ash **1:**43, **2:**126, **5:**576, *577;*
  Alpine **1:**43, **2:**135;
  American **3:**341;
  American mountain **3:**319;
  black **1:**43;
  blue **1:**43;
  blue mountain **1:**43;
  Canary **1:**43;
  European **1:**43, **3:**341;
  European mountain **3:**319;
  flowering **1:**43, *43;*
  Japanese **1:**31, **3:**341;
  Manchurian **3:**341;
  manna **1:**43, *43*, **2:**219, **3:**328;
  mountain **1:**43, **2:**135, **233**, **3:**318, *319;*
  Northern prickly **3:**362;
  prickly **1:**39, 43, **3:**362;
  quaking **1:**43;
  red **1:**43, **3:**341;
  Southern prickly **3:**362;
  stinking **3:**283;
  white **1:**43, **3:**341;
  see also Fraxinus
Asimina **2:**241, **3:**380
Asparagus **1:**43, **3:**317, **5:**662, 664
asparagus **1:**43, *44*, **3:**350, *351;*
  common **1:**43;
  fern **1:**43, *44;*
  garden **1:**43;
  wild **3:**350
asparagus bean **1:44**
asparagus pea **1:44**
asparagus stone **8:**1084
aspect and exposure **6:**800
aspect societies **6:**729
aspectation **6:**710
aspen **1:**44, **3:**279, **4:**467;
  American **1:**44, **3:**279;
  Chinese **1:**44;
  European **1:**44, **3:**279;
  Japanese **1:**44;
  large-toothed **1:**44;
  quaking **1:**44, **3:**279;
  trembling **1:**44
Aspergillus **1:**44
Asperula **1:**44, **5:**607, *608*, 609
asphalt **8:**1112
asphodel **1:44;**
  bog **1:**45;
  giant **1:**45;
  Scottish **1:**45;
  white **1:**45;
  yellow **1:**45
Asphodeline **1:**45
Asphodelus **1:**44
Aspidistra **1:**45
Aspidium **1:**125
Aspidosperma **2:**258
Asplenium **1:**45
Asplundia **5:**654, *655*
assegai **1:**45
assegai wood **1:**45, **4:**518
associations **6:**708, *728*, 729;

vicariant **7:**908
Astelia **7:**905
Aster **1:**45, **2:**229, **5:**618, **7:**890;
  tripolium **7:**889
aster **1:**45, **5:**618;
  beach **2:**133;
  China **1:**45, *45, 71, 71*, **3:**325;
  garden **1:**45;
  New England **2:**229;
  New York **2:**229;
  Stoke's **3:**325;
  tree **2:**248
Asteraceae **5:**613
Asterales **5:**606, 613-8
Asteranthera **5:**596
Asteranthus **4:**450
Astereae **5:**618
Asteridae **5:**572-618
Asterionella **1:**45
asteroid belt **8:**972, 983, 988, *989*
Asteroideae **5:**617-8
asteroids (fauna) **9:**1189, 1223
Asterolasia **5:**552, 554
Asteropeiaceae **4:**432
Asteroxylon mackei **6:**734
Astilbe **1:**45, **4:**497, 498
Astilboideae **4:**497
Astragalus **1:**46, **2:**203, **3:**354, 4:527, **6:**817, **7:**843
Astrantia **1:**46, **5:**569, 571
Astrocarpeae **4:**472
Astronia **4:**514
Astronioideae **4:**514
Astrophytum **4:**415
Aswan Dam **8:**1052, *1068*
Asyneuma **5:**604
Atherosperma **3:**384, 385
Atherospermataceae **3:**384
Athyrium **1:**46
Atlantia **5:**554
Atlantic North American region **7:**897, 902
Atlantic period **6:**750-1
Atlantic province **7:**898
atmosphere **6:**785, **8:996-7**, 1009, 1034, 1038, **9:**1122, 1143, 1151, 1153;
  circulation of **6:**787, *788;*
  and light **6:**793, **7:**869;
  origin of life in **9:**1202
  oxygen in **6:**757, 758, 766, **7:**941;
  pollution of **7:**941-2, *942-3*, 944, 946
atolls **8:**1056, **1063-4**, *1064*, **9:**1166, 1266, 1267
atomic number **8:**997, 1101, **9:**1142
Atraphaxis **4:**428
Atrichum **1:**46
Atriplex **1:**46, **2:**254, **3:**305, **4:**423, *423;*
  littoralis **7:**887
Atropa **1:**46, **2:**241, **5:**579
atropine **1:**26, **2:**227
Atroximia **5:**566
Attalea **1:**49, **2:**145, **3:**271, **5:**654
attar of roses **1:**46, **2:**136
Atwood, Alice **6:**702
aubergine **1:**46, **3:**317, 350, *352*, **5:**579
Aubrieta **1:**47, **4:**470, 472
aubrietia **1:**47, *47*, **4:**469
Aucoumea **3:**341, **5:**547
Aucuba **1:**47, **2:**198, **4:**516, 517, *518, 518*
Aufnahme **6:**727
augengneisses **9:**1139
augite **8:**1079, **1085**, 1089, 1092, 1097
Aulacomnium **1:**47
Aurantioideae **5:**552, 554
aureole, metamorphic **9:**1139
auricula **1:**47, **3:**280, **4:**484
auricula tree **1:**72, *72*
Auricularia **2:**188
Aurinia **1:**25
Austral realm **7:896**, *897, 897,* 898, 904

Australia nut **2:214**
Australian bower plant **5:**600
Australian cherry **4:**522
Australian laurel **4:**489
Australian region **7:897,** 897;
  explorations in **6:687**
Australian sassafras **3:**384
Australopithecus **9:**1198, **1250-2**, 1266, 1271
Austrobaileya **3:**383
Austrobaileyaceae **3:383**
Austrocedrus **2:**203
Austromyrtus **2:**187
autecology **6:689**, *691*, **9:**1211
autochory **6:**818-9, *819*
autotoxicity **6:**823
Auxemma **5:**583, *584*
auxins **7:**943
Avena **1:**47, **2:**246, **3:**358, **5:636**, 638, 640, **7:**863, 950;
  fatua **6:**822;
  sativa **7:**943
Aveneae **5:**638
avens **4:**494;
  mountain **1:**125, *see also Dryas octopetala;*
  water **2:**161, *161;*
  wood **2:**161
Averrhoa **2:**151, **5:**560
Averrhoaceae **5:**560
Avetra **5:**670
Avicennia **2:**218, **4:**508, **7:**891;
  marina **7:**890
avocado **1:**47, *48*, **2:**151, *153*, **3:**266, 350, *352, 387, 387*, 388, **7:**931
avodiré **3:**341
avoidance of drought **7:**848
awl-leaf **3:**302
Axonopus **1:**48, **5:**638
Ayapana **5:**617
Ayers Rock **8:**1043
Azadirachta **5:**552
azalea **1:**48, *48*, **4:**475, 477, **6:**681;
  Pontic **3:**293;
  summer **2:**263
Azara **1:**48, **4:**451, 452
Azima **4:**530
Azolla **1:**48, **6:**725, 747;
  nilotica **6:**770
azonal soils **6:**807, **810**
azonal vegetation **7:**872-91
Azorella **1:**48, **5:**569, 571, **6:**722, **7:**905
Azotobacter **1:**48
azurite **8:1085**, 1089, 1094, 1106

babaco **4:**455
babassu oil **2:**250, 255
baby-blue-eyes **2:**239
baby's breath **2:**167, **4:**419
baby's-tears **3:**318
Baccharis **1:**49, **5:**618
Bacillus **1:**49
Backhousia **2:**187
Bacon, Francis **6:**740
Bacopa **1:**49
bacteria **1:50**, **8:**1021, 1114-5, **9:**1208;
  and evolution **6:**739;
  nitrogen-fixing **6:**806, 806-7;
  and plant-life **6:**785, 785;
  sulfur **8:**1096
bacteriophage **1:**51
Bactris **5:**653
Bactritoida **9:**1226
baddeleyite **8:**1108
badlands **9:**1187
bael **1:**11
bagasse **1:**49, **2:**231
Bahia **2:**133

bahia piassaba **1:**49, **2:**145
Bailey, Sir E. **9:**1264
Baileya **2:**219
Balanites **5:**554
Balanocarpus **1:**116
Balanopaceae **4:**412
Balanophora **4:**526
Balanophoraceae **4:525-7**, *526*
Balanops **4:**412
Balanopsidaceae **4:**412
balata **1:**49, **2:**219, 230, **3:**300, 4:482, 483
balau **3:**315
Balbisia **5:**559
bald cypress **7:**837
Baldellia **5:**620
balds, Appalachian **7:**873
balisier **2:**171
Ball, John **6:**682
ballistic dispersal **6:**818-9, *819*
balloon flower **2:**215, **5:**606
balloon fruits **6:**817
balloon vine **1:**75, **5:**544
Ballota **1:**49
Balls, Ernest **6:**682
balm **1:**49, **2:**174, 224;
  bastard **2:**224;
  bee **1:**57, *112*, **2:**232;
  field **2:**162;
  fragrant **2:**232;
  lemon **2:**147, 174, *175*, 224, *224;*
  Molucca **2:**232;
  sweet **2:**224
balm of Gilead **1:**6, *99*, **3:**279
balsa **1:**49, **2:**144, **3:**341, **4:**443, 444
balsam **1:**49, **2:**237, **5:**561;
  garden **2:**185;
  Himalayan **2:**185, *185;*
  Indian **2:**185;
  Peru **2:**227, 237;
  Tolu **2:**237
balsam apple **2:**232, **4:**467
balsam of Peru **2:**227, 237
balsam pear **2:**232
balsam-bog **1:**48
Balsaminaceae **5:**559, *561*, **561-2**
Balsamita **1:**89, *106*, **2:**174
Baltic raised bogs **7:**877, *878*, 879
Baltic Shield **9:**1160, 1191
Baluchitherium **9:**1247-8
bamboo **1:**49, **2:**144, **3:**395, *396*, **5:**635, 636, 640, **6:**685, **7:**836;
  black **3:**270;
  Calcutta **1:**118;
  dwarf **7:**861;
  fishpole **3:**270;
  forage **3:**270;
  giant **1:**118, **3:**270;
  golden **3:**270;
  hardy **3:**270;
  hedge **1:**52;
  Himalayan **1:**43;
  Japanese timber **3:**270;
  Mexican **3:**277;
  Meyer **3:**270;
  Moso **3:**270;
  sacred **2:**238;
  Simon **1:**43;
  spiny **1:**52;
  stake **3:**270;
  sweetshoot **3:**270;
  timber **3:**270;
  Tonkin **1:**43;
  yellow-groove **3:**270
bamboo grass **7:**861
bamboo shoots **3:**350
Bambusa **1:**52, **5:**636
Bambuseae **5:**636
bambusoid grasses **7:**862
Bambusoideae **5:**636, 640
banana **1:**52, *52*, **2:**151, *153*, 236, **5:**646, 647, 649, **6:**720, *722*, **7:**863, 926, 931, 933, 959;
  Abyssinian **2:**131, *131*, 145;

Fehi 2:151, 236;
flowering 1:52;
Japanese 1:52;
wild 3:326
Bancroft, H. 6:733
Bandulska, H. 6:733
baneberry 1:10, 3:399
Banister, Revd John 6:682
Banisteria 5:563, 564
Banisteriopsis 2:226, 5:563-4
Banks, Sir Joseph 6:687, 687
Banksia 1:52, 4:518, 520, 7:874;
serrata 6:687
banksia:
bull 1:52;
coast 1:52;
swamp 1:52
banyan 1:32, 52, 2:142, 4:447;
Indian 2:142
baobab 1:10, 4:443, 444, 6:719
Baptisia 1:52, 2:185, 4:502
Barbacenia 5:667
Barbaceniopsis 5:667
Barbarea 1:108, 3:295, 4:470;
vulgaris 7:949
Barberetta 5:668
barberry 1:26, 52, 53, 3:395, 396,
6:825
Barbeuia 4:421
Barbeuiaceae 4:421
Barbeuieae 4:421
barchans 8:1046
Barclaya 3:394, 395
Barclayaceae 3:394, 395
barite (barytes) 8:1047, 1079,
1085, 1085-6, 1087, 1101,
1104, 1109
barium 8:996, 1086, 1109-10
Barleria 1:53, 5:601
barley 1:53, 53, 58, 83, 3:328,
348, 358, 5:635, 638, 640,
7:880, 932, 934, 957;
pearl 2:262;
six-rowed 1:83, 83;
two-rowed 1:83
barnacles 6:828
Barnadesia 5:617
Barneoudia 3:399
Barosma 5:554
barrel cactus 2:127, 6:722, 7:849,
895
Barrell, J. 9:1263
barren wort 2:131, 132
Barringtonia 4:449, 449, 6:826
Barringtoniaceae 4:450
Barrois, C. 9:1264
Barteria 4:453
Bartram, John 6:683
Bartramia 3:268
barytes *see* barite
basal area 6:716
basal forest 7:866
basalt 8:973, 979, 982, 996,
1001, 1008, 1034, 1042,
1057, 1060, 1064, 1083,
1085, 9:1123, 1124, 1125,
1126, 1127-8, 1128, 1129,
1132, 1150, 1181;
debates over nature of 9:1259,
1265, 1268;
tholeiitic 8:1092
Basella 4:425, 426, 426
Basellaceae 4:425-6, 426
Baselleae 4:425
basil 1:53, 2:147, 5:589;
holy 2:247;
sweet 1:53, 2:174, 175
basket plants 1:11
basketflower 1:81, 2:183
basswood 3:336, 341, 4:440, 441
bastard balm 2:224
bastard breadnut 4:447
bastard bullet tree 5:556
bastard cypress 1:84
bastard jasmine 1:84
bastard teak 1:68
bastnaesite 8:1104
bat flower 3:331

batchelor's button 1:81, 3:287;
white 3:287
batholiths 8:1031, 1032, 9:1125,
1126
Batidaceae 4:426-7, 427
Batis 4:426-7, 427
Batrachium 3:396, 6:725
Batrachospermum 1:53, 7:944
bats 9:1246;
and pollination 6:786
batu, Senegal 3:315
Bauhin, Caspar 6:699
Bauhinia 1:53, 4:502, 502
bauriamorphs 9:1243-4
bauxites 8:1010, 1045, 1074,
1087, 1089, 1103, 1106,
9:1135
Baventian phase 6:748-9
Baxteria 5:666
bay:
bull 2:215;
red 3:266;
rose 2:240;
sweet 2:174, 198, 215, 3:266
bay fat 2:198
bay laurel 3:387, 388, 7:941
bay rum 1:53, 4:511
bayberry 2:237
bayonet plant 1:9
baywood 1:9
Bdallophyton 4:528
bdellium 1:99
beachgrass 1:27
bead tree 2:224
bean 1:53, 4:499, 502, 5:599,
7:948;
adzuki 2:201;
African locust 2:201;
algarrobo 3:281;
asparagus 1:44, 107;
baked 2:169, 3:267;
Bengal 2:149, 233;
bonavist 2:195;
broad 2:149, 200, 201, 3:354,
354, 4:502, 7:932;
butter 2:200, 201, 207, 3:267;
butterfly 1:92;
carob 2:201;
Carolina 2:201, 3:267;
castor 3:295;
Cherokee 2:134;
civet 2:201;
cluster 2:201;
common 3:267;
dry shell 2:169;
dwarf 2:169;
dwarf sieva 2:207;
field 3:354;
French 2:169, 200, 201, 3:267,
267;
Goa 1:44, 2:201;
green 2:169, 201;
green shell 2:169;
haricot 2:169, 200, 201, 3:267;
horse 3:354;
hyacinth 1:123, 2:195, 201;
Indian 1:79;
jack 1:73, 2:201, 201;
jumping 2:189;
kidney 1:123, 2:169, 200, 201,
3:267;
Lima 2:200, 201, 207, 3:267;
locust 2:201;
Madagascar 2:201, 3:267;
manioc 3:360;
mescal 3:318;
moth 2:201;
mung 1:123, 2:201, 236, 236;
navy 3:267;
pinto 7:943;
potato 3:350, 360;
rice 2:201;
runner 2:169, 201, 3:267;
salad 2:201;
scarlet runner 2:200, 201,
3:267, 267;
sieva 2:201, 207, 3:267;
snap 2:169, 3:267;

soya *see* soybean;
string 2:201, 169;
sweet 2:162;
sword 1:73, 2:201;
tepary 2:201, 3:267;
tick 3:354;
tongue 3:342;
tonka 3:342;
velvet 2:149, 233;
wax 2:169, 201;
yam 2:201, 3:299, 350, 360;
yardlong 1:107, 2:201
bean sprouts 2:236, 236
bean-tree 2:195
bearberry 1:39, 39, 77, 4:477,
6:800
beard lichen 3:348
beard tongue 5:595
bear's breeches 1:8, 5:601
bear's ear 1:47
bear's tail, Cretan 1:81
bearwind 1:72
bearwood 1:77
Beatsonia 4:461, 462
beauty berry 1:71
beauty leaf, Ceylon 1:72
beauty-of-the-night 2:231
beaver's tail 3:312
bedding conehead 3:326
bedstraw 5:607, 608, 6:723;
dye 2:154;
ladies' 2:126;
marsh 7:876, 880, 885;
yellow-flowered 2:154
bee balm 1:57
beech 1:54, 4:410, 412, *see also*
Fagus;
American 1:54, 3:341;
Australian 2:242;
black 2:242;
blue 1:54, 2:179;
brown 1:54, 110;
copper 1:54;
European 1:54, 3:341, 6:791;
hard 2:242;
Japanese 3:341;
myrtle 2:242;
Oriental 1:54, 3:341;
roble 2:242, 242;
silver 2:242;
southern 2:242, 6:801, 7:904,
see also Nothofagus
beefwood 4:413;
red 1:78
beer 1:16, 58
beerseem 1:93
bees and pollination 6:767, 773,
777, 780
Beestonian phase 6:749
beet 3:298, 4:423;
field 2:218;
garden 1:54;
seakale 1:54, 85, 3:350;
spinach 1:54, 3:321, 350;
sugar 3:298, 299, 327, 327;
wild sea 1:57, 57
beetroot 1:54, 54, 3:298, 298,
299, 4:422, 423
beggar's tea 3:302
beggarweed 1:119, 2:149
Begonia 1:54, 4:463, 463, 464,
6:722;
evansiana 6:684
begonia 1:54, 54;
watermelon 3:264;
wild 3:301;
winter 1:57
Begoniaceae 4:463, 463-4, 465,
5:606
Begoniella 4:463, 464
behavioral isolation 6:780-1
Beilschmiedia 1:43, 3:388
bel fruit 1:11
belemnoids 9:1189, 1226
bell, scarlet 3:321
belladonna 1:26, 46, 2:226, 227,
5:579
Bellevalia 2:183

bellflower 1:54, 57, 5:604, 606;
Chilean 2:197;
Chinese 3:275
Belliolum 1:125, 3:378
Bellis 1:54, 116, 5:615, 617, 618;
perennis 7:949
bells, yellow 3:334
bells of Ireland 2:232
Bellus 6:680
Belon, Pierre 6:680
Beloperone 2:191, 5:600, 601
Bembridge flora 6:747
ben oil 2:232, 250, 4:473
beneficial weeds 7:949
Benincasa 2:163, 222, 3:350,
4:465, 467
Benincaseae 4:465
Bennettitales 6:733, 739, 740,
9:1217
bent 1:14
benteak 2:196
bent-grass 1:14, 14, 2:149, 6:705,
776, 7:862
Bentham, George 6:701, 702
Benthamidia 4:517
Benthamiella nordenskjoldi 6:801
benthic cryptogams 6:725
bentonite 8:1094, 9:1190
benzoin 2:227, 3:327, 4:483
Berberidaceae 3:395, 395-6, 399,
400
Berberideae 3:396
berberidine 1:26
Berberidoideae 3:396
Berberidopsis 4:452
Berberis 1:52, 3:395, 395, 396;
bealei 6:684;
vulgaris 6:825
Berchemia 4:537
bergamot 1:57, 3:314;
lemon 2:174;
red 2:174;
sweet 1:57, 2:232
bergamot oil 1:57, 2:136, 3:314,
5:554
bergamot orange 5:554
Bergenia 1:57, 4:497, 497
Bergia 4:437, 437, 438
bergschrunds 8:1048
Beringia land bridge 7:909
Berkheya 1:57
Berlinianche 4:528
Bermuda buttercup 5:559, 560
Bermuda grass 5:638
Berneuxia 4:481
berry:
baked-apple 3:300;
buffalo 3:314;
cockroach 3:317;
coral 3:330;
Himalaya 3:300;
honey 2:224;
male 2:213;
nanny 3:354;
rabbit 3:314;
raccoon 3:276;
sapphire 3:330;
sheep 3:354;
yellow 3:300
berry tree, China 2:224
Bersama 5:541, 541, 542
Berteroa 4:470, 470
Bertholletia 1:63, 2:245, 4:449,
450
beryl 8:1080, 1084, 1086, 1089,
1102
beryllium 8:995, 1102
Berzelia 4:491
Besleria 5:596
Beslerieae 5:596
Beta 1:54, 57, 85, 2:218, 3:321,
3:327, 4:423
betaxanthin 1:26
betel 1:112
betel nut 1:57, 2:245, 245, 3:388,
5:654
betel palm 1:57

betel pepper 1:57, 75
Betonica 2:174
betony 2:174;
  wood 3:323
Betula 1:59, 4:409, *409*, 410,
  6:*717*, 717, 749, 817, 825,
  826, 827, 7:841, 855, 873,
  876, 901, 902, 903;
  nana 6:749, 750, 789, 7:841,
    855;
  pubescens 6:*703*, 7:884, *894*;
  pumila 7:*903*;
  tortuosa 6:721
Betulaceae 4:408, *409*, **409-10**,
  6:746
Betuleae 4:409
Betuloideae 4:409
beverage plants 1:58
bezetta rubra 1:88
bibisi tree 2:247
Bicornes 4:477
Bidens 1:57, 2:219, 5:617, 618,
  7:921;
  populifolia 7:921
Biebersteinia 5:559
Biebersteiniodeae 5:559
biennial herbs 6:*724*, 724
biennials, winter 6:724
big tree 3:289, 313
bigarade 3:314
Bignonia 1:57, 5:599, 600
bignonia, yellow 3:334
Bignoniaceae 5:593, 598, *599*,
  599-600, 601, 603
bilberry 1:59, *59*, 2:151, *152*,
  4:475, 477, 7:903;
  European 3:*349*
bilimbi 2:151
Billardiera 1:59, 4:488, *488*, 489
Billardiereae 4:488
Billbergia 1:59, 5:644, *644*, 646
Billia 5:544, *545*, 545
bilsted 3:325
bilva 1:11
bindweed 1:59, 5:579, 580, 6:825;
  field 1:59, 99;
  greater 1:*72*;
  hedge 1:59, 72;
  Japanese 1:72;
  lesser 1:99, *99*, 6:*772*;
  pink 1:99;
  riviera 1:99;
  sea 6:825
binomial system of nomenclature
  6:698, 699-700
biocides 7:946-7
biogenic theory 6:757-8
biological control of weeds 7:950
biomass 6:709
biomes 6:692, 712
Biophytum 5:559, *559*, 560
biotherms 9:1191
biotic factors and the environment
  6:785, 814-29
biotite 8:1009, 1068, *1082*, **1086**,
  1094, 1095, 1101, 9:1124,
  1125, 1126, 1138, *1139*
bipolar distributions 7:910, *910*,
  911
birch 1:59, 2:126, 145, 3:341,
  4:409, 410;
  dwarf 6:749, 750, 789, 7:841,
    855;
  shrub 7:*903*;
  silver 1:59, *59*, 2:247, 3:341;
  see also Betula
bird cherry 4:494
bird of paradise 7:*960*
bird of paradise flower 3:325, *326*,
  4:502, 5:647
bird of paradise tree 3:326
bird-catcher tree 3:273
bird-on-the-wing 3:277
birds 9:1181, 1187, 1189, 1191,
  1209, 1210, 1236, 1239,
  1244, **1244-5**;
  and dispersal 6:816, 7:905
bird's head 1:40, 3:392

bird's-foot trefoil 2:211, *211*,
  6:*825*, 7:*908*
bird's-nest, yellow 1:32, 2:232,
  232
bird's-nest fungi 1:60, 3:284, *284*,
  6:818
bird's-nest orchid 5:*675*
bird's-tongue flower 3:326
birefringence *see* double refraction
birthroot 3:344
birthwort 3:392;
  European 1:40
Bischofia 1:60, 4:537
Biscutella 4:470, *470*
bishop's caps 2:231
bishop's head 2:131
bishop's weed 1:27
bishop's wort 3:323
bishop's-weed 1:11
bismuth 8:1111
bismuthinite 8:1111
bistort 3:277, *277*;
  amphibious 6:826, 7:947
bitter aloes 5:664
bitter cress 1:75
bitter leaf 3:353
bitter melon 4:467
bitter root 2:203
Bitter Springs chert 6:*757*, 757
bitter wood 3:286
bitternut 1:77
bittersweet 2:241, 3:317, 7:884;
  climbing 1:80
bitterweed 2:171
bitterwood 3:315
bivalves 8:1015, 9:1154, 1156,
  1165, 1178, 1185, 1188,
  1189, 1221, 1224, **1227**
Bixa 1:31, 60, 2:126, 4:455, *456*,
  456
Bixaceae 4:455-6, *456*, *457*, *459*
bixin 1:31
black currant 4:498
black drink 2:177
black earths 6:808, *809*
black gum 4:516
black henbane 5:579
black Jack 5:618
black pot herb 3:317
black wattle 4:502
blackberry 1:60, *60*, 2:126, 151,
  3:300, 4:494, 6:*772*, *778*,
  826;
  American 2:210;
  cut-leaf 3:300;
  European 3:300;
  evergreen 2:151, 3:300;
  Pacific 3:300;
  see also bramble
blackbutt 2:135
black-eyed Susan 3:300, 336, *336*,
  5:*600*, 601
blackfellows bread 2:156
blackfingers 2:254
blackgram 2:201
black-gum 6:*747*, 747
Blackstonia 5:574
blackthorn 1:60, *60*, 2:126, 3:316
blackwood 4:502;
  African 1:116;
  Australian 1:7
bladder fucus 2:150
bladder nut 5:540
bladder senna 1:98
bladderwort 5:603, 644, **3:348**
bladderwrack 2:150, 6:828
blaeberry 1:59, *see also* bilberry
Blake, Sidney 6:702
Blancoa 5:668
blanket bog 7:*877*, 877, *879*
blanket flower 2:154, *154*
  blanket leaf 2:233
blanket weed 1:91, 7:944
blaspheme 3:317
blastoids 9:1223
blastomylonites 9:1139
blazing star 2:203, 225, 4:464
Blechnum 1:60

Blechum 5:601
bleeding heart 1:120, 4:404
Blepharis 5:601
Bletia 1:60, 5:675
Blighia 1:14, 2:151, 5:543, 544
blimbing 2:151
blister cress 2:134
blonde Lilian 2:135
blood flower 1:43
bloodberry 1:60, 3:295, 4:421,
  422
bloodleaf 2:186
bloodroot 2:126, 3:306
bloodstone 8:1087
bloodwood 3:283, 4:512
bloodwort 3:306
blowball 3:332
blowholes 8:*1014*, 1056
blue blossom 1:79
blue devil 2:128
blue John 8:*1090*
blue schists 8:1036, 1091, 9:1137
blue throatwort 5:606
blue weed 2:128
bluebell 1:35, 54, 6:*697*, 7:838;
  California 3:267;
  English 2:*182*, 183, 3:311;
  Scottish 1:57;
  Spanish 2:183, *183*
blueberry 1:60, 2:151, 4:474, 477;
  European 1:59;
  highbush 1:60, 2:151, *152*;
  lowbush 1:60, 2:151;
  rabbit-eye 1:60;
  velvet-leaf 1:60;
  see also bilberry
bluebottle 1:81
blue-buttons 2:194, 3:355
blue-eyed Mary 1:98, 2:249
bluegrass:
  annual 3:276;
  Canada 2:149, 3:276;
  Kentucky 2:149, 3:275, 6:823;
  rough 3:275;
  Texas 2:149, 3:276
blue-green algae 1:50;
  in evolution 6:*739*
bluelips 1:98
bluestem 2:149
bluestem grass 7:863
bluet 2:182;
  creeping 2:182;
  mountain 1:81
bluewings 3:342
Blumea 1:60, 5:617
Blumenbachia 4:464
blusher 1:*27*
Bocconia 1:60, 4:402
body waves *see* seismic waves
Boehmeria 1:60, 2:241, 4:448,
  449;
  nivea 7:936
Boehmerieae 4:448
boehmite 8:1103
Boerhavia 4:420
bog moss *see* Sphagnum
bog rosemary 1:29, *29*
bog rush 2:189
bogbean 2:225, *225*, 5:581,
  7:876, 880
bogs 7:875-80, *876-80*;
  boreal 7:*902-3*, 903;
  hummock and hollow on 6:716;
  and peat 6:810;
  valley 7:876, 880, 883
bois de rose 1:99
Boisduvalia 4:512
Bolax gummifera 6:722
bolbonal 2:212
boldo 3:385
Boletus 1:61
Bomarea 1:61, 5:666
bomb, volcanic 8:*1034*
Bombacaceae 4:441, 442, *443*,
  443-4, 7:896
Bombax 1:61, 4:443, 444;
  buonopozense 6:*771*
Bonner, J. 6:822

Bonnetiaceae 4:432, 436
Bonpland, Aimé 6:682, 7:966
Bonplandia 5:583
Bonplandieae 5:583
Bontia 5:593
bony fishes 9:1164, **1232-5**, *1233*
Boopis 5:613
bootlace fungus 1:40, *41*
Boquila 3:400
borage 1:61, *62*, 112, 5:586
Boraginaceae 5:579, 580, 582,
  583, **585-6**, *586*, 590, 591
Boragineae 5:586
Boraginoideae 5:586
Borago 1:61, 5:586
borassoid palms 5:653
Borassus 1:61, 5:651, 653, 654,
  7:896
borax 8:1102
Bordetella 1:51
Boreal element in Britain 7:894
Boreal forest 7:838-9, 866, 903,
  938
Boreal phase 6:750
Boreal provinces 7:898, *898*
Boreal region 7:898
Boreal zone 7:841, *902-3*, **902-4**
borecole 1:64
Borlaug, Norman 7:957
Bornemann, J. 6:732
bornhardts 8:1010, 1043
bornite 8:1086, 1106
boron 8:995, 1074, 1100, **1102**;
  in plant nutrition 6:807
Boronia 1:61, 5:552, 554
boronia 1:61
boronia oil 2:136
Boronieae 5:554
Borya 5:662
Bosqueia angolensis 6:*771*
bosses 8:1030-1, *1032*
Boswellia 1:61, 2:148, 5:546, *547*,
  547
botanic gardens 6:681, 7:963;
  Calcutta 6:686;
  Glasgow 6:683;
  Kirstenbosch 7:*960*;
  Melbourne 6:687;
  Missouri 7:*960*;
  Oratava (Tenerife) 7:963;
  Oxford University 7:951;
  St Petersburg 6:688;
  see also gardens
Botanical Code 6:699-701
Botany Bay tea tree 1:105
Botrychium 1:51, **62**
bottle gourd 4:467
bottle tree 1:10, 6:*719*
bottlebrush 1:71, *71*, 4:512
bottle-stem trees 6:*719*, 719
bottom-living cryptogams 6:725
botulism 1:51
boudinage 8:1029
Bougainvillea 1:62, 4:419, *419*,
  420
Bougueria 5:591
boulder clay *see* till
bouncing bet 3:307
bouquet garni 1:62
boura 1:16
bournonite 8:1109
Boussingaultia 4:426
Bouteloua 1:62, 5:638, 7:860, 863,
  940;
  gracilis 7:860
Bouvardia 1:62, 5:609
bow wood 2:256
Bowen, N. 9:1264-5
Bowenia 1:112
bower actinidia 1:10
bower plant 2:259
Bowlesia 5:56*9*
bowman's root 2:161
bowstring hemp 5:666
box 1:62, 4:533, 534, 535, 6:749;
  bastard 3:*277*;
  Cape 1:62;
  common 1:62;

flooded 2:137;
   fragrant 3:307;
   jasmine 3:268;
   rattle 3:290;
   sweet 3:307;
   Victorian 3:274
box-elder 1:8
box-within-box classification
   6:696, 699
boxwood 1:62
Boykinia 1:62
boysenberry 2:151, 3:300
Brachiaria 5:638, *638*
brachiopods 9:1153, 1154, 1156,
   1159, 1160, 1161, 1162,
   1163, 1164, 1167, 1170,
   1176, 1177, 1185, 1189,
   1221-3, 1227
Brachiosaurus 9:1181, 1241
Brachychiton 4:442;
   rupestre 6:719
Brachycome 1:62, 5:618
Brachylaena 5:618
Brachypodium pinnatum 7:940
Brachysiphon 4:509, 509
Brachythecium 1:62
bracken 1:62, *63*, 2:126, 141,
   247, 3:283, 6:801
Bragantieae 3:391
Brahea 1:63
brake 3:283
bramble 1:60, *63*, 2:151, 6:*690*,
   721, see also blackberry
Branchiopoda 9:1228
branchiosaurs 9:1235
brandy 1:16, 58
brandy bottle 2:243
Brasenia 3:394-5
brass buttons 1:107
Brassavola 1:79
Brassia 1:63, 5:675
Brassica 1:64, 66, 67, 69, 79, **87**,
   98, 99, 2:192, 194, 2:236,
   3:288, 301, 308, 330, 346,
   4:470, 472, 6:767, 780, 781,
   7:932, 934
Brassiceae 4:470
Brassolaeliocattleya 2:196
Braun-Blanquet, Josias 6:689, 729,
   7:964
Braun-Blanquet scale 6:716
Braun-Blanquet school of plant
   sociology 6:727
braunite 8:1105
Braya 4:470
Brayulinea 4:420
Brayulineae 4:420
Brazil nut 1:63, 2:245, *245*, 250,
   4:449, 450
Brazil wood 1:69, 2:126
Brazilian plume 2:191
Brazzeia 4:439
bread tree 2:130, 3:328
breadfruit 1:42, 2:151, 258,
   3:350, *352*, 4:447, 5:656,
   7:*926*;
   Mexican 2:232
breadnut 1:42, 4:447
breadnut tree 1:66
breadroot 3:283
bread-tongues 3:**264**
break-axe tree 3:286
breastwort 2:173
breathing roots 7:*891*, 891
breccias 6:802, 8:979, 9:1132-3
Bredemeyera 5:566, *566*
breeding 6:769, 7:**931-4**, *932-4*;
   and genetic resources 7:956,
   957
Breynia 4:537
briar root 1:63
bridal wreath 2:148, 3:322
Bridelia 4:537
Bridelieae 4:537
bridewort 3:322
Brimeura 2:183, 3:312
brinjal 1:46, 3:317
bristle agrostis 6:800

British approach to plant sociology
   6:**729**
British Ecological Society 6:704
British Museum 6:682
Briza 1:63, 5:638
Brizula 5:633
broad bean 2:149, *200*, 201,
   3:354, *354*, 4:502, 7:932
broad-leaf trees, evergreen 6:720
broads 7:882, *944*
broccoli 1:64, 65, **66**, *66*, 69,
   4:472
Brodiaea 1:66, 5:664, 665
brodiaea, harvest 1:66
brome 1:66, 2:149;
   upright 7:862
Bromeae 5:638
Bromelia 1:66, 5:644, 646
Bromeliaceae 5:644, **644-6**, 7:896
Bromeliales 5:644-6
Bromelioideae 5:644
bromine 8:1109, 1121
Bromus 1:66, 5:638, *638*, 7:863
Brongniart, Adolphe 7:964
Brongniart, Alexandre 6:731,
   7:**964**, 9:1260
Brontosaurus 9:1181
brontotheres *see* titanotheres
bronze 8:1087
Bronze Age Man 6:751
bronzite 8:1086, 1089, 1092,
   1097
bronzite-chondrites 8:1086
brooklime 3:353
broom 1:66, 114, 2:126, 227,
   4:499, 502;
   butcher's 3:301;
   common 1:114, *114*;
   Dalmation 2:160;
   dyer's 2:126;
   Genoa 2:160;
   hedgehog 2:133;
   Madeira 2:160;
   Spanish 3:320, *321*;
   Warminster 1:114;
   weaver's 3:320;
   white 1:114
broomrape 2:256, *256*, 5:598,
   599, 7:948
broomroot 1:66
Brosimum 1:66, 4:447
Broussonetia 1:66, 2:233
Browallia 1:66, 5:579
browallia, orange 3:326
Brown, 'Capability' 7:960, **964**
Brown, Robert 7:**964**
brown algae 1:66, *66*
brown cabbage tree 4:420
brown earths 6:808, *809*
Brucea 5:550
brucine 1:26, 3:326
brucite 8:1103
Brugmansia 2:226
Bruguiera 4:*508*, 508, 7:891
Brunella 4:490
Brunellia 4:490
Brunelliaceae 4:**490**, 5:542
Brunfelsia 1:67, 5:579
Brunia 4:491
Bruniaceae 4:490-1
Brunnera 1:67
Brunnichia 4:427
Brunonia 5:607
Brunoniaceae 5:**607**, 618
Brussels sprout 1:64, 65, **67**,
   4:472
bryoid epiphytes 6:721
Bryonia 1:67, 4:465;
   dioica 6:772
bryony 1:67, 6:*772*;
   black 3:332, 6:697;
   redberry 1:67;
   white 1:67, *67*, 6:697
Bryophyllum 2:191
bryophytes in evolution 6:*739*
bryozoans 9:1154, 1156, 1160,
   1162, **1221**
Bryum 1:67;

pendulum 6:825
Bubbia 1:125, 3:378
Buch, C. von 9:1260, **1265**
Buchloe 2:149, 5:638;
   dactyloides 7:860
buckbean 2:225
buckeye 1:12, 5:544, 7:838
Buckland, W. 9:1261, 1262,
   1265, 1271
buckrams 2:155
buckthorn 1:67, 4:537, 6:769,
   7:843;
   alder 1:15, 2:148, 227, 7:*881*,
   884;
   European 1:67;
   purging 1:67;
   redberried 1:67;
   sea 2:177, *177*, 6:*706*, 750,
   825, 7:888
buckwheat 1:67, 83, 2:139,
   4:427, 428;
   bush 1:67;
   common 2:139, *139*;
   kangra 1:67;
   Siberian 1:67, 2:139;
   Tartary 1:67, 2:139;
   wild 1:67, 2:133
buckwheat tree 4:474
Buddleia 1:67, 5:**572**, *572*, 573
buddleia 1:67
Buddleieae 5:572, 573
Buddleioideae 5:572, 573
Buddleiaceae 5:572
buds, perennating, and life-forms
   6:725, 725-7, *726*
buffalo berry 4:519
buffalo grass 5:638, 7:860
Buffon, G. 9:1258, **1265**
bugbane 1:10, 89
bugle 1:14, *15*, 5:589
bugloss 1:15, 29;
   viper's 2:128
Buhsia 4:468
building stone 8:*1120*, **1121**,
   9:*1132*, *1136*, *1139*, *1171*,
   1219
bukhara 3:277
Bulawayan stromatolites 6:*757*,
   757
bulb of daffodil 6:778
bulb-tuber plants 6:*723*, 723
Bulbocodium 1:67
Bulbophyllum 1:68, 5:**673**, 675
bullace 1:116, 2:151, 3:275
bullock's heart 1:31, 2:151
Bulnesia 5:554
bulrush 1:68, 3:264, 301, 5:643,
   6:747, 826, 7:894;
   cattail 3:346, 347;
   common 3:311;
   reedmace 1:68, 6:826, *827*,
   7:880
bulrush millet 5:638, 640
bunch grasses 6:723
bunch spear grass 7:940
bunchgrass, feather 3:325
Bunchosia 5:563
Bunium 5:571
bunny ears 2:254
bunya bunya 1:39, 7:837
Buphthalmum 1:68, 5:617
Bupleurum 1:68, 5:569, 571
bur, New Zealand 1:7
bur marigolds 1:57, 7:921
Burchell, William John 6:683-4
Burgess Shale 9:1154
Burgundy pitch 3:323
burlap 2:191
Burmannia 5:671
Burmanniaceae 5:**670-1**, *671*, 675
Burmannieae 5:671
Burmeistera 5:606
Burnatia 5:620
burnet:
   great 3:306;
   salad 2:174, 3:306, *306*
burning 6:811-2, 7:*874*, 875,
   941, 949, *see also* fire

burning bush 1:68, 5:554
bur-reed 6:747, 826, 5:643;
   unbranched 7:885
burro's tail 3:312
burs and dispersal 6:816
Bursaria 4:488
Bursera 1:68, 2:129, 5:546, 547
Burseraceae 5:**546-7**, *547*, 548,
   552
Bursereae 5:547
bursting-heart 2:137
Busbecq, Ghislaine de 6:680
bushmans-poison 1:9
bushy poppy 4:403
busy lizzie 2:185, 5:562
butcher's broom 3:301
Butea 1:68, 193, 2:195
Butomus 1:68
Butomaceae 5:**619**, 620, 622,
   623, 631
Butomus 5:619
butterbur 3:266
buttercup 1:68, 3:395, 396, 399;
   Bermuda 2:257;
   bulbous 1:68, 3:287;
   Colombia 2:249;
   common 3:287;
   creeping 3:287, 7:950;
   early 3:287;
   great mountain 7:*915*;
   meadow 1:68;
   Persian 3:287;
   tall 3:287;
   water 1:68, 3:287, 6:826;
   white 1:68, 2:260;
   yellow 3:287;
   see also Ranunculus
buttercup tree 4:457
buttercup winter hazel 1:106
butterfly flower 1:53, 3:310,
   5:575, 576
butterfly tree 1:53
butterfly weed 1:43
butternut 1:77, 2:126, 245, *245*;
   Chinese 3:356;
   North American 3:356
butterwort 3:*272*, *273*, 5:598, 603
buttes 8:*1013*, *1043*, *1046*,
   9:*1180*
buttonball 3:330
buttonball tree 3:274
buttonwood 3:274, 330, 4:405,
   406
buttress roots 7:*891*, *see also* prop-
   roots
Butyrospermum 4:483
Buxaceae 4:**533-5**, *534*, 537
Buxbaumia 1:68
Buxus 1:62, 4:*534*, 534, 535, 537,
   6:749
Byblidaceae 4:490
Byblis 4:490
Byrsocarpus 5:542
Byrsonima 5:563
bytownite 8:1096

C$_4$ photosynthetic pathway 6:799
caapi 2:226
cabbage 1:64, 69, *69*, 3:308,
   4:472, 6:823;
   Chinese 1:87, *88*;
   flowering 1:65;
   Portuguese 1:64;
   red 1:65;
   round 1:65;
   Savoy 1:64, 65;
   skunk 2:213, 3:353;
   wild 1:65;
   see also Brassica
cabbage tree 1:104, 2:258, 3:313,
   4:420, 5:613;
   black 7:919;

brown 3:273
Cabomba 3:395
Cabombaceae 3:395
Cacalia 2:130, 3:312, 5:617
cacao 1:26, 58, 69, **96**, 3:335,
    4:441, 442, 7:932
cacao black pod 3:270
cacao butter oil 2:250
cachi 1:48
Cachrys 5:571
Cactaceae **4:413-5**, *414*, 495,
    6:721, 7:848, 896, 908
Cacteae 4:415
Cactoblastis cactorum and weed
    control 7:950
Cactoideae 4:415
cactus 1:69, 4:413, 415, 6:*722*,
    7:*849, 895*;
    barrel 1:69, 2:127, *128*, 139;
    candelabra 2:138;
    Christmas 2:132, 3:310;
    claret-cup 2:128;
    claw 3:310;
    cochineal 2:242;
    cotton pole 2:254;
    crab 3:310;
    cushion 2:254;
    Dane 2:253;
    devil 2:254;
    dumpling 2:211;
    Dutchman's pipe 2:132;
    Easter 2:132, 3:290;
    Easter lily 1:128;
    Eve's pin 2:253;
    feather 2:217;
    fishbone 2:132;
    giant 1:76;
    golden ball 2:127;
    grizzly bear 2:254;
    hedgehog 2:139;
    leafy 3:265;
    Mexican dwarf tree 2:254;
    mistletoe 3:290;
    old lady 2:217;
    organ-pipe 1:69;
    paper 2:254;
    pencil 2:254;
    rainbow 2:128;
    redbird 2:263;
    ribbon 2:263;
    rose 3:265;
    snowdrop 3:290;
    strawberry 2:128;
    teddy-bear 2:254;
    Thanksgiving 3:310;
    thimble 2:254;
    toad 3:324;
    torch 2:128;
    yoke 3:310
cade 2:136
cadmium 8:1099, **1108-9**
Caesalpinia 1:69, 122, 4:*502*, 502
Caesalpiniaceae 4:499
Caesalpinioideae 4:499, 502,
    5:566, 567
caesium 8:1109
caffeine 1:26, 58, 69, 2:227,
    3:333
caffeol 1:97
Cain, S. A. 7:906
cajan 2:201
cajang 1:107
Cajanus 3:271, 4:502
cajuput 2:227
cajuput oil 2:221, 4:511
cajuput tree 2:221
Cakile 1:69, 4:470;
    edentula 7:*921*;
    maritima 7:*887*, 920
calabash 4:467;
    sweet 2:151, 261
calabash gourd 1:69
calabash tree 1:69, 5:600
calabazilla 2:222
calabozo 1:69
calabrese 1:64, *65*, 69, 4:472
Caladium 1:70
Calamagrostis 3:290

calamint 2:174;
    lesser 1:70
Calamintha **1:70**
Calamites 6:732, *739*, 739, *740*,
    740, 743, *765*, 765, 766,
    9:*1163*, 1217
Calamus 1:70, 2:216, 3:289,
    5:651, 653, 654
Calandrinia 1:70
Calanthe 1:70, 5:675
Calathea 1:70, 3:*342*, 5:*650*, 650,
    651
Calathodes 3:399
calcarenites 9:*1191*
calcareous rocks 9:*1130, 1131*,
    1133-4, *1133, 1134, see also*
    chalks
Calceolaria 1:70, 5:593, 595
calcicole plants 6:786, 787, 806
calcifuge plants 6:*786*, 786, 806
calcinomorphic soils **6:810**
calcite 8:1009, 1015, 1021, 1023,
    1075, 1080, 1081, *1082*,
    1084, *1086*, **1086-7**, 1089,
    1091, 1093, *1096*, 1099,
    1101, 1102, 1104, 9:*1123*,
    1129, 1131, *1133, 1134*,
    1136, 1213, 1220
calcium 8:972, 996, 1084, 1089,
    1090, **1104**, 9:*1123*, 1124,
    1126, 1127, 1128, 1133,
    1141;
    bicarbonate 8:*1045*;
    carbonate 8:1021, 1043, *1044*,
    1045, 1061, 9:*1130, 1131*,
    1135;
    see also aragonite, calcite
calcium in plant nutrition 6:806
calcrete 6:805, 8:1046
calcsilicates 9:1136
Calcutta Botanic Garden 6:686
calderas 8:*1074*
Caldesia 5:620
Calea 2:226
Calectasia 5:666
Caledonian Sea 6:742
Caledonian-Appalachian orogeny
    9:*1154*, 1158, 1159, 1165
Calendula 1:70, 2:219, 5:618
Calenduleae 5:618
Caley, George 6:687
calf's snouts 1:36
caliches 9:1165
calico bush 2:192
California rose 1:72
Californian floral province 7:898
Californian poppy 4:403, 7:*951*
calisaya bark 2:227, 3:286
Calla 1:70;
    palustris 7:*903*
calla 3:362;
    florist's 3:362;
    golden 3:*362*;
    red 3:308;
    yellow 3:362
Calliandra 1:71, 4:499
Callianthemum 3:399
Callicarpa 1:71, 5:587
Calliergon 7:855
Calligonum 4:428
calliopsis 1:104
Callirhoe papaver 6:683
Callisia 5:629, 631
Callistemon 1:71, 4:*511*, 512,
    7:874
Callistephus 1:71, 5:618
Callisthene 5:564, 565
Callitrichaceae 5:589, *590*, **590-1**
Callitriche 5:*590*, 590, 591;
    verna 7:*944*
Callitris 1:71, 3:272, 306
Calluna 1:71, 2:133, 170, 4:474,
    475, 477, 7:875;
    vulgaris 6:814, 826, 829, 7:*872*,
    873, *874*, 875, 876
Calocarpum 2:151, 3:307, 4:483
Calocedrus 2:203
Calocephalus 1:71

Calochortus 1:72, 5:*662*, 664
Calodendron 5:554
Calophylloideae 4:436
Calophyllum 1:72, 2:198, 4:436,
    436, 437
Caloplaca:
    marina 6:*829*;
    thattincolor 6:*829*
Calotropis 1:72
Caltha 1:72, 2:220, 3:396, 399;
    palustris 7:880, 884, 885
calumba 3:401
calvados 1:16
Calvin-Benson cycle 6:*794*
Calycanthaceae 3:381, 384, *385*,
    385-6
Calycanthus 1:17, 76, 3:*385*, 385,
    386
Calycera 5:*613*, 613
Calyceraceae 5:**612-3**, *613*, 618
Calycophysum 4:465
Calylophus 4:512
Calyptrothecium 2:237
Calystegia 1:72, 2:233, 5:*580*, 580;
    soldanella 6:*825*, 7:*887*
Camarea 5:564
camas 3:362
camass 1:72
Camassia 1:72, 5:664
Cambrian 6:*738-9*, 739, 742, 743,
    9:*1149*, **1152-5**, 1156, 1158,
    1159, 1177, 1213, 1219,
    1220, 1261, 1271, 1273;
    faunal provinces 9:*1155*;
    faunas 9:*1152-4, 1153*;
    floras 9:*1153*;
    geography 9:*1153*, 1154-5
Camelina 1:72, 4:470
Camellia 1:72, 3:333, 4:432, 433,
    433
camellia 1:72;
    mountain 3:324;
    silky 3:324
Camellieae 4:432
camel's foot tree 1:53
camembert cheese 3:264
Camissonia 4:512
camomile *see* chamomile
camp-following weeds 7:925
Campanula 1:54, 3:287, 5:604,
    604, 606;
    uniflora 7:*907*, 911
Campanulaceae 5:*604*, **604-6**,
    607, 618, 7:*919*
Campanulales 4:465, 5:604-7
Campanulinae 5:604
Campanumoea 5:604
camphor 1:73, 2:136, 227, 3:388;
    Ngai 1:60
camphor as chemical defense
    6:*822*
camphor oil 2:136
camphor tree 1:89
camping forest 7:835
campion 3:315, *315*, 4:417, 419,
    6:*781*;
    rose 2:213;
    sea 6:750
Campsis 1:73, 5:599, 600
Camptotheca 4:516
Camptothecium 1:73
Canacomyrica 4:408, *408*
Canada balsam 1:6
Canadian Shield 8:1043-4,
    9:*1150*, 1160, 1171, 1172
Canadian waterweed 5:621, 622,
    see also Elodea
Cananga 3:361, 380, 381
Canangium 3:361
Canarieae 5:547
Canarina 1:73, 5:604, *604*
Canarium 1:24, 2:129, 245, 249,
    5:546, 547, 547
canary bird bush 1:110
canary bird flower 3:345, 5:563
Canary creeper 3:345, 5:562, 563
Canary Island ivy 5:568
Canary Islands wallflower 7:*915*

Canavalia 1:73, 4:502, 6:826
cancer weed 3:302
candelabra succulents 6:721, *722*
candelabra tree 1:39, 2:258, 6:*768*
candelilla 2:138
candle plant 2:193, 3:275
candleberry tree 1:15
candlenut 1:15, 2:250
candlenut oil 4:537
candle-snuff fungus 3:*360*
candle-tree life-form 6:720
Candolle, Alphonse de 6:689, 821,
    7:964
Candolle, Augustine de 7:*964*, 965
Candollea 5:607
candytuft 2:184, 4:470, 472
cane 1:73, 5:635;
    dumb 1:120;
    Malacca 2:145, 216;
    rattan 2:145;
    small 1:43
cane grass 7:862
cane-tree life-form 6:720
Canella 1:73, 3:379, 380
canella bark 1:73, 3:380
Canellaceae 3:**379-80**
canistel 2:128
canker brake 3:278
Canna 1:73, 5:648, *649*, 649
Cannabaceae 4:447
cannabinoids 1:73
Cannabis 1:73, 2:173, 4:446, 447
Cannaceae 5:647, **648-9**, *649*,
    650, 7:896
cannonball tree 1:107, 4:449, *450*
cantala 3:316
cantaloupe 1:110, 2:222, 4:467
canterbury bell 1:54
Cantleya 4:531
Cantua 5:583
Cantueae 5:583
Caoutchoua 1:74
caoutchouc 1:74, 2:142
cap shells *see* monoplacophora
Cape box 4:535
Cape daisy 3:353, *353*
Cape floristic region 7:897
Cape gooseberry 5:579
Cape heath 4:477
Cape honeysuckle 5:600
Cape jasmine 5:607
Cape lance tree 1:45
Cape leadwort 3:275
Cape marigold 1:*121*
Cape pondweed 5:622
caper 1:74, 2:146, 147, 4:469
caper bush 1:74
Caperonia 4:535, 537
cappan 2:126
Capparaceae 4:403, 468, **469**,
    470, 472, 473
Capparales 4:432, 469-73
Capparis 1:74, 4:468, 469
Capraria 5:593
caprifig 2:142
Caprifoliaceae 5:*609*, **609-10**, 618
Capsella 1:74, 4:470, *470*
Capsicum 1:74, 79, 87, 2:164,
    260, 3:265, 272, 289, 330,
    5:579, 7:880
captorhinomorphs 9:1236, 1238
carabeen 4:440
Caracasia 4:439
Caragana 1:74
Caraipa 4:436
Caralluma 5:576
caramba 2:151
carambola 2:151, *153*
Carapa 2:250, 5:552
carapa 2:250
caraway 1:111, 2:136, *146*, 147,
    174, 5:571
caraway oil 2:136
carbon 8:971, 995, 997, 1084,
    1089, 1091, 1102, 1105,
    1114, 1115, 9:*1130*, 1138,
    1143-6, 1149;

dioxide 8:975, 982, 997, 1009, 1021, 1034, 1043, 1044, 9:1122, 1128, 1135, 1136, 1143;
monoxide 8:982, 997
carbon fixation and water conservation 6:795, 799, 799
carbonaceous chondrites 8:972, 987, 988
carbonates 8:997, 1087, 9:1126, 1134
carbonatite 8:1087, 9:1126
carbon-14 dating 9:1143, 1146, 1199
Carboniferous 6:738-9, 739-40, 740, 740, 741, 743, 766, 8:1002, 1117, 9:1152, 1163, 1166-71, 1170, 1172, 1179, 1206, 1209, 1216, 1217, 1223, 1229, 1235, 1236, 1261;
climate 9:1166;
fauna 9:1167, 1170, 1177;
flora 9:1167, 1175;
formation of coal in 8:1118, 9:1170, 1171;
geography 9:1166, 1167;
Mississippian 9:1171, 1172;
Pennsylvanian 8:1001, 9:1171-2;
stratigraphic correlation 9:1166-7
carbuncle 8:1091
Cardamine 1:75, 4:470
cardamom 1:58, 75, 2:146, 147, 5:647, 648
cardinal, red 2:134
cardinal flower 5:606
Cardiospermum 1:75, 5:544
cardol 1:28
cardoon 1:42, 75, 113, 3:350
Cardueae 5:615, 617
Carduus 1:75, 3:335, 5:617, 618, 7:940
Carex 1:75, 3:312, 5:642, 642, 643, 6:810, 826, 827, 7:854, 869, 883, 901, 903;
appropinquata 7:894;
arenarius 6:825;
elata 7:876;
lachenalii 7:910;
lasiocarpa 7:876;
limosa 7:876;
maritima 7:921;
monostachya 7:879;
paniculata 6:723, 7:882, 884;
pauciflora 7:876;
pseudocyperus 7:903;
rostrata 7:876;
runssoroensis 7:879
carex fen 7:903
Careya 4:449, 450
Caribbean region 7:897;
explorations in 6:682-3
Carica 1:75, 2:259, 4:455, 7:880
Caricaceae 4:455, 465
caricachi 1:48
Caricoideae 5:643
Carlemannia 5:610
Carlemanniaceae 5:610
Carlina 1:75, 5:617
Carludovica 1:75, 5:654, 655, 655
Carludovicoideae 5:654
Carmichaelia 1:76
carnallite 8:1104
carnation 1:76, 119, 4:417, 419, 7:943;
American spray 1:76;
border 1:76, 76;
perpetual 1:76, 76, 119
carnauba wax 1:76, 5:654
Carnegie Institute 6:705-6
Carnegiea 1:76, 4:415, 415;
gigantea 7:843, 849, 850
Carnegieodoxa 3:384
carnivores 6:772, 772, 7:878, 9:1195, 1246, 1249
carnosaurs 9:1241

carnotite 8:1105, 1111
caroa 2:144, 5:644
carob 1:76
carob tree 1:15, 2:209, 3:281
Carolina allspice 1:76, 3:385, 386
carotenoids 6:794
carpenter's-square 3:311
carpet grass 1:48, 2:149
Carpinaceae 4:409
Carpineae 4:409
Carpinus 2:179, 187, 4:409, 6:747, 749;
betulus 7:898
Carpobrotus 4:415-7, 6:722
Carpodinus 5:575
carpolestids 9:1249
Carpolobia 5:566, 566
Carpolobium 4:533
carr 7:881, 882-3, 883, 884
carrageenan 1:18, 2:161, 3:289
carragheen 1:77
Carrierea 4:452
carrion flower 3:323, 323
Carrissa 5:574, 575
carrizo 3:269
carrot 1:77, 77, 3:298, 298, 350, 5:569, 571
Carthamus 1:77, 5:617, 618
cartilaginous fishes 9:1232
Carum 1:77, 5:571
carvone 2:227
Carya 1:77, 2:262, 5:555, 6:749, 765, 7:838, 896
Caryocar 1:77
Caryocaraceae 4:432
Caryophyllaceae 4:417-9, 418, 425, 428, 484
Caryophyllales 4:413-27, 429, 455
Caryophyllidae 4:413-29
Caryopteridoideae 5:587
Caryopteris 1:77, 5:587
Caryota 1:77, 5:653, 653, 654, 6:747
caryotoid palms 5:653, 654
casabanana 2:223
cascara 1:77, 2:227
cascara sagrada 4:538
cascarilla verde 3:286
Casearia 1:62, 4:452
cashau 3:281
cashew 5:547, 548
cashew apple 2:151, 244
cashew nut 2:244, 245, 245
cashew nut kernel oil 2:250
cashew nut tree 1:8, 28, 2:244
Casimiroa 3:307
cassa banana 4:467
cassada wood 5:541
cassava 1:77, 78, 83, 2:219, 3:298, 299, 299, 328, 4:535, 537, 7:926, 932
Cassia 1:78, 3:313, 4:499, 502, 7:843;
closiana 7:843
cassia 1:78, 89;
Padang 1:90;
purging 1:78;
tanner's 1:78
cassia-flower tree 1:90
cassie 1:7, 78
cassina 1:58, 2:178
Cassine 4:528, 529
cassine 2:177
Cassinopsis 4:531
Cassiope 1:78, 4:475, 477, 477, 7:855, 873;
mertensiana 7:873;
tetragona 7:854, 873
Cassipourea 4:507, 508
cassiterite 8:1079, 1087, 1101, 1109, 1110
Cassytha 3:387
Cassythoideae 3:387
cast fossils 6:731-2, 732
cast iron plant 1:45
Castanea 1:86, 4:410, 410, 7:841, 866

Castaneoideae 4:410
Castanopsis 4:410, 412
Castanospermum 2:245
Castelnavia 4:503
Castilla 1:78, 3:297
Castilleja 5:593
Castilloa 4:447
castor cake 1:78
castor oil 1:78, 79, 2:250, 250, 4:535, 537
castor oil plant 1:26, 79, 3:295
Casuarina 1:78, 2:187, 4:412, 412, 413, 6:824, 7:919;
equisetifolia 6:825, 826
Casuarinaceae 4:407, 412-3
Casuarinales 4:412-3
Catalpa 1:78, 5:599, 599, 600
catalpa 1:78
Catamoches 1:79
Catamodes 1:79
Catananche 1:79, 5:617
catapulted seeds 6:819
Catasetum 1:79, 5:675
catastrophic selection 6:777
Catastrophic Theory of fossil origins 6:731
Catastrophism 9:1147, 1149, 1262, 1265, 1266
catawba tree 1:79
catchfly 3:315, 4:419
catchweed 2:154
catechu 1:7, 2:126, 154;
black 2:154;
pale 2:154
catena 9:1141
Catesby, Mark 6:683
catgut 3:334
Catha 1:58, 69, 2:192, 193, 4:529
Catharanthus 1:79
Cathaysia 9:1175, 1176, 1179
Cathaysian province 6:740, 741, 743
cathedral bell 1:93
Catherine the Great 6:688
catmint 2:174, 240, 5:589
catnip 2:240
cat's-claw 5:600
cat's ear 2:184
cat's foot 1:31
cat's tail 3:268
cat's whiskers 3:331
catstail, meadow 7:861
catta 1:58, 2:192
cattail 1:68, 3:346, 5:643, 7:903, 903;
common 3:347;
narrow leaf 1:68, 3:347;
red-hot 1:8
Cattleya 1:79, 5:675
cattleya, yellow 3:282
Caucalideae 5:571
Caucalis 5:571
caucho 1:74, 78
cauliflower 1:64, 65, 79, 79, 4:472
Caulophyllum 3:396
Cavanillesia 4:443, 444, 6:817
Cavendishia 4:477
caves 8:1012, 1044, 1045;
phreatic 8:1044;
vadose 8:1043, 1070
caviomorphs 9:1249
cayenne pepper 1:74, 79, 5:579
Cayluseea 4:472
Cayluseeae 4:472
Caytonia 6:740, 744
Caytoniales 9:1217
Ceanothus 1:79, 4:537, 538, 538, 7:843;
lobbianus 6:683
ceanothus 1:79
ceara rubber 4:537
Cecropia 1:80, 4:448
cedar 1:80, 7:895;
Alaska 1:84;
Algerian 1:80;
Atlas 1:80, 3:341;
blue 1:80;

Burma 3:341;
California incense 2:203, 203;
Chinese 3:341;
cigar box 3:341;
Colorado red 2:190;
Japanese red 1:110, 110;
Lebanon 1:80, 100, 3:341;
Northern white 3:335;
pencil 2:127, 190, 3:341;
red 1:80, 2:190, 3:342, 341;
Southern red 2:191;
West Indian 1:80, 3:341;
Western red 3:335, 335, 341, 7:837;
white 1:84, 2:127, 3:335, 341
cedar wood oil 1:80, 2:136
cedar-of-Lebanon 1:80, 100, 3:341
Cedrela 1:80, 2:215, 3:342, 5:551, 552
cedrela tree 1:80, 3:342
Cedrus 1:80, 7:895
Ceiba 1:80, 4:443, 444, 2:192
celandine 3:399;
common 6:816;
creeping 3:287;
early 3:287;
tree 1:60, 2:214
Celastraceae 4:528-9, 529, 530, 531, 532, 534, 537, 5:540
Celastrales 4:474, 523, 528-33, 537
Celastrus 1:80, 4:529, 529
celeriac 1:80, 80, 3:298, 350
celery 1:80, 80, 2:174, 3:350, 351, 5:569, 571;
turnip-rooted 1:80, 3:350;
water 3:349;
wild 3:349
celery oil 2:136
celestine 8:1079, 1100, 1108
cellonia 3:279, 5:627
Celmisia 1:80, 7:920
Celosia 1:80, 4:420
Celosieae 4:420
Celsia 1:80
celsian 8:1109
Celtideae 4:445, 446
Celtis 1:81, 3:324, 4:445, 446, 446, 6:747
cementation 9:1131
Cenozoic 6:738-9, 740, 745-51, 9:1191-200, 1209-10, see also Tertiary, Quaternary
Centaurea 1:81, 3:313, 5:615, 617;
cyanus 6:821
Centaurium 5:574
centaury 5:574
Centella 5:571
centers of diversity, origin and variability 7:906-7
centers of domestication 7:927-9
Centosteca 5:636
Centosteceae 5:636
Centostecoideae 5:636
Centranthera 5:595
Centranthus 1:81, 5:610, 611
Centrobium robustum 6:817
Centrolepidaceae 5:633, 634
Centrolepideae 5:633
Centrolepis 5:633
centromeres 6:762-3
Centroplacus 4:537
Centropogon 5:606
Centrosema 2:149, 262
Centrospermae 4:419, 420, 422, 423, 424, 425, 426, 427, 455
century plant 1:13, 6:786
cepe, edible 1:61
cephaeline 2:186
Cephaelis 2:186, 227, 5:609
Cephalanthera 1:81, 2:172, 5:675
Cephalaria 1:81, 5:611, 612
Cephalaspis 9:1231
cephalopods 9:1154, 1166
Cephalostemon 5:629
Cephalostigma 5:604

Cephalotaceae 4:496, *496*
Cephalotaxus 1:81
Cephalotus 1:81, 4:496, *496*
Ceramium 1:82
cerargyrite 8:1108
Ceraria 4:425
Cerastium 1:82, 87, 4:417;
  arvensea 7:949
Cerasus 1:86, 2:219, 3:282, 4:494
Ceratiola 4:478, 479, *479*
Ceratiosicyos 4:462, 463
ceratites 9:1225
Ceratocapnos 4:404
Ceratocystis 2:130
Ceratodon 1:82
Ceratonia 1:15, 76, 2:209
Ceratopetalum 3:308, 4:488
Ceratophyllaceae 3:**393**, 393-4
Ceratophyllum 1:82, 3:393, 393-4,
  6:826, *827*;
  submersum 7:948
ceratopians 9:1242
Ceratostigma 1:82, 4:429
Ceratotheca 5:601
Ceratozamia 1:112
Cerbera 5:574, 575
Cercidiphyllaceae 4:**405**
Cercidiphyllum 1:82, 4:405, 6:746,
  746
Cercis 1:82, 4:499, 502
Cercocarpeae 4:494
Cercocarpus 4:494;
  betularis 7:843
Cereeae 4:415
Cereus 1:82, 4:415, 6:721;
  giganteus 6:722
ceriman 2:232
Cerinthe 5:586
Ceriops 2:218, 4:508
cerium 8:1111, 9:1126
Ceropegia 1:82, 5:575, 576
ceroxyloid palms 5:653
Ceroxylon 1:84, 3:357, 5:654
cerrado 7:856
cerussite 8:1087, 1090, 1111
cesium *see* caesium
Cespedesia 4:433, 434
Cesteae 5:579
Cestrum 1:84, 5:579
Cetraria 1:84
Ceylon olive 4:440
chabazite 8:1101
Chaenomeles 1:84, 3:286, 4:494,
  494
Chaerophyllum 1:84, 5:571
Chaetomium 1:84
Chailletiaceae 4:532
chain fern 3:359
chain plant 3:342
chalcedony 8:*1082, 1083*, **1087**,
  1093, 1097, 1101
chalcopyrite 8:992, 1078, *1079*,
  1087, 1096, 1104, 1106
chalicotheres 9:1248
chalk 8:1087, 9:*1130, 1131*,
  1187, *1190*, 1191
chalybite *see* siderite
Chamaecyparis 1:84, 113;
  lawsoniana 6:719
Chamaedaphne 7:876;
  calyculata 7:*903*, 903
Chamaedorea 1:85, 5:*653*, 7:896
chamaedoroid palms 5:654
Chamaemelum 1:36, **85**, 2:219
Chamaenerion 1:85
Chamaepericlymenum 4:517, *518*
chamaephytes 6:725, *725*, 727
Chamaerops 1:85, 5:651, 7:895,
  896
Chamaespartium 2:160
Chamaexeros 5:666
Chamberlin, T. 9:**1265-6**
Chambers, Robert 6:759
Chamira 4:470
Chamireae 4:470
chamise chaparral 7:843
chamomile 1:36, **85**, 2:174,
  5:618;

lawn 1:85;
  ox-eye 1:36;
  Roman 2:219;
  stinking 1:85;
  sweet 1:85;
  wild 1:85;
  yellow 1:36, 2:126
Chamomilla 1:**85**;
  suaveolens 7:951
chamosite 8:1087, 9:1135
champaca oil 2:229
champedak 1:42
chandelier plant 2:192
chandelier tree 2:258
Chandler, Marjorie 6:765
chaparral 6:*822*, 822, 7:842, *843-*
  4, 843-4
character-species 6:729
charcoal consumption 7:937
chard 1:85;
  Swiss 1:54, 85, 3:350
charity 3:276
charlock 1:**85**, *85*, 3:316, 7:948;
  white 3:288
charnockites 8:1086, 1092
chaste tree 3:355, 5:587
chat 1:58, 2:**192**
chatterbox 2:131
chaulmoogra oil 1:**85**, 2:250,
  4:451, 452
chaulmoogra tree 6:686
chaura 3:266
chayote 1:**85**, *85*, 2:223, 3:350,
  4:465, 467
checker bloom 3:315
checkerberry 2:155
Cheilanthes 1:86
Cheiranthera 4:488, 489
Cheiranthus 1:**86**, 3:356, 4:470,
  470, 472;
  scoparius 7:915
cheirotoxin 3:356
chelicerates 9:1227, 1228, **1229**
Chelidonium 1:26
Chelone 1:86
chelonians *see* tortoises, turtles
Chelsea Physic Garden 6:683,
  7:963
chemical control of weeds 7:**950**
chemical defenses 6:**821-3**, *822*
chemical pans 6:805
chenille 1:8
chenille honey-myrtle 2:221
Chenopodiaceae 4:419, 420,
  422-3, *423*, 427, 525, 6:772
Chenopodium 1:86, 4:423;
  album 6:795, 7:949
cherimoya 1:26, 31, 2:151, *153*
Cherleria sedioles 7:907
chernozems 6:808, *809*, 7:859,
  860, 862, 9:1141
cherry 1:86, *87*, 4:491, 494;
  Barbados 2:217;
  bird 3:282;
  bladder 3:270;
  Brazil 2:137;
  cooking 6:151;
  cornelian 1:105, 123;
  European dwarf 1:86;
  false Jerusalem 3:*317*, 318;
  flowering 3:282, *282*, 6:685;
  fluted 2:137;
  ground 3:270;
  Japanese cornelian 1:105;
  Japanese flowering 3:*282*;
  Jerusalem 3:317;
  maraschino 1:86, 2:**219**;
  mazard 1:86;
  oshima 3:282;
  red Surinam 2:137;
  sour 1:86, 2:151, 3:282;
  Spanish 2:230;
  sweet 1:86, 2:151, *152*, 3:282;
  West Indian 2:217;
  winter 1:270
cherry elaeagnus 4:519
cherry laurel 4:494
cherry pie 2:172

cherry tomato 7:927
cherts 8:*1074*, 1087, 1097,
  9:1134, **1135**, 1150, 1191,
  1202, 1214, 1220
chervil 1:84, 2:126, 174, *175*,
  5:571;
  bulbous 1:84;
  garden 1:36;
  salad 1:36, 84;
  turnip-rooted 1:84, 3:350;
  wild 1:36
chestnut 1:86, 2:126, 145;
  American 1:86, 2:130, 245;
  Chinese 1:86, 2:245;
  Chinese horse 1:12;
  Chinese water 2:129, 3:357,
    5:642, 643;
  dwarf 1:86;
  horse 1:12, 88, 6:680, 7:959,
    see also horse chestnut;
  Japanese 1:86, 2:245;
  Moreton Bay 2:245;
  Spanish 1:86;
  sweet 1:87, *87*, 2:130, 245, *see*
    also sweet chestnut;
  water 2:245, *245*, 3:356, *356*,
    357, 4:506, 6:749, 818
chestnut soils 6:808, 7:859, 860,
  862
chewing gum 1:87, 2:219
chiasmata 6:*763*
chiastolite 8:1084
chick pea 4:502
chickasaw lima 1:73
chicken-claws 3:302
chickweed 1:87, 3:324, *324*, 343,
  4:417, 6:724, 751, 7:920;
  common 1:87;
  field mouse-ear 1:87;
  mouse-ear 1:82, 7:949;
  umbellate 1:87;
  water 1:87
chicle 1:49, 87, 2:219, 4:482, 483
chicory 1:58, 87, *87*, 89, 3:350,
  351, 5:618;
  wild 2:130
chiku 2:219, 4:483
Childe, V. Gordon 7:925
chilling, overwinter 6:*793*
Chimaphila 4:480, *480*
Chimonanthus 1:87, 3:*385*, 385,
  386
Chimonobambusa 1:43;
  quadrangularis 6:685
china clay *see* kaolinite
China grass 1:60, 4:449
China jute 1:87, 4:444, 445
China root 5:670
China wood oil 2:250, 3:346
chincherinchee 2:256, 5:664
chin-chin 2:256
Chinese cabbage 4:472
Chinese date 4:538
Chinese date plum 4:483
Chinese explorations 6:680, 681,
  684-6
Chinese fir 1:111
Chinese green indigo 4:538
Chinese hat plant 5:587
Chinese lantern 5:579
Chinese mat grass 5:643
Chinese silk plant 1:60
Chinese tallow tree 4:537
Chinese water chestnut 2:129,
  3:357, 5:642, 643
chinquapin 1:86;
  water 2:239
Chionochloa 5:636, 7:905
Chionodoxa 1:87, 5:664;

lucilliae 6:682
chipire 2:138
chirata 3:330
chiretta 3:330, 5:574
Chirita 5:596
Chironia 5:573, 574
Chisocheton 5:551, 552
chittamwood 3:317
chives 1:17, **87**, 2:147, 174,
  3:350, *351*, 5:664;
  Chinese 1:17
Chlaenaceae 4:440, 445
Chlamydomonas 1:88, 3:289
Chlamydophytum 4:526
chloanthite 8:1107
Chloranthaceae 3:383, *386*,
  386-7, 389
Chloranthus 3:*386*, 386-7
chlorapatite 8:1084
Chlorella 1:20
Chlorideae 5:638, 640
chloridoid grasses 7:862-3
chlorine 8:979, 997, 1034, 1109,
  1121, 9:1126;
  in plant nutrition 6:807
Chloris 1:88, 5:638
chlorite 8:1021, **1087-8**, 1100,
  9:1138, 1139, 1150
Chlorococcum 1:88
Chlorophora 2:126, **187**, 4:447;
  excelsa 6:771
chlorophylls 6:794, 795
Chlorophytum 1:88
chloroplast origin 6:759
Chloroxylon 1:88, 3:308
choco 1:85
chocolate 2:227
Choisya 1:88, 5:552, 554
cholla 1:69, 2:253, 6:722, 7:843,
  849;
  jumping 2:254
Chondrilla 5:617, 618
chondrites 8:974, 987, *988*, 1089,
  1092, 9:1122, 1202
Chondrodendron 1:111, 2:227,
  3:401
Chondropetalum 5:634
Chondrorhyncha 3:363
chondrosteans 9:1189, *1206*,
  1234
chondrules 8:987
Chondrus 1:77, 88, 3:289
Choricarpia 2:187
Chorisia 4:443, 444
Chorisodontium aciphyllum 6:810,
  7:853, 855
Chorizema 1:88
chorogi 3:323
chorology 6:707, 7:**893-919**
Chorthippus parallelus, meiosis in
  6:*763*
Chosenia 4:468
Christensenia 1:88
Christmas bush, Victorian 3:281
Christmas cactus 4:415
Christmas flower 2:138, 3:276
Christmas rose 1:88, 2:172, 3:*396*,
  399
Christmas star 3:276
Christmas tree 1:88;
  New Zealand 2:228, *228*
Christmas-berry tree 3:309
christophine 1:85, 2:223, 3:350
Christ's thorn 2:258
chromatids 6:*762-3*
chromite 8:1083, **1088**, 1099,
  1105
chromium 8:1060, 1074, 1088,
  1089, 1091, 1092, 1098,
  1105, 9:1151
Chromolaena 5:617, 618
chromophores 6:794
chromosome numbers:
  and endemics 7:914-5;
  and rapid speciation 6:(*776*),
    776-7
chromosomes 6:761, *762-3*;
  inversions in 6:*777*, 819;

manipulation of 7:933-4, 958;
translocations in 6:777, 7:958
chronistics 6:696
Chrozophora 1:88, 4:537
Chrysalidocarpus 1:88
Chrysanthemum 1:89, 2:219,
3:278, 5:613, 615, 618,
6:684, 769, 781, *793*, 7:915,
946
chrysanthemum 1:89, 88, 5:613,
615, 618
Chrysobalanaceae 4:*498*, **498-9**,
502
Chrysobalanus 1:89, 4:498, 499
Chrysolepis 4:410
Chrysophyllum 1:116, 3:324,
4:483
chrysoprase 8:1087, *1093*
Chrysosplenium 4:497
Chrysothemis 5:596
chrysotile 8:*1085*, 1099
chufa 1:113, 5:643
Chukrasia 1:80, 5:552
Chusquea 3:636
Cibotium 3:342
cicely 1:36;
sweet 2:174, 237
Cicer 1:87, 89, 4:502
Cichorium 1:87, 89, 2:130, 5:*615*,
617, 618
Cicuta 1:89
cidaroids 9:1185
cider 1:16, 37, *88*, **89**
cigar box tree 1:80
cigar flower 1:111
Cimicifuga 1:89, 3:399
Cinchona 3:286, 5:607, 609
cinchona 3:286
cinchonine 1:26
Cinchonoideae 5:608
Cinclidium 7:855
Cinderella-slippers 3:316
cineole 2:227;
as chemical defense 6:822
Cineraria 1:89, 3:312, 5:617
cineraria (*Senecio*) 1:89, 3:313,
5:618
cinerins 3:285
cinnabar 8:*1088*, 1110
cinnabar moth and weed control
7:950
cinnamein 2:227
cinnamic acid as chemical defense
6:822
Cinnamodendron 3:380
Cinnamomeae 3:388
Cinnamomum 1:73, 89, 3:*387*, 388
cinnamon 1:89, 2:146, 147,
3:387, 388;
Batavia 1:90;
Ceylon 1:89;
Chinese 1:89;
Saigon 1:*90*;
true 1:89;
white 1:73;
wild 1:73
cinnamon stone 8:1091
Cinnamosma 3:379, 380
cinquefoil 3:280, 4:494
Circaea 1:90, 2:241, 4:512, *513*;
alpina 7:904
Circaeaster 3:399
Circaeasteraceae 3:399
Circaeeae 4:512
Circaeocarpus 3:389, *389*
circumboreal distributions 7:903-
4, 908
circumpolar distributions 7:910,
911
cirques 8:*1012, 1018*
cirripedes 9:1228
Cirsium 1:90, 3:335, 5:617, 618,
6:724, 817, 7:940;
acaulon 7:940;
vulgare 6:724
Cissampelos 3:401
Cissus 1:90, 4:538, *539*, 539
Cistaceae 4:458, **458-9**

Cistanche 5:598
Cistus 1:90, 4:*458*, 458, 459,
7:836
Citharexylum 5:587
citrine 8:1084, 1098
Citriobatus 4:488
citron 1:91, 2:151, 222, 4:467,
5:554
Citronella 4:*531*, 531
citronella (*Cymbopogon*) 5:640
citronella oil 2:136
Citrullus 1:91, 2:222, 224, 3:*357*,
4:465, 467
Citrus 1:91, 92, 2:163, 199, 207,
217, 254, 256, 3:278, 308,
314, 332, 347, 4:525, 5:552,
552, 554, 7:926
citrus fruits 1:91
ciupo 4:443
cladistics 6:696
Cladium 3:312, 5:642, 643, 6:810,
7:885;
mariscus 6:724, 750, 826,
7:880-1, 885
cladograms 6:*696*, 696, *697*
Cladonia 1:91, 6:825
Cladophora 1:91, 7:944;
glomerata 7:944
Cladosporium 1:91
Cladothamnus 4:477
Clappertonia 4:441
claret-cup cactus 2:128
Clark, William 6:683
Clarkia 1:91, 2:163, 4:512, 6:777,
7:917;
biloba 6:777;
lingulata 6:777
clary 1:91
clary wort 1:91
class, phytocoenal 6:*728*
classification 6:694;
artificial 6:*695*;
box-within-box 6:696, *699*;
history of 6:698-9;
and ordination 6:730;
phenetic and phylogenetic
6:696-7;
and scientific taxonomy 6:694-6;
Sexual System of 6:679, 759;
types of 6:696-7
clastic rocks 8:1097, 9:1131,
1133
Clathrus 3:284, 324
Clausena 5:554
Clavaria 1:91
Claviceps 2:132, 227
Clavija 4:486
clay 6:802, *802-3*, 803-4
clay minerals 8:1009, 1084, **1088**,
1092, 1093, 9:1130, 1131,
1132
clays 8:*1068*, 1070, 1088,
9:1122, **1130**, 1136, 1138
Claytonia 1:91, 4:425
clear-felling 7:*922*, 935
clearing nut tree 3:327
cleavage:
mineral 8:1081, *1082*, 1086,
1089;
rock 9:1137, *1138*
cleavers 2:154, *155*
Clematideae 3:399
Clematis 1:92, 3:396, 399, *399*,
5:562;
lanuginosa 6:684;
montana 6:*686*
Clematopsis 3:399
clementine 1:92, 2:151, 217
Clements, Frederick 6:689, 709,
718, 7:964
Cleome 1:92, 4:468, 469, 470
Clermontia 5:606
Clerodendrum 1:92, 5:587, 587
fragrans 6:684
Clethra 1:92, 4:473, 7:906
Clethraceae 4:473-4, 477
Clianthus 1:92
Cliftonia 1:67, 4:474, 475

climate 6:787-99, *788*;
and climax vegetation 6:712;
of deserts 7:*845*;
and desert types 7:844-5;
and floristic provinces 7:898;
and forest types 7:834-8;
and grassland types 7:855-60;
Mediterranean 7:836, 843;
and scrub types 7:842-3;
and soil types 6:*807*, 807-8;
of tundra 7:851-3
climatic formation-types 6:718
climatic zones 8:998-9, *999*, 1037,
9:1130, 1140, 1141, 1159,
1198, 1210
climatron 7:*960*
climax vegetation 6:692, **711-4**,
712-3, 7:*894*;
on peatland 7:879, 884;
and succession 6:823, 827-8
climbing adaptations 6:771-2, *772*
climbing annuals 6:724
clines 6:706
clinopyroxene 8:996
Clinostigma 5:653
Clintonia 1:92
Clitocybe 1:92
clitocybin 1:92
Clitoria 1:92
Clivia 1:92, 5:664, *665*, 666
clones 7:932, 933
Closterium 1:21
Clostridium 1:51
cloud forest 7:866-7, *867*
cloudberry 2:151, 3:300
clove 1:93, 2:146, 147, 227,
4:511
clove oil 1:93, 2:136
clove tree 1:93, 2:136, 137
clover 1:92, 4:499, 502, 6:*718*,
7:932, 948;
alsike 1:93, 2:149;
Aztec 1:93;
Bokhara 2:224;
bush 2:202;
Calvary 2:221;
crimson 1:93, 2:149;
Dutch 1:93;
Egyptian 1:93;
holy 2:252;
hop 3:314;
Italian 1:93;
Japanese 2:202;
Korean 2:202;
musk 2:134;
pin 2:134;
red 1:92, 93, 122, 2:149, 3:*343*,
7:934;
sour 2:224;
strawberry 1:93, 2:149;
subterranean 1:93, 2:149;
suckling yellow 1:93;
Swedish 1:93;
sweet 2:174, 224;
tick 2:149;
water 2:*220*, 221;
white 1:93, 2:149, 3:314,
6:706, 7:940;
white sweet 2:149, 224;
yellow 3:314;
yellow sweet 2:149
club moss 1:94, *94*, *95*, 2:213,
6:*739*, 9:1209, **1216-7**;
common 2:213;
small sand 1:94, *95*;
true sand 1:94
club mosses (lycopsids) 9:1209,
1216-7;
in evolution 6:*739*
club root 2:174
clubrush 1:68, 3:311
clumping 6:716
Clusia 4:436, 437
Clusieae 4:436
Clusioideae 4:436
Clusius 6:680

clymenids 9:1166
Clytostoma 1:93
Cneoraceae 5:552
Cneorum 5:552
Cnestis 5:542, 542, 543
Cnicus 1:93, 3:335, 5:617
Cnidoscolus 3:323
coachwood 7:837
coal 8:1003, 1021, *1072*, 1102,
1105, 1115-9, *1115, 1116,
1117*, 9:1130, 1135, 1170,
1171, *1172*, 1173, 1181,
1187;
limnic 8:1117;
paralic 8:1116-7;
rank of 8:1117-8;
world resources 8:*1116*,
1118-9;
see also Carboniferous, Jurassic
coal areas 6:*741*
Coal Measures 9:1167
Coastal Plain province 7:*898*
coastal plains 8:1051-2, *1052*
coastal sage 7:843
coastal vegetation 7:885-91;
see also seashores
coastlines 8:1055-6, *1055, 1056*
Cobaea 1:93, 5:583
Cobaeaceae 5:583
Cobaeeae 5:583
cobalt 8:979, *1075*, **1105**
cobaltite 8:1078, 1105
cobnut 2:170, 4:410;
Turkish 2:245
cobra plant 1:117
coca 1:26, 93, 5:560;
truxillo 1:93
cocaine 1:26, 93, 2:227, 5:560
Coccinia 2:222, 4:465, 467
coccolithophores, coccoliths
8:1015, 1087, 9:*1131*, 1134,
1163, 1185, 1186, 1189,
1190, 1191, 1215, **1216**
Coccoloba 1:96, 2:193, 4:427, 428,
428
Cocculus 3:401
cochineal 2:242
cochineal berries 3:270
cochineal cactus 2:242
Cochlearia 1:96, 4:470;
officinalis 7:920, *921*
Cochliostema 5:631
Cochlospermaceae 4:445, **455-7**,
457
Cochlospermum 4:*457*, 457
cockle:
corn 1:14;
sticky 3:315;
white 3:315
cocklebur 3:359, 5:618, 6:816
cockpits 8:1045
cockroach berry 3:317
cockscomb 1:80, *81*, 4:420
cocksfoot 1:115, 2:149
cocksfoot grass 6:705, 7:940
coco bolo 1:116
coco de mer 1:123, 6:818
coco plum 1:89, 4:498, 499
cocoa 1:26, 58, 69, 96, 3:335,
4:441, 442, 7:932
cocoa butter 4:435
cocoa butter oil 2:250
cocona 5:579
coconut 1:96, *96*, 2:126, 145,
151, 245, *245*, 250, *250*,
5:651, 653, 654, 6:*818*, 818,
7:932, 950;
double 1:123, *123*
coconut apple 1:97
coconut oil 2:250
coconut water 1:58
Cocos 1:41, 96, *97*, 5:651, 653,
654;
nucifera 6:*818*, 818
cocosoid palms 5:653
cocoyam 3:328, 359, 5:659,
7:931
codeine 1:26, 2:227

codes of nomenclature 6:698, **699-701**
Codiaeum 1:97, 4:537
Codium 1:97
codominance 6:711
Codonocarpus 4:421
Codonopsis 1:97, 5:604, 606
coelacanths 9:1164, 1232, 1234
coelenterates 9:1152, 1209, 1220
Coeloglossum 1:97, 5:675
Coelogyne 1:97, 5:673, 675
Coelophysis 9:1181
coelurosaurs 9:1241
Coffea 1:97, 2:227, 5:607, 608, 609
coffee 1:26, 58, 69, 97, 2:227, 5:607, 608, 608, 609, 7:880, 926, 950;
  fig 1:58;
  liberica 1:97;
  mogdad 1:78;
  negro 1:78
coffee plant 1:58
coffee tree, Kentucky 2:167
coffeeberry 1:77
cognac 1:16
cohosh, black 1:10, 89
coigue 3:341
coir 1:96, 97, 2:145, 145, 5:651, 654
Coix 1:97, 5:638, 640
Cola 1:98, 2:194, 4:442, 442;
  acuminata 6:771;
  mellenii 6:771
cola 1:26, 58, 98, 2:194
cola tree 1:58
colanin 2:194
Colchic forest 7:838
colchicine 1:26, 98, 5:664
Colchicum 1:98, 5:662, 664, 6:781
cold steppe 7:832-3, 859
cold winter deserts 7:845
Coldenia 5:583, 584
cole 1:64
colemanite 8:1102
Colenso, William 6:687-8
Coleogeton 5:624
Coleonema 5:554
Coleosporium 1:98
Coleotrype 5:629
Coleus 1:98, 5:589, 589
coleus, Brazilian 3:275
colewort 1:64
collards 1:64, **98**
collections:
  crop 7:957, 958-9;
  herbarium 6:680, 694, 703, 7:963;
  living 6:681, 683-8, 7:959-61
collembolids 9:1229
Colletia 1:98, 4:537, 538, 538
Colletotrichum 1:98
Colliguaia 4:537
Collinsia 1:98, 5:595
Collomia 5:583
collophane 8:1084, **1088**
Colobanthus 4:417, 7:905;
  quitensis 7:855, 910, 920
Colocasia 3:328, 333, 5:659, 7:931
colocynth 1:88, 2:222
Colocynthis 1:91, 2:224
colonization 6:819, 820, 7:887;
  and aliens 7:951;
  of islands 7:920-1, 921;
  of nunataks 7:911;
  and succession 6:823-7, 824-5;
  and tolerance 6:815, 815
colophony 3:296
color index 9:1124
coltsfoot 3:347
colubroids 9:1238
columbine 1:38, 3:399, 6:773, 779
Columellia 5:591
Columelliaceae 5:591-2, 7:896
columnar succulents 6:721, 722
Columnea 1:98, 5:596, 596, 598

Colutea 1:98;
  arborescens 6:817
colza 1:64, 99, 4:472
comb hedgehog 2:128
comb. nov. 6:699
Combretaceae 4:440, 507, 508, **514-6**, 515
Combretodendron 4:449
Combretum 4:514, 515, 515, 516, 6:818
comfrey 3:330, 330, 5:585, 586
Commelina 1:99, 5:629, 631, 631
Commelinaceae 5:628, **629-31**, 631, 632, 633, 640, 643, 644
Commelinidae 5:627-51
Commelinales 5:627-31, 641
Commelinoideae 5:629
Commidendron 7:919
Commiphora 1:99, 2:237, 5:546, 547, 547
common ancestry 6:696, 697, 7:908
communities 6:709, **709-14**;
  and phytosociology 6:727-30;
  in tundra 7:854-5
community-wide adaptation 7:848, 890
Comoranthus 5:577
companions, phytocoenal 6:729
compass flowers 7:853
compass plant 3:315
competition 6:710, 820-3, 821-2;
  for light 6:771-2, 792
competitive exclusion 6:786-7
complementary species 6:710
Compositae 4:415, 520, 525, 535, 5:569, 606, 607, 610, 612, **613-8**, 615, 617, 7:919
composting and weed control 7:949
compression fossils 6:732-3, 732
comptie 3:361
Compton, Henry, Bishop of London 6:682
Condoron 5:596
Conanthera 5:669, 669
conchita 2:149
concretion 8:1020
condylarths 9:1192, 1195, 1246-7, 1249
cone flower 3:300;
  purple 2:127
cone-sheets 8:1030
conglomerates 9:1131, 1132, 1133
Congo jute 1:39
Conicosia 4:417
Coniferae 7:919
coniferophytes 9:1218
coniferous forest 7:838-9, 895, 902, 938
coniferous shrubs, xeromorphic 6:721
conifers 1:100, 6:739, 9:1176, 1179, 1185, 1188, 1189, 1218
coniine 1:26, 2:227
Conium 1:99, 2:172, 5:571
Connaraceae 5:542, **542-3**
Connaropsis 5:560
Connarus 5:542, 542, 543
connate water 8:1069
Conocarpus 4:515
Conocephaleae 4:448
Conocephalum 1:99
conodonts 9:1154, 1159, 1162, 1163, 1166, 1167, **1229**
Conophytum 1:99
Conopodium 1:99, 5:571
Conostyleae 5:668
Conostylis 5:668
consequents 8:1037
conservation 7:952-9, 953, 963
Conserved Names 6:700
consociations 6:729

Consolida 6:704
constancy, phytocoenal 6:727
constant final yield 6:820
continental drift 6:736, **740-5**, 742, 8:1001-3, 1001, 1007, 1025, 9:1263, 1264, 1267, 1268, 1275;
  and endemism 7:916;
  and long-distance dispersal **7:919**
continental islands 7:917-8
continua 6:711, 711
continuous and discontinuous distributions 6:745, 7:905, 906-11, 906, 907-11
continuous and discontinuous variation 6:761-2
contra hierba 1:123
control of weeds 7:949-50
Convallaria 2:206, 5:662, 664, 6:723
convallatoxin 2:206
convergent evolution:
  in deserts 7:850;
  in forests 7:833;
  in hydrophytes and xerophytes 6:769-70;
  and phylogenetic classification 6:696;
  and polytopy 7:908;
  in tundra 7:853-5
Convolvulaceae 4:506, 5:579-80, 580, 583, 586
Convolvulus 1:99, 2:233, 5:580;
  arvensis 6:772
Conyza 5:618
conyza 2:133
Cook, Captain James 6:687
Cooksonia 6:766, 9:1216
cool coastal and cool winter deserts **7:845**
coolabah 2:137
coolwort 2:231
coontie 3:361
Copaifera 1:49, 104, 2:187
copals 1:99, 2:192;
  East African 2:183
Cope, E. 9:1262, **1266**, 1272
Copepoda 9:1228
Copernicia 1:76, **104**, 3:357, 5:654
copihue 2:197
copper 8:992, 1071, 1073, 1074, 1075, 1078, 1081, 1085, 1086, 1087, 1089, 1094, 1100, **1106**, 1106-7, 1110, 1121, 9:1126, 1151;
  in plant nutrition 6:807
copper pyrites *see* chalcopyrite
copper-leaf 1:8
copra 2:250, 5:651, 654
Coprinus 1:104
Coptis 1:104, 3:399
coquitos palm 5:654
coral bells 2:173
coral flower 2:173
coral fungi 1:91
coral gem 2:211
coral plant 2:188
coral tree 2:144, 135;
  Hawaiian 2:134
coral vine 4:428
coralberry 1:40, 5:610
Corallina 1:104, 9:1215
Corallocarpus 4:465, 467
Corallorhiza trifida 7:903
corals (anthozoans) 8:1015, 1056, 1064, 9:1134, 1154, 1159, 1160, 1161, 1162, 1163, 1166, 1167, 1170, 1178, 1188, 1213, 1214, 1220-1;
  rugose 9:1156, 1164, **1220-1**;
  scleractinian 9:1178, 1185, 1221;
  tabulate 9:1156, 1164, 1220;
  see also atolls, reefs
Corchorus 1:104, 2:191, 4:441, 441
cord grass 6:777, 7:945

Cordaitales 6:739, 740, 9:1176, 1218
Cordaites 9:1176
Cordia 1:104, 5:583, 584, 584
cordierite 8:1088, 9:1138
Cordilleran province 7:898
Cordioideae 5:586
Cordyceps 1:104
Cordyline 1:104, 5:666
core 8:972, 973, **974**, 989, 991, 996, 997, 998, 1003, 9:1122
Corema 4:478, 479, 479, 7:873
Coreopsis 1:104, 5:617
coreopsis 2:126, 174, 175;
  green 1:105
coriander 1:104, 5:571
Coriandreae 5:571
Coriandrum 1:104, 2:147, 174, 5:571
Coriaria 5:550, 550, 551
Coriariaceae 5:550, **550-1**
Coridaceae 4:484
Corideae 4:484
Coris 4:484
cork 1:105
cork oak 4:410
cork tree 3:267, 5:554
cork-bark tree 2:168
corkwood 2:144
corm of crocus 6:778
corn 1:83, 2:216;
  dent 2:216;
  flint 2:216;
  Guinea 3:319;
  Indian 2:216;
  kafir 3:319;
  squirrel 3:319;
  sweet 2:216
corn cockle 1:14, 4:419
corn root, sweet 3:342
corn salad 3:349, 5:610
Cornaceae 4:506, 516, **517-8**, 518, 5:568, 571, 618
Cornales 4:516-8, 5:571
cornel 1:105
cornelian 8:1087
cornelian cherry 1:123
cornflour 1:105
cornflower 6:821;
  American 1:81
Cornoideae 4:518
Cornus 1:105, **122**, 3:389, 4:517, 518
Corokia 1:105, 4:518
Coronanthereae 5:596
Coronilla 1:105
Coronopus 4:470
Correa 1:105, 5:554
Corrigiola 4:419
Corsia 5:671
Corsiaceae 5:671, 675
Corsican curse 3:318
Corsieae 5:671
Cortaderia 1:105, 5:638, 7:904
Cortesia 5:583
Cortinarius 1:105
cortisone 7:925
Cortusa 1:106
corundum 8:1080, 1082, **1088**, 1098, 1103, 9:1135
Corybas 5:675
Corydalis 1:106, 4:403, 403, 404
Corylaceae 4:409
Coryleae 4:409
Coryloideae 4:409
Corylopsis 1:106, 4:407
Corylus 2:170, 4:409, 410, 6:726, 749, 7:838;
  avellana 6:703, 750
Corynanthe 1:26
Corynebacterium 1:51
Corynephorus canescens 6:792
Corynocarpaceae 4:530
Corynocarpus 4:530
Corynostylis 4:450, 451
Corypha 1:106, 5:651, 653
Coryphantha 1:106
coryphoid palms 5:653

Coscinieae 3:401
Coscinium 3:401, 401
cosets 8:1017
Cosmos 1:106, 5:617, 618
Costaceae 5:648
costmary 1:106, 2:174, 175
Costus 1:106, 5:647, 648, 648
Cotinus 1:106, 3:317, 5:547, 548
Cotoneaster 1:106, 4:491, 494, 494;
  microphylla 6:686;
  rotundiflora 6:686;
cotton 1:107, 107, 2:144, 145, 250, 4:444, 445, 6:691, 7:932, 943;
  bog 7:902;
  devil's 2:145;
  Egyptian 1:107;
  lavender 3:307, 307;
  okra-leaf 7:924;
  sea island 1:107;
  tree 2:163;
  wild 2:176
cotton grass 2:133, see also Eriophorum
cotton rose 2:176
cotton seed 4:472
cotton seed oil 2:250
cottonweed 2:163
cottonwood 3:279, 341, 6:826;
  black 3:279
Cotula 1:107, 5:618
Cotuleae 5:618
Cotyledon 1:107, 4:495
cotylosaurs 9:1176, 1236, 1238
couch, sand 1:13
couch grass 1:13, 14, 7:948;
  East African 7:950;
  sea 6:825, 825
Couepia 4:498
Coula 3:356, 4:524
coumarin 1:36, 2:227
Coumarouna 3:342
courbaril 2:183
courgette 1:107, 2:222, 223, 4:465, 467
Couroupita 1:107, 4:449, 450
Cousinia 5:617
cover 6:715-6
cow parsley 5:571
cow parsnip, common 2:173
cow tree 1:66
cowage 2:233
cowbane 1:89
cowberry 1:108, 2:151, 3:354
cow-itch 2:233, 3:276
cowpea 1:107, 123, 2:201, 201, 262, 3:326, 4:502
cowslip 3:280, 281;
  blue 3:284;
  Cape 2:195;
  common 3:277;
  Himalayan 3:281;
  Jerusalem 3:284;
  Virginian 2:228
cow-tang 3:264
coypu in fens 7:882-3
crab apple 1:108
crab's eyes 1:6
crakeberry 2:130
Crambe 1:108, 4:470, 470, 7:936;
  abyssinica 7:936;
  maritima 6:818
crampbark 3:354
cranberry 1:108, 2:151, 152, 4:474, 475, 477, 7:880, 885, 903;
  American 1:108;
  European 1:108;
  highbush 3:354;
  mountain 1:108;
  rock 1:108;
  small 1:108
cranberry bush 3:354
cranberry tree 3:354
crane flower 3:326
cranesbill 2:160, 5:558, 559, 6:819;

bloody 2:161, 6:706;
  dove's foot 2:161;
  meadow 2:161;
  wild 2:161
Craniolaria 5:602
Crassocephalum 3:312, 5:617, 618
Crassula 1:108, 4:495, 503, 5:590
Crassulaceae 4:495, 495, 503
crassulacean acid metabolism 6:799, 799, 7:848
Crataegus 2:169, 219, 4:491, 494, 7:838;
  monogyna 6:751, 800, 7:940
Crateranthus 4:449, 450
craters, impact:
  lunar 8:977, 978, 983, 989;
  Martian 8:982, 983, 984, 985, 989;
  Mercurian 8:981, 983, 989;
  terrestrial 8:986, 987, 989, 1089
craters, volcanic 8:1057
Cratoneuron 1:108
Cratoxylum 4:436, 437
cream of tartar tree 1:10
creambush 2:178
creeper:
  Canary 3:345;
  New Guinea 2:233;
  Rangoon 3:286;
  Virginia 2:260, 261
creeping annuals 6:724, 724
creeping berries 3:313
creeping boobialla 5:593
creeping dwarf shrubs 6:722
creeping grasses 7:855
creeping herbs 6:723
creeping jenny 2:213
creeping sailor 3:309
crème de violette 3:355
Cremolobeae 4:470
Cremolobus 4:470
creodonts 9:1192, 1195, 1246
creosote bush 2:197, see also Larrea
creosote plant 5:554
crepe myrtle 4:507
Crepis 1:108, 5:617
Crescentia 1:69, 108, 5:600
cress 1:64, 65, 108, 2:202;
  American 1:108;
  bitter 1:75;
  blister 1:134;
  brown 3:357;
  common 1:108, 2:202;
  garden 1:108, 2:202;
  hairy rock 1:39;
  Indian 3:345;
  land 1:108;
  Lebanon 1:12;
  rock 1:38;
  true 1:108, 2:202;
  violet 2:186;
  water 1:108;
  yellow 3:296
crestal mountains 8:1060, 1061, 1063, 1064
Cretaceous 6:738-9, 740, 742-4, 743, 744, 765, 8:1001, 1052, 9:1130, 1131, 1133, 1134, 1173, 1181, 1187-91, 1209, 1214, 1215, 1216, 1219, 1226, 1233, 1261;
  climate 9:1188, 1242-3;
  fauna 9:1188, 1189-90, 1244;
  flora 9:1188, 1188-9, 1218;
  geography 9:1187-8, 1188, 1191
Cretan bear's tail 1:81
Crick, Francis 6:761
Crinodendron 4:439, 440
crinoids 9:1154, 1156, 1160, 1170, 1185, 1189, 1222, 1223
Crinum 1:109, 5:664, 666
cristobalite 8:979, 1088-9, 1095-6
Crithmum 1:109
critical resources 6:820
Crocanthemum 2:171, 4:458

Croceae 5:662
crocidolite (blue asbestos) 8:1085, 1089, 1098
crocodiles 9:1181, 1187, 1206, 1209, 1235, 1236, 1239, 1243
Crocosmia 1:109, 5:662
Crocus 1:109, 5:661, 661, 662, 664, 6:682, 778, 781;
  balansae 6:762;
  sativus 6:681
crocus 1:109, 109;
  autumn 1:26, 98, 6:781;
  Indian 3:275
Cro-Magnon Man 9:1252
Cromerian interglacial 6:749
crook root 3:322
crookneck, summer 2:222
Croomia 5:668
Croomiaceae 5:668
crops:
  collections of 7:957, 958-9;
  damaged by weeds 7:949;
  domestication of 6:791, 7:924-9, 926-8;
  future 7:935-6;
  improvement of 7:931-4, 932-3, 935;
  primitive and advanced 7:956-8
crop-spraying, aerial 7:947
cross profiles 8:1039-40
cross-bedding 8:1017, 9:1129, 1136
cross-lamination 8:1017
cross-vine 1:57
Crossandra 1:109, 5:601
crossopterygians 9:1232, 1234
Crossosoma 4:432
Crossosomataceae 4:430, 432, 5:542
crotal 2:126
Crotalaria 1:109, 2:173
crotalism 1:109
Croton 1:110, 4:535, 537, 537
croton 1:97, 110;
  purging 1:110
croton oil 2:250
croton oil plant 1:110
Crotoneae 4:537
crottle 2:126
crowberry 2:130, 4:478, 479, see also Empetrum
crowding 6:820
Crowea 5:552
crowfoot 2:129, 3:399;
  alpine white 6:698;
  bulbous 3:287;
  Persian 3:287;
  water 3:287, 287, 6:764, 7:944
crown imperial 2:150, 150
crown of thorns 2:138
crown trees 6:719
Crucibulum 1:60, 3:284
Cruciferae 4:403, 469-72, 471, 5:562, 6:697, 7:936
crust 8:972, 973, 974-5, 989, 1089, 9:1122, 1124, 1136;
  continental 8:973, 975, 1002, 1003, 1005, 1036, 9:1125;
  formation of 9:1150, 1151;
  oceanic 8:973, 975, 1002, 1003, 1005, 1036, 9:1140
crustaceans 9:1156, 1170, 1189, 1228
cryolite 8:1089
Cryptanthe 5:586
Cryptanthus 1:110, 5:644, 646
Cryptocarpus 3:273
Cryptocarya 1:54, 110, 3:324, 388
Cryptocaryeae 3:388
cryptoendemism 7:915
cryptogams:
  aquatic 6:725, 725;
  mat-forming 6:724, 724
Cryptogramma 1:110
Cryptomeria 1:110
cryptophytes 6:725
Cryptostegia 2:214, 3:297
crystal habit 8:1075, 1082

crystallography 8:1075-80, 1075, 9:1269;
  X-ray 8:1078
crystal systems 8:1075-80, 1077;
  cubic 8:1076, 1077, 1078, 1079, 1082, 1089, 1090, 1091;
  hexagonal 8:1077, 1080;
  monoclinic 8:1077, 1079-80, 1080, 1084;
  orthorhombic 8:1077, 1079, 1084, 1100;
  tetragonal 8:1077, 1078-9, 1079;
  triclinic 8:1077, 1080;
  trigonal 8:1077, 1080, 1083, 1086, 1097
Ctenolophon 5:557, 558
Ctenolophonaceae 5:557
Ctenopharyngodon idella and weed control 7:950
cuachalala 5:544
cubbra borrachero 2:232
Cubeba 3:273
cubic system see crystal systems
cuckoo bread 2:257
cuckoo flower 1:75, 2:212, 213
cuckoo pint 1:42
cucumber 1:110, 2:161, 222, 223, 3:350, 4:465, 467, 7:943;
  bitter 3:350;
  serpent 2:223;
  squirting 2:127, 223;
  wild 1:110
cucumber tree 2:215
Cucumeropsis 4:465, 467
Cucumis 1:110, 2:161, 163, 2:178, 222, 224, 4:465, 467;
  sativum 4:465
Cucurbita 1:107, 111, 2:163, 222, 3:284, 323, 4:465, 467, 467
Cucurbitaceae 4:453, 455, 463, 465-7, 466, 7:919
Cucurbiteae 4:465
Cucurbitoideae 4:465
cuddle-me-to-you 2:259
cudweed 2:163
cultivars:
  advanced 7:956, 957-8;
  naming of 6:698;
  obsolete 7:958;
  primitive 7:927, 956-7;
  see also crops
cultivated grassland 7:862, 938-41, 939-40
cultivated plants see crops, cultivars
cultivation:
  areas of 7:926;
  and domestication 7:925
cultural methods of weed control 7:949-50
cumin 1:111, 2:146, 147, 249, 5:571;
  black 2:241
Cuminum 1:111, 2:147, 5:571
Cunningham, Allan 6:687
Cunninghame, James 6:684
Cunninghamia 1:111
Cunonia 4:487, 487
Cunoniaceae 4:407, 487, 487-8, 490, 513, 5:540
cup and saucer plant 1:93
cup flower 2:241
cup plant 3:315;
  Indian 3:315
Cupaniopsis 5:543
Cuphea 1:111, 4:506, 507, 507
cupid's dart 1:79
cupolas see domed bogs
× Cupressocyparis 1:111
Cupressus 1:113, 4:521, 6:747
cuprite 8:1089, 1106
curare 1:111, 2:227, 3:326, 400, 401, 5:572
curare poison nut 1:26, 111
curarine 1:26
Curculigo 5:665
Curcuma 1:111, 2:126, 3:346, 5:648

currant 1:111, 4:496, 497, 498, 538, 539;
American black 1:112, 3:294;
black 1:58, 111, 112, 2:151, 152, 3:294;
buffalo 3:294;
common 1:112;
flowering 1:112, 3:294;
garden 1:112;
golden 3:294;
Missouri 3:294;
Northern 3:294;
red 1:112, 2:151, 152, 3:294, 294
Curtisia 1:45, 4:517, 518, 518
Curtisioideae 4:518
curub 2:151, 223
Cuscuta 1:122, 5:580, 6:724, 773, 7:948
Cuscutaceae 5:580
Cuscuteae 5:580
cushaw 1:111
cush-cush 3:328
cushion bush 1:71
cushion flower 3:315
cushion plants 6:722, 722
Cusparia 1:30, 112, 2:147, 5:554
Cusparieae 5:554
Cussonia 5:568
custard apple 1:31, 2:151
cutch 1:7, 112, 2:126
cuticle, fossil 6:732
Cutleria 1:112
Cuvier, Baron Georges 6:731, 7:964, 9:1207, 1260, 1261, 1262, 1263, 1266, 1271
Cyamopsis 2:201
Cyananthus 5:604
Cyanastraceae 5:669, 669-70
Cyanastrum 5:669, 669
Cyanchoideae 5:576
Cyanea 5:606
Cyanella 5:669, 669
Cyanotis 5:629, 631
Cyathea 1:112, 6:740
Cyatheaceae 6:720
Cyathus 1:60, 3:284;
striatus 6:818, 818
Cycadales 6:739
cycadophytes 6:740, 9:1217, 1218
cycads 1:112, 9:1176, 1179, 1185, 1188, 1189, 1217
Cycas 1:112
Cyclamen 1:112, 4:484, 484
cyclamen, florists' 1:112, 113
Cyclamineae 4:484
Cyclanthaceae 5:654-5, 655, 656
Cyclanthales 5:654-5
Cyclanthera 4:465, 467
Cyclanthereae 4:465
Cyclantheropsis 4:465, 467
Cyclanthoideae 5:654
Cyclanthus 5:654, 655
cyclic vegetation 6:716-7
Cyclobeae 4:423
Cydonia 1:112, 3:286, 4:494
Cylicodiscus 2:164
Cylicomorpha 4:455
cymarin 5:575
Cymbalaria 1:112, 3:264, 337, 5:595
Cymbidium 1:112, 5:675
Cymbopogon 1:112, 5:638, 640
Cymodocea 5:627
Cymodoceaceae 5:626, 627
Cynanea:
gayana 6:774;
leptostegia 6:774;
pilosa 6:774
Cynara 1:42, 75, 113, 5:617, 618
Cynoches 1:79
Cynocrambaceae 4:504
Cynodon 1:113, 5:638, 638
cynodonts 9:1176, 1244
Cynoglosseae 5:586
Cynoglossum 1:113, 5:586
Cynometra 2:187, 3:341, 4:502
Cynomoriaceae 4:525, 527

Cynomorium 4:525
Cynosurus 1:113, 5:638, 7:863
Cypella 1:113, 5:662
Cyperaceae 5:638, 641, 642, 642-3
Cyperales 5:642-3
Cyperus 1:113, 4:506, 5:642, 643;
latifolia 7:883;
papyrus 6:724, 724, 826, 7:885, 885
Cyphia 5:604
Cyphiaceae 5:604
Cyphomandra 1:113, 5:579
cypress 1:113, 6:747;
Arizona 1:111, 113, 114;
bald 3:333, 7:837;
bastard 1:84;
Bhutan 1:114;
false 1:84;
funeral 1:113;
Himalayan 1:114;
Hinoki 1:84;
hybrid 1:111;
Italian 1:113;
Lawson 1:84, 6:719;
Mediterranean 1:113;
Mexican 1:111, 3:333;
Monterey 1:111, 113;
Montezuma 3:333;
Nootka 1:84, 111;
Patagonian 2:143;
pond 3:333;
Portuguese 1:113;
rough-barked Arizona 1:113;
Sawarra 1:85;
smooth Arizona 1:111, 114;
summer 2:194;
swamp 1:84, 6:747;
white 1:85;
yellow 1:84, 111
cypress pine 1:71
Cypripediaceae 5:675
Cypripedioideae 5:675
Cypripedium 1:114, 5:675, 675
Cyrilla 2:187, 4:474, 475
Cyrillaceae 4:474, 475, 6:748
Cyrtandra 5:596
Cyrtandreae 5:596
Cyrtandroideae 5:596
Cyrtanthus 1:114, 5:664, 665, 666
Cyrtomium 1:114
Cyrtosperma 3:328, 5:659
Cysticapnos 4:403
cystoids 9:1223
Cystopteris 1:114;
fragilis 7:921
Cytineae 4:528
Cytinus 4:527, 528;
hypocistus 6:724
cytisine 2:227
Cytisus 1:114, 2:195, 4:499, 502, 521
cytogenetics:
and breeding 7:933-4, 958;
and endemism 7:914-5;
and tobacco 7:927
cytotaxonomy and circum-Antarctic distributions 7:911

2,4-D 7:946
Daboecia 1:115, 4:477
dacites 8:1058, 9:1126, 1127, 1150, 1180
Dacrydium 1:115, 3:272, 6:721, 7:837, 904
Dacryodes 2:129, 5:546, 547
Dactylanthus 4:526
Dactylis 1:115, 5:638, 6:690, 7:863;
glomerata 6:705
Dactyloctenium 5:638
Dactylorhiza 1:115, 5:675, 675

Daemonorops 1:115, 124, 3:289, 5:654
daffodil 1:115, 2:238, 238, 5:664, 666, 6:778, 7:830;
Peruvian 2:183;
petticoat 2:238, 239;
winter 3:324
Dahlia 1:115, 3:278, 5:613, 615, 617, 618
dahlia 1:115;
bedding 1:116;
bell tree 1:116;
candelabra 1:116;
flat tree 1:116;
garden 1:115, 115
daisy 1:54, 116, 7:949;
African 1:40, 3:353;
Alpine 1:116;
Barberton 2:161;
blue 2:139;
blue-eyed African 3:353;
bush 1:116;
butter 3:287;
Cape 3:353, 353;
common 1:116;
double orange 2:133;
Easter 3:342;
globe 2:162;
gloriosa 3:300, 300;
kingfisher 2:139;
Michaelmas 1:45, 116, 2:229;
moon 2:202;
Mount Atlas 1:28;
ox-eye 1:89, 116, 2:202;
Paris 1:89;
rock tree 1:116;
seaside 2:133;
shasta 1:89, 116, 2:203;
Swan River 1:62, 63, 116;
Transvaal 2:161;
see also Bellis
daisy bush 2:248, 5:618
daisy tree 2:248
dal 2:199
dalapon 7:950
Dalbergia 1:116, 3:296, 346
Dalbergieae 4:502
Dalechampia 4:535, 537
Daly, R. 9:1266
damask oil 2:173
Damasonium 5:619, 620, 620
damiana 3:346
dammar 1:116, 3:315, 4:435;
almond 1:116
Dampier, William 6:687
Dampiera 5:607
dams 8:1065, 1066, 1067-8, 1069
damson 1:116, 2:151, 152, 3:275, 4:494;
butter 1:116;
West African 1:116
damson plum 2:164
Dana, J. 9:1260, 1263, 1266, 1269
dandelion 1:116, 3:332, 5:613, 618, 6:723, 817, 817, 7:949;
common 1:116, 116, 3:332, 332;
Russian 3:300, 333
dandelion coffee 1:58
danewort 3:306
Danthonia 5:636, 7:905;
pallida 7:862
Danthonieae 5:636, 638
Dapedius 9:1231
Daphne 1:116, 2:198, 3:323, 4:509, 510, 510, 511
Daphniphyllum 1:116, 4:537
Darlingtonia 1:117, 4:404, 404, 405
darnel 7:949
Dart, R. 9:1266, 1271
Darwin, Charles 6:679, 688, 691, 731, 759-60, 761, 766, 7:964, 964, 8:1064, 9:1126, 1152, 1203, 1259, 1260, 1262, 1266-7, 1270, 1271, 1273

Darwin, Erasmus 6:759, 7:964
Darwin, George Howard 9:1267
Darwinia 4:511
Daryphora 7:837
dasheen 3:328, 5:659
Dasylirion 1:117, 6:720
Dasypogon 5:666
date 1:117, 117, 2:151;
Chinese 3:363;
cliff 3:269;
Jerusalem 1:53;
wild 1:117
date palm 1:117, 117, 3:268, 5:651;
India 3:269;
Senegal 3:269;
wild 3:269
date plum 1:121, 4:483
dating 9:1142-6, 1149;
of continental drift 6:741-3;
of fossils 6:734-5, 734-5, 759
Datisca 4:464
Datiscaceae 4:464
Datura 1:117, 5:579, 579
datura, sacred 1:117
Datureae 5:579
Dauceae 5:571
Daucus 1:77, 117, 5:569, 571, 571
Davallia 1:117
David, Armand 6:684
Davidia 1:118, 4:516;
involucrata 6:684
davidia tree 6:685
Davidiaceae 4:516
David's harp 3:277
Davidsonia 4:487
Davis, W. 9:1263, 1267, 1268
Davis, W. 9:1266
dawn flower, blue 2:186
Dawsonia 1:118
day flower 1:99
day-length:
and dormancy 7:854;
and flowering 6:793, 795, 795
daylily:
dwarf yellow 2:172;
fulvous 2:172;
lemon 2:172, 173;
orange 2:172;
tawny 2:172;
yellow 2:172, 173
DDT 7:941, 946
De Geer, G. 9:1267
De la Beche, H. 9:1260, 1262, 1267, 1271
De Vries, Hugo 6:761, 762
deadly nightshade 5:579
dead-men's fingers 3:360
dead-nettle 2:196;
giant 2:196;
red 2:196;
spotted 2:196;
white 2:196, 196
deal, yellow 3:272
death cap 1:25
Decaisnea 3:399, 400, 400
Decaphalangium 4:436
Decaryia 4:423, 424
Decumaria 1:118
Deeringia 4:420, 421
de-etiolation 6:794-5
deformability 8:1065-6
Degeneria 3:382
Degeneriaceae 3:378, 379, 382
Deherainia 4:486
dehydration 7:845
Deimos 8:985-6
Deinosuchus 9:1243
Deinotherium 9:1197
Delavay, Jean-Marie 6:684
Delissea 5:606
Delisseae 5:606
Delonix 1:118, 4:502
Delphineae 3:399
Delphinium 1:118, 3:396, 399, 6:704;
gypsophilum 7:915
delphinium 1:118, 118

deltas 8:*1015*, **1052-5**, *1053,*
1054, 9:1135;
arcuate 8:*1053, 1054*;
elongate (birdfoot) 8:1053-5;
lobate 8:1053-5
demarcation knots 7:895
demethion 7:946
Dendranthema 1:89, 5:618;
morifolia 6:769;
sinensis 6:769
Dendrobangia 4:530
Dendrobenthamia 4:517
Dendrobium 1:118, 5:*673*, 675;
cunninghamii 6:687;
gibsonii 6:687
Dendrocalamus 1:118, 5:636
dendrochronology (tree-ring
dating) 6:*735*, 735, 9:1146
dendrograms 6:696
dendroids 9:1230
Dendromecon 1:119, 4:403
Dendrophthora 4:524
Dendrosenecio 3:313, 6:769
Dendrosicyos 4:465, 7:919
Dendrosonchus 6:774, 7:915
density 6:716, 820-1
Dentaria 1:75
deodar 1:80, 3:341
dependence 6:*709*, 710
deposition 8:*1015, 1016,*
1017, 1021, 1038, 1052,
1056, 9:1130, 1134, 1147
Derris 1:119
derris root 1:119
Deschampsia 1:119, 5:638;
antarctica 7:855, 920;
caespitosa 6:791, 7:854;
flexuosa 7:875
Descole, H. R. 6:(*702*)
description:
of species 6:*698*, 699, *700, 704*;
of vegetation 6:*708-30*
desert candle 2:132
desert roses 8:*1047*, 1085
deserts 6:798-9, 7:*832-3*, 832,
844-8, *845-7*;
polar 7:845, 902;
soils of 6:808, *809*;
see also arid landscapes
desert-steppe 7:859
Desfontainea 1:119
Desmodium 1:119
destroying angel 1:25
detergents and aquatic plants
7:944
determinism, evolutionary 6:764-5
Deutzia 1:119, 4:498
developing countries, conservation
in 7:954-5
development hypothesis (Lamarck)
6:759
Devensian glaciation 6:749
devil flower 3:331
devil-in-a-bush 2:241
devil's backbone 2:263
devil's coachwhip 7:848, *see also*
ocotillo
devil's cotton 1:6
devil's fig 1:40
devil's herb 1:46
devil's leaf 3:348
devil's paintbrush 2:177
devil's tongue 1:27, 2:139
devil's walking stick 1:39
Devonian 6:*738-9*, 739, 743, 766,
9:1152, **1163-6**, *1165*, 1170,
1172, 1209, 1214, 1229,
1231, 1232, 1234, 1261,
1271, 1273;
climate 9:1163, 1165;
fauna 9:1163-5, *1164*, 1166;
flora 9:1163, *1164*, 1175;
geography 9:1163, *1164*
Devonshire, Duke of 6:686
dewberry, Pacific 2:151, 3:300
dhak 1:68
dhal 2:199
Dhobi's nut 5:548

diachronism 9:1149
diagenesis 6:731, 8:**1020-1**, *1020,*
1021, 9:1129, 1134
diakinesis in meiosis 6:763
Dialyceras 4:445
diamonds 8:1073, *1081*, 1082,
1088, **1089**, 1102, 9:1128,
1129
Dianthus 1:76, **119**, 4:417, *419,*
419, 7:943
diapensia 4:480, 481, *481*
Diapensiaceae 4:477, **480-1**, *481*
Diapensiales 1:**480-1**
diaspores 6:816-9, 8:1103
diatomites 9:1215
diatoms 1:120, 7:881, 8:1061,
9:1163, 1191, **1215**
Dicentra 1:120, 4:*403*, 403-4
Dichanthium 2:149
Dichapetalaceae 4:**532-3**, *533*
Dichapetalum 4:532, *533*, 533
Dichelostemma 1:66
Dichondra 5:580, *580*
Dichondraceae 5:580
Dichondreae 5:580
Dichorisandra 5:631
Dichrostachys 4:502
Dicksonia 1:120, 6:740;
antarctica 6:720
Dicoma incana 7:916
dicotyledons 9:1218
Dicraeia 4:*503*, 503
Dicranopygium 5:654
Dicranum 1:120, 7:884;
elongatum 7:855
Dictamnus 1:68, **120**, 5:554
Dictyonema 9:1230
Dictyophora 3:284
Dictyosperma 1:120, 3:271
Dictyostelium 1:120
Dictyota 1:120
dicynodonts 9:1236, 1243-4
diddle-dee 7:*873*, *see also Empetrum*
Didiereaceae 4:**423-4**, *424*, 7:897
Didierea 4:*424*, 424
Didymocarpeae 5:596
Didymoglossum 2:141
Didymotheca 4:421
Dieffenbachia 1:120, 5:659
dieldrin 7:946
Dierama 1:120, 5:662
Diervilla 1:120, 5:610;
florida 6:684
differentiated table 6:*728*
digitalin 2:148
Digitalis 2:148, 5:593, 595, *595,*
6:724;
purpurea 6:762, 7:950
Digitaria 2:149, 230, 5:638, 640;
scalarum 7:950
digoxin 2:148
dikes 7:*881*, 883, 8:*1030, 1031,*
1032, 1034, 9:*1125*;
swarms 8:*1030, 1031*, 9:1149,
1151
dilatancy hardening 8:1026-7
Dilatris 5:668
dill 1:121, *121*, 2:161, 174, *175,*
5:569, 571
Dillenia 4:*430*, 430-1
Dilleniaceae 4:*430*, **430-1**, 432,
436, 452, 456, 5:542
Dilleniales 4:430-2
Dilleniidae 4:430-86
Dillwynia 1:121
dilpasand 4:467
Dilsea 3:289
Diluvial Theory 6:731
Dimerocostus 5:648
Dimetrodon 9:1176, 1243
Dimocarpus 2:203
Dimorphotheca 1:121, 2:219, 5:618
dinocephalians 9:1243
Dinochloa 1:49
dinoflagellates 9:1185, 1189,
1190, **1215-6**;
and food poisoning 7:945

dinosaurs 9:1205-6, 1209, 1236,
1239, *1240*, **1241-3**, *1241,*
1271;
Triassic 9:1178;
Jurassic 9:1181, 1187;
Cretaceous 9:1189, 1191
Diocoryphe 4:407
dioecious species 6:769, 7:921
Dionaea 1:121, 3:313, 4:489, *489,*
490;
muscipula 6:683, 710
Dionysia 1:121
Dioon 1:121
diopside 8:996, **1089**, 1097
diorites 8:1085, 1086, 1092,
9:1124, 1125, **1126**
Dioscorea 3:360, 5:670, 7:925,
931
Dioscoreaceae 5:669, *670*
Dioscorides 6:680
diosgenin 3:360
Diosma 5:552, 554
Diosmeae 5:554
Diospyros 1:121, 2:127, *191,*
3:266, 307, 4:483, 7:921
Dipelta 1:121
Dipholaena 5:554
diphtheria 1:51
Diphylleia 3:395, 396
Dipladenia 2:217
Diplarche 4:481
Diplazium 2:140
Diplococcus 1:51
Diplodocus 9:1181, 1241
Diplophyllum 1:121
Diplotaxis 2:174, 4:470
diplotene in meiosis 6:763
Diplusodon 4:507
dipnoans *see* lungfish
Dipsacaceae 5:607, **611-2**, *612,*
613, 618
Dipsacales 5:608, 609-13
Dipsaceae 5:611
Dipsacus 1:122, 5:*612*, 612
Diptera and pollination 7:854
Dipteridaceae 6:743
Dipterocarpaceae 4:432, **434-5**,
435, 445, 461, 522, 5:546,
6:745, 7:897, 935
Dipterocarpoideae 4:435
Dipterocarpus 1:122, 4:*434*, 435,
435
Dipteronia 5:545, 546
Dipterygium 4:468
Dipteryx 3:342
Dirachma 5:559
Dirachmoideae 5:559
direct gradient analysis 6:730
directional selection 6:769
Disa 1:122, 5:*675*, 675;
caerulea 6:683
Disanthoideae 4:407
Disanthus 4:407
Discaria toumatou 7:861
Disciphania 3:401
dis-climax 6:*713*, 714
Discocapnos 4:403
discontinuous distributions 6:*745;*
7:905, *906-11*, **906, 907-11**
discontinuous variation 6:762
disease resistance 7:932, 933, 934,
935, 957, 958
disease vectors 7:949
dispersal 6:816-9, *817-9*;
and aliens 7:950-2;
of desert annuals 7:850;
long-distance 7:905, 909, 911,
919
disruptive selection 6:769
Dissotis 4:513, 514
Distichia 5:641, 641
distribution 6:707-8, 7:893-919;
and continental drift 6:743-5,
7:919;
continuous and discontinuous
6:745, 7:905, *906-11*, **906,**
907-11;
and islands 7:917-21;

mapping of 6:*706-7*, **707-8**;
patterns of 7:906-21;
restricted 7:912-7
districts, floristic 7:894
ditch grass 5:626
dittany 1:68
dittany of Crete 2:256
diversity, centers of 7:906, 927,
957
divi-divi 1:69, **122**
divine flower 1:119
Dizygotheca 1:112, 5:568;
veitchii 6:687
DNA 6:761, 8:1075, 9:1203-4
Dobera 4:530
dock 6:751;
Alpine 3:301;
broad-leaved 3:*300*, 301;
curled 7:888
docodonts 9:1184
dodder 1:*32*, **122**, *122*, 5:580,
6:*773*, 7:948
Dodecatheon 1:122, 4:484, *484*
Dodonaea 2:249, 5:543, *543*
dogbane:
hemp 1:37, 2:144;
spreading 1:37
dogberry 1:123, 3:319
dog-hobble 6:203
dogrose 3:296, *296*
dog's mercury 6:792
dog's tail, crested 1:113
'dog-tooth' calcite 8:*1075, 1086*
dogwood 1:122, 3:281, 4:517;
blood-twig 1:123;
flowering 1:71, *105*, 123;
giant 1:123;
mountain 1:123;
red barked 1:123;
red osier 1:123;
Tartarian 1:123;
Western flowering 1:123
Dokuchaiev, V. 9:1140, 1141
dolerite 8:1030, 1085, 9:*1125*
Dolichos 1:123, 2:195, 4:502
dolines 8:1043, *1044*
dolomite:
mineral 8:1009, 1021, 1080,
1081, 1084, **1089**, 1103,
1104, 9:*1123, 1133, 1134,*
1135, 1136;
rock 8:1043, 1088, 1089,
1090, 1104, 9:*1134*, 1136,
1180
domains:
clay 6:803-4;
floristic 7:894
Dombeya 1:123, 4:442, *442*
domed raised bogs 7:877, *878,*
879
domestication of plants 7:924-34,
926-8
Domin, K. 6:716
dominance 6:711, 820-1, 7:*884*
dominions, floristic 7:897
Donatia 5:606, 607, 7:905;
fascicularis 7:*908*;
novaezelandicae 7:*908*
Donatiaceae 5:607
Donatioideae 5:607
donkey's tail 3:312
Doona 4:435
Dorema 1:123
dormancy 6:815;
and day-length 7:854
Doronicum 1:123, 5:617
Dorotheanthus 4:417
Dorstenia 1:123, 4:446
Doryanthes 1:123, 5:666
Doryphora 3:384, 385
Dose, K. 6:752
doub 1:113
double coconut 5:653
double refraction (birefringence)
8:*1082*, 1087
Douglas, David 6:683, 7:965
Douglas fir 1:123, *124*, 3:341,
6:683, 7:837, 866, 867, 942

dove tree 1:118, 6:*684*
dove's foot 2:161
Downingia 5:606
downy mildew 3:266
Doxantha 1:57, 5:600
Draba 1:**124**, 4:470, 472
Dracaena 1:**124**, 5:666, 6:720
dracaena 6:687
Dracocephalum 1:**124**
Dracontomelon 6:747
Dracophyllum 4:478, *478*
Dracunculus 1:**124**, 5:659
dragon arum 1:*124*
dragon mouth 2:**178**
dragon root 1:40
dragon tree 1:**124**, 5:666
dragonhead 1:**124**;
   false 3:270
dragon's blood 1:110, **124**;
   Malayan 1:115
dragon's blood tree 1:**124**
drainage:
   and afforestation 7:879-80;
   in bogs 7:877, 879;
   in fens 7:*881*, 881, 882-3;
   in soils 8:804-5
drainage basins 8:1037
Draparnaldia 1:**124**
drape folds 8:1028
Draperia 5:585
Drepanocladus 1:**124**, 2:234, 7:855
Drimys 1:**125**, 3:378, *379*, 6:744,
   745, 766, 7:837, 904;
   winteri 6:745
dropwort 2:142
dropworts 6:826
Drosanthemum 4:417
Drosera 1:**125**, 4:489, *489*, 490;
   anglica 7:884;
   arcturi 7:908;
   uniflora 7:908
Droseraceae 3:393, 4:405, *489*,
   489-90
Drosophyllum 1:**125**, 4:489, *489*,
   490
drought 6:*798*, 7:849;
   avoidance of 7:848-50;
   and domestication of crops
   7:925;
   evasion of 7:850;
   injury from 6:798, *799*, 7:845;
   response to 6:798-800;
   tolerance to 7:848;
   in tundra 7:853
Drude, Carl 6:689, 719, 7:965
drumlins 8:1050
Drummond, James 6:687
Drummond, Thomas 6:683
Drusa 5:569
dry rot 3:313
dry steppe 7:859, *860*
dry surfaces, succession on
   6:824-6
dry zone grasslands 7:859-60
dryad's saddle 3:278
Dryas 1:**125**, 4:494, 6:826, 7:869;
   drummondii 7:912;
   integrifolia 7:854;
   octopetala 6:750, 789, 7:912
Dryas glacial phase 6:750
Dryobalanops 1:73, 3:341
Dryopteris 1:**125**, 6:825;
   thelypteris 7:884
Du Rietz, Gustaf 6:729, 7:965
Duabanga 4:506
dubia 3:268
Duchesnea 3:325
Duckesia 5:556, *556*
duckweed 1:**125**, *125*, 5:656, *see
   also Lemna*;
   tropical 3:273
Dudleya 1:**125**
Duguetia 1:**125**
dulse 1:19
dumb plant 1:120
dumb-bell model of origin of life
   6:*753*, 753
Dunalia 5:579

dunes 6:*825*, **825-6**, 7:*886-7*,
   886-8, 8:*1017*, **1046-7**, 1048,
   1052, 1056, 1062, 9:1165,
   1213
dunite 8:979, 1095
Dupontia 7:854, 901
durable resistance 7:933
durian 2:**127**, 151, *153*, 4:443,
   444
duricrusts 8:1047
Du Toit, A. 8:1002, 9:1267
Durilignosa formation-type 7:836
Durio 2:**127**, 151, 4:*443*, 444
Durvillea antarctica 6:782
dust diaspores 6:817
dust pollution 7:941
dusty miller 1:81, 3:313
Dutch elm disease 2:130
Dutchman's breeches 1:120, 4:404
Dutchman's pipe 1:40, 3:392
dwarf bamboo meadows 7:861
dwarf heath 7:872
dwarf shrubs 6:722, **722**
dwarf succulents 6:721-2
Dyckia 2:**127**, 5:644, 646
Dyera 3:341, 5:574
dyer's greenweed 2:160
dyer's woad 2:187
dyes 2:**127**
Dysosma 3:396
Dysoxylum 2:**127**, 215, 234, 5:552

E

early domestication, theories of
   7:925-7
early history of plant life 6:752-7,
   765-6
Earth, the *passim, et*:
   age of 8:971, 976, 997, 9:1142-
   6, *1144-5*, 1149, 1257, 1263,
   1265-6, 1269, 1275;
   atmosphere 8:996-7, 1009,
   1034, 1038, 9:1122, 1143,
   1151, 1153, 1202;
   chemical differentiation 8:972,
   996;
   composition 8:972-5, 995,
   995-6;
   gravitational field 8:991-2, *993*;
   heat flow within 8:1032-3,
   1050, 9:1122;
   internal temperatures 8:974-5,
   992, 9:1136;
   magnetic field 8:980, **993-4**,
   1003-4, *1004*, 1027-8,
   9:1149, 1190, 1199;
   magnetic poles 8:994;
   Man's ideas of 9:1254-63;
   natural vibrations of 8:991;
   oblateness of 8:1002;
   obliquity of axis 8:998;
   origin of 8:971-2, 976, 997,
   9:1142, 1258, 1265-6;
   origin of life on 8:1034, 9:1201-
   3, 1264;
   physical measurements 8:972-5;
   structure 8:972-5, 991, 9:*1257*;
   year, length of 9:1208;
   see also core, crust, mantle
earth almond 5:643
earth balls 2:127, 3:284
earth pillars 8:*1011*, 1043, *1053*
earth smoke 2:154
earth stars 1:110, 2:127, 3:284
earthnut 1:38, 99
earthquakes 8:990, 1002, 1023,
   1024-8, *1025*, 1027, 1037,
   1062, 1063, 1068;
   associated phenomena
   8:1027-8;
   prediction and control 8:1026-7;
   Mercalli intensity 8:1026;
   Richter magnitude 8:1026;

in relation to plate movements
   8:1005, 1006, *1024*, 1025-6,
   1033, 1040
East African region 7:897
East Indian arrowroot 5:648, 668
eau d'ange 2:237
eau de creole 2:217
Ebenaceae 4:483
Ebenales 4:432, 482-4
ebony 1:53, 121, 2:**127**, 4:483,
   7:921;
   black carving 3:341;
   Calabar 2:127;
   Ceylon 3:341;
   coromandel 2:127;
   East Indian 1:121, 3:341;
   Gaboon 2:127, 3:341;
   green 3:334;
   greenheart 3:334;
   Macassar 1:121, 2:127;
   North American 3:266;
   Senegal 1:116;
   Texas 3:274
ebony wood 1:53
ecads 6:706
Ecballium 2:**127**, 4:465
Eccremocarpus 2:**127**, 5:599, 600
Ecdeiocolea 5:634
Ecdeiocoleaceae 5:634
Echeveria 2:**127**, 4:495, *495*
Echieae 5:586
Echinacea 2:**127**, 5:617
Echinocactus 2:**127**, 4:415;
   acanthodes 6:722, 7:849, 895
Echinocereus 2:**128**, 4:415
Echinochloa 2:230, 5:638
Echinocystis lobata 6:724
echinoderms 9:1154, 1185, 1189,
   1222, **1223-4**
Echinodorus 5:620
echinoids 8:1015, 9:1156, 1185,
   1189, 1223, **1224**
Echinophora 5:571
Echinophoreae 5:571
Echinops 2:**128**, 5:615, 617, 618
Echinopsis 2:**128**, 4:415
Echinospartium 2:160
Echinospermum 5:586
Echioides 1:41
Echium 2:**128**, 5:585, 586, *586*,
   6:774
eclogite 8:973, 1093, 9:**1129**,
   1137
Ecluse, Charles de l' 6:680
ecoclines 6:706
ecological control of weeds 7:950
ecological gradients 6:706, 828
ecological isolation 6:778, 779,
   779-80, *780*
ecology:
   of early domestications 7:925-7;
   of forests 7:841-2
ecology of plants:
   history of 6:689-91;
   methods and concepts of 6:693-
   735
economics:
   and breeding 7:934;
   and conservation 7:952
ecosystem 6:689-90, 708-15, 784
ecotones 6:*710*, 710-1
ecotypes 6:*705*, 705-6, 773, 776,
   779, 815
Ectocarpus 2:**128**
edaphic climax 6:714
edaphic factors in growth and
   distribution 6:802
Edaphosaurus 9:1176, 1243
eddo 5:659
edelweiss 2:**128**, 202
edentates 9:1195, **1248**, *1266*
edge effect 6:711
Ediacaran metazoa 6:757
edrioasteroids 9:1154
eel grass 3:363, *363*, 5:626, 7:885
eelworms suppressed by weeds
   7:949

Eemian interglacial 6:749
effective publication 6:699
Egeria 5:621
egussi 4:467
egg fruit 1:46, 2:128
eggplant 1:46, 3:317, 350, *352*;
   Chinese 1:46;
   snake 1:47
eglantine 3:296
Ehretia 5:583, 584, *584*
Ehretiaceae 5:**583-4**, *584*
Ehretioideae 5:586
Eichhornia 2:**129**, 5:659, *660*, 660,
   661;
   crassipes 6:820, 826, 7:948
Eichleria 5:559, 560
einkorn 7:927
Elaeagnaceae 4:**518-9**, *519*, 520
Elaeagnus 1:**129**, 4:518, *519*, 519
Elaeis 2:**129**, 5:651, 653, *653*,
   654
Elaeocarpaceae 4:**439-40**, *440*
Elaeocarpus 2:249, 4:**440**, 440
Elaeodendron 4:529, *529*
Elaphomyces 1:104, 2:**129**, 3:345
elapids 9:1238
Elateriopsis 4:465
elaterite 8:1112
elaterium 2:127
Elatinaceae 4:437, **437-8**
Elatine 4:437, *437*, 438
Elatostema 4:448
elder 1:47, 3:306, 5:609, *610*;
   American 3:306;
   American red 3:306;
   common 3:306;
   Dane's 3:306;
   dwarf 3:306;
   European 3:306;
   European red 3:306;
   ground 1:11, 7:948;
   prickly 1:39;
   red-berried 3:306;
   rose 3:354;
   sweet 3:306;
   yellow 3:334
elderberry 3:306, 5:610
elecampane 2:185
electromagnetic geophysical studies
   8:**992-3**, *993*;
   resistivity methods 8:1067
electromagnetic (EM) prospecting
   techniques 8:993
electron microprobe analyzer
   8:996
Elegia 5:*634*, 634
elements 8:997, **1101-11**, *1102*;
   Aristotelian 9:**1255**, 1258,
   1263, 1264;
   cosmic abundances of 8:995;
   periodic table of 8:**1101**, 1102
   in phytochoria 7:894-5
elemi 1:68, 2:**129**
Eleocharis 2:**129**, 5:643
Elephantopus 5:615
elephants 9:1197, 1198, 1246,
   1247
Elettaria 1:75, 5:648
Eleusine 2:**129**, 230, 5:638, 640
eleven o'clock 3:279
elfin woodland 7:867, 868
Elie de Beaumont, L. 9:1260,
   1262, **1267-8**
Elliottia 4:477
elluviation 6:802
elm 2:**129**, 4:445, 6:749;
   American 2:129;
   Chichester 2:129;
   common 2:*130*;
   Cornish 2:129;
   Dutch 2:129, 3:341;
   English 2:129, 3:341;
   European field 2:129;
   hickory 3:341;
   Holland 3:341;
   Huntingdon 2:129;
   red 2:129;
   rock 2:130, 3:341;

Scotch 2:129;
September 2:129;
slippery 2:129, 3:341;
Spanish 1:104;
white 2:129;
wych 2:129, 168
Elmerrillia 3:378
Elodea 2:130, 5:621, 622, 6:826, 7:944;
 canadensis 6:816, 827, 7:947
Elster ice advance 6:749
Elton, Charles 6:689
Elwes, Henry John 6:681, 687
Elymus 2:130, 5:638;
 arenarius 6:825, 7:886, 887, 920, 921
Embelia 4:486, 486
emblic 3:269
embolomeres 9:1235
Embothrium 2:130, 4:520, 6:744
emerald 8:1080, 1081, 1084, 1086, 1089
emergence marshes 7:889
emergents 7:834
emery 8:1088
emetine 1:26, 2:186, 227
Emilia 2:130, 5:617
emmer 7:927
Empetraceae 4:474, 477, 478-9, 479
Empetrum 2:130, 4:478, 479, 479, 7:905, 910, 910;
 hermaphroditum 7:910;
 nigrum 7:873, 873, 875, 910;
 rubrum 7:873, 873, 910, 910
empress tree 2:261
Empusa 2:131
emu bush 5:592
Enallagma 1:108
Encelia farinosa 6:822
Encephalartos 2:130
Endeavour (Captain Cook's ship) 6:687
endemics 7:894, 897, 913-7, 914-6, 920
endemism 7:913-7, 914-6
Endiandra 3:388
endive 1:87, 89, 2:130, 3:350, 351, 5:618;
 Batavian 3:350;
 Belgian 3:350
Endodesmia 4:436
Endonema 4:509
Endonemeae 4:509
Endopleura 5:556
endosymbiotic view of chloroplast origin 6:759
Endothia 2:130
endothion 7:946
endozoochory 6:816-7
endrin 7:946
Endymion 5:662
energy:
 in food chains 6:709;
 radiant 6:787, 792-4;
 see also light, solar radiation
eng oil 1:122, 2:250
eng tree, Indian 1:122
Engellardtia 5:555
engineering geology 8:1065-9, 1065, 1066, 1067, 1068, 1072
Engler, Adolf 7:914, 965
Enhalus 2:130, 5:622
Enkianthus 2:131, 4:477
Ensete 2:131, 5:646, 646, 647
enstatite 8:972, 996, 1089, 1097
Entandrophragma 2:215, 3:307, 341, 5:552
enteldonts 9:1248
Enteromorpha 2:131
Entomophthora 2:131
environment 6:784-6;
 and grassland types 7:862;
 and growth 6:704;
 pollution of 7:941-7;
 and tundra vegetation 7:851-3

environmental stability:
 of islands 7:916-7, 919-20;
 of salt marshes 7:889;
 and tourism 7:937
enzian 2:160
enzymes and temperature 6:789, 791
eobionts 6:752
Eocene 6:738, 740, 742, 746-7, 8:1001, 9:1191, 1192, 1193-5, 1193, 1194, 1216, 1245-6
Eocoelia 9:1161-2
eocrinoids 9:1154
Eohippus 9:1248
Epacridaceae 4:474, 477-8, 478
Epacrideae 4:478
Epacris 4:478, 478, 7:874
Eperua 3:341
epharmony 7:833
Ephedra 2:131, 4:413
ephedra 2:227
ephedrin 2:131, 227
ephemerals 6:724, 799, 7:849, 850
epibionts (epibiotics) 7:914, 915-6
Epicampes 1:66
Epicattleya 2:131
Epidendreae 5:675
Epidendrum 2:131, 5:675
epidiorite 9:1137
epidote 8:1079, 1089, 9:1140
Epigaea 4:477
Epilobieae 4:512
Epilobium 2:131, 4:512, 513, 6:781, 817, 826, 7:920;
 hirsutum 6:793, 7:885
Epimedieae 3:396
Epimedium 2:131, 3:395, 396
Epipactis 2:131, 172
Epiphyllum 2:132
epiphyllum 2:132
epiphytes 6:721, 721, 771-2, 7:867
Episcia 2:132, 5:596, 598
Episcieae 5:596
epizoochory 6:816
epsomite 8:1077
Equisetum 2:180, 6:740, 7:884, 9:1217;
 arvense 6:759
Eragrostideae 5:638
Eragrostis 2:132, 230, 5:638, 640
Eranthemum 2:132, 5:601
Eranthis 2:132, 3:396, 396, 399
Erblichia 4:454
Ercilla 4:421
Eremolepideae 4:525
Eremophila 3:306, 5:592, 592, 593
Eremothamneae 5:617
Eremothamnus 5:617
Eremurus 2:132, 5:662
Erepsia 4:417
ergot 1:26, 2:132, 226, 227
ergotamine 1:26, 2:227
ergotism 1:26
ergs 8:1047
Eria 2:132, 5:675
Erianthus 2:132, 5:638
Eriastrum 5:583
Erica 1:63, 2:133, 170, 4:474, 475, 477, 477, 6:786, 826, 7:874, 898;
 arborea 7:898, 907;
 cinerea 6:829, 7:873, 875;
 scoparia 6:829, 7:873;
 tetralix 6:829, 7:873;
 vagans 7:873
Ericaceae 4:474-7, 476, 478, 479, 480, 481, 5:564
Ericales 4:432, 473-80, 5:582
ericoid shrubs:
 dwarf 6:722, 7:872;
 xeromorphic 6:721
Ericoideae 4:477
Erigeron 2:133, 5:618
Erinacea 2:133
Erinus 2:133, 5:595
Eriobotrya 2:133, 4:494

Eriocaulaceae 5:628, 631, 631-2
Eriocaulales 5:631-2
Eriocaulon 5:631, 632;
 septangulare 7:909
Eriogonum 2:133, 4:428, 7:843
Eriophorum 2:133, 5:643, 6:810, 7:854, 855, 869, 880, 901;
 augustifolium 6:829, 7:876;
 latifolium 7:876, 880;
 vaginatum 7:876, 902
Eriophyllum 2:133, 5:617
Eriostemon 5:554
Eriotheca 4:444
Erisma 5:564, 565
Erismadelphus 5:564, 565
Eritrichieae 5:586
Eritrichium 5:586
Erodium 2:133, 5:558, 558, 559
erosion 8:1010-4, 1011, 1012, 1013, 1016, 1021, 1030, 1032, 1036, 1037, 1038, 1039, 1040, 1042, 1043, 1045, 1046, 1056, 1057, 1062, 9:1122, 1125, 1130, 1133, 1135, 1147, 1150, 1268;
 cycle of 9:1267;
 by ice 8:1011-2, 1012, 1020, 1037, 1048, 1051;
 lunar 8:977;
 Martian 8:983, 985;
 Mercurian 8:981;
 of meteorites 8:989;
 of soil 7:935, 936, 940, 940, 944;
 Venusian 8:982;
 by water 8:1010-1, 1013-4, 1051-2, 1055, 1068, 9:1139;
 by wind 8:1012-3, 1013, 1046;
 see also soil erosion
erratics, glacial 8:1049, 1050
Eruca 2:174, 3:295, 4:470
erucic acid from crop plants 7:936
Erycibe 5:580
Eryngium 2:134, 5:569, 571, 571;
 maritimum 7:887
Erysimum 2:134, 3:295, 4:472
Erysiphe 2:134, 6:773
Erythrina 2:134, 185, 4:502, 502
Erythrochiton 5:554
Erythronium 2:134, 5:664
Erythrospermum 4:452
Erythroxylaceae 5:560
Erythroxylum 1:93, 2:135, 5:560
Escallonia 2:135, 4:498;
 virgata 6:728
Escalloniaceae 4:489, 498
Escallonioideae 4:489, 498, 5:610
escarolle 1:89, 3:350
Escherichia 2:135
Eschscholzia 2:135, 4:402, 402, 403;
 minutiflora 6:800;
 californica 7:951
Esenbeckia 5:554
Eskola, P. 9:1268
esparcet 2:149, 252
esparto 2:135, 144, 145, 5:640, 6:723
Espeletia 5:617, 6:720
essence of roses 1:46
establishment 6:819;
 of aliens 7:951;
 on islands 7:920-1
Estonian school of phytosociology 6:729
estragon 3:333, *see also* tarragon
Ethiopian floristic region 7:897, 897
ethological isolation 6:780-1
ethylene gas and leaf fall 7:943
Etna 8:1033, 1034
Eucalyptus 2:126, 135, 187, 193, 227, 233, 4:511, 511, 512, 6:721, 723, 770, 773, 814, 7:836, 837, 842, 916, 920, 926;

eucalyptus oil 2:136
Eucharis 2:137, 5:666
Eucheuma 3:289
Euchlaena 2:216, 3:334, 5:638
Euclea 4:483
Eucnide 4:464
Eucomis 2:137, 5:664
Eucommia 4:407
Eucommiaceae 4:407, 446
Eucommiales 4:407
Eucryphia 2:137, 4:490
Eucryphiaceae 4:490, 5:590
Eudorina 1:20, 21
Eugenia 2:137, 187, 4:511, 512, 6:818;
 longiflora 7:891
eugenol 2:227
Euglena 2:137
Euglypha 3:391
eukaryotes, first 6:739, 753, 757, 759
eulittoral zone 6:828
Eulophia 2:137, 5:675
Euodia 2:137
Euonymus 2:137, 4:528, 529, 529
Euparkeria 9:1211, 1239
Eupatorieae 5:615, 617
eupatorin 2:138
Eupatorium 2:138, 5:617;
 microstemon 7:949
Euphorbia 2:138, 3:276, 323, 4:413, 535, 537, 6:768, 770, 7:842, 893, 936, 949;
 amydaloides 6:768;
 aphylla 6:768;
 canariensis 6:768;
 candelabrum 6:768;
 fulgens 6:768;
 helioscopia 6:768;
 kamerunensis 6:768;
 marginata 6:683;
 paralias 6:768, 7:887;
 poissonii 6:768;
 pulcherrima 6:768;
 regis-jubae 6:768;
 splendens 7:850
Euphorbiaceae 4:522, 530, 534, 535-7, 537, 6:721, 7:848, 897
Euphorbiales 4:424, 533-7
Euphorbieae 4:535, 537
Euphrasia 2:138, 5:593, 7:965
Euphronia 5:564
Eupomatia 3:383
Eupomatiaceae 3:383
Euptelea 4:405
Eupteleaceae 4:405
Euramerican province 6:740, 741, 743
Eurhynchium 2:138, 6:824, 7:944;
 ripariodes 7:944
European ash 5:577, *see also* ash
European plant explorations 6:680-1
Euro-Siberian region 7:897, 898, 902
europium 8:979
Eurya 4:432, 433
Euryalaceae 3:395
Euryale 3:394, 395
Euryops 5:617
eurypterids 9:1229
Eurystemon 5:659
Euscaphis 5:540
Eusideroxylon 2:187
eustatic sea-level changes 7:909
Euterpe 2:138, 7:896
Euthemis 4:434
eutrophic water in peatland 7:875, 881-3
eutrophication 7:945
Euxylophora 3:308
evaporites 8:1015-6, 1023, 1074, 1083, 1084, 1091, 1096, 1100, 1102, 1103, 1104, 1119, 9:1130, 1133, 1134, 1135, 1155, 1166, 1170, 1177, 1179, 1197

evapotranspiration 7:845
evasion of drought 7:850
evening primrose 4:512, 6:762, 799, *see also* primrose
evergreen broad-leaf trees 6:720
evergreen crown-trees 6:719
evergreen shrubs, life-forms of 6:721
everlasting 4:420, 429, 5:618, 631, 632;
    mountain 1:31
Evodia 5:554
Evodianthus 5:654, 655
evolution 8:1001, 9:1142, **1203-6**, *1204*, *1206-7*, 1208, 1213-4, 1260, 1263, 1266, 1267, 1270, 1271, 1272;
    and adaptability 6:768, **769**;
    and classification 6:696, *697*;
    and fossil record **6:765-6**;
    and the Galapagos 7:917;
    and geology 6:739, *739-51*;
    and natural selection **8:759-65**;
    and origin of life 6:752-7;
    and polar floras **7:910-1**
evolutionary theory **6:759-65**
Exacum 2:138
Exbucklandia 4:407
Exbucklandioideae 4:407
excessive enrichment of water 7:941, **945**
exclusion, competitive **6:786-7**
exclusive species 6:729
exfoliation 8:1008
exhausts from engines 7:942-3
exines 6:734
Exocarpos 4:521, 522
Exochorda 2:138, 4:491, 494
Exochordeae 4:491
Exospermum 1:125, 3:378
Exotic Theory of fossil origins 6:731
exotics 7:959
expanding Earth hypothesis 8:1004
exploitation:
    of heathland **7:874-5**;
    of tropical forests 7:935, 937-8
explorations 6:*680-8*, **680-8**
exposure **6:800-1**, *801*
Extermination Theory of fossil origins 6:731
external reproductive isolation **6:780-1**
extinction, man-made 7:921, 952, 963
eye rot 2:239
eyebright 2:138

Fabaceae 4:499
Fabales 4:494, 499-502
facies, phytocoenal 6:729
Fagaceae 4:409, **410-2**, *411*
Fagales 4:407, 409-12, 494
Fagoideae 4:410
Fagara 5:554
Fagopyrum 1:67, 2:139, 4:428
Fagraea 5:572, 573
Fagus 1:54, 4:410, *410*, 6:711, 717, *717*, 747, 749, 827, 7:838, 841, 866, 867, 868;
    grandifolia 7:896;
    sylvatica 6:791, 7:896
fair maids of France 3:309
fairy castles 2:254
fairy clubs 1:91
fairy crosses (fairy stones) 8:1099
fairy ring 4:527
Falkia 5:580
Falkland Islands province 7:904;
    aliens of 7:952

fallowing 7:949
false aralia **1:122**
false cypress **1:84**
false nettle, Hawaiian 1:61
false-trunk trees 6:720
Falya 4:533
families 6:696;
    endemic 7:913;
    and floral realms 7:894;
    and isolation 7:917
fan-palm **6:748**
FAO 7:959
Far North of Europe explored **6:688**
farm effluents **7:946**
farmer's lung 1:44
Farrer, Reginald 6:686, 7:965
fat hen 1:86, *86*, 7:949
× *Fatshedera* 2:139, 5:568
Fatsia 2:139, 5:568
fatty acids from crop plants 7:936
Faucaria 2:139, 4:417
fault, transform 8:1026
faulting **8:1022-3**, *1022*, 1026, 1029, 1036, 1060, 1066, *1072*, *1113*, 9:1126, 1139, *1275*
fault-plane solutions 8:1026
Favarger, Claude 7:914
fayalite 8:1081, 1095
feather top 3:264
feather-grass *see Stipa*
federations, synusial 6:729
Fedia 5:610;
    cornucopiae 6:817
Feijoa 2:139, 4:512
feldspars 8:973, 974, 979, 980, 996, 1009, 1031, *1080*, *1083*, 1086, 1088, **1090**, 1092, 1096, 1104, 9:*1124*, *1125*, 1126, *1127*, 1129, 1130, 1131, *1132*, 1136, *1137*, *1139*
feldspathoids **8:1090**, 1095, 1098, 9:*1124*, 1126
Felicia 2:139, 5:618
fell-field 7:855, 902
felonwood 3:317
felt bush 2:192, *192*
Fenestraria 4:415
fennel 1:31, 2:139, 174, *175*, 5:569, 571, 7:876;
    Florence 2:139, 3:350, *351*;
    giant 2:139, *139*;
    sweet 2:139
fennel flower 2:139, 241, 3:399
fens 7:875, 878, **880-3**, *881-2*;
    carex 7:*903*;
    and carr woodland 8:989;
    and peat 6:810, **7:881-2**
fenugreek 1:26, 2:*146*, 147, 3:343
ferallitic soils 6:808
fern 2:140, 6:*739*, 9:*1163*, 1176, 1179, 1185, 1209, *1210*, 1216, 1217;
    African 3:276;
    American maidenhair 1:10;
    American wall 3:278;
    Anderson's holly 3:278;
    asparagus 1:43, *44*;
    ball 1:117;
    beech 1:47;
    bird's nest 1:45, *45*, 2:141;
    black maidenhair 1:10;
    black-stemmed tree 3:343;
    bladder 1:114;
    blue 3:278;
    Boston 2:240;
    buckler 2:140;
    chain 3:359;
    Christmas 3:278;
    cinnamon 2:256;
    cliff 1:125;
    climbing 2:141;
    coastal wood 1:125;
    comb 3:310;
    common maidenhair 1:10, *10*, 2:*141*;

cotton 2:242;
    crested buckler 1:125;
    crested wood 1:125;
    curly grass 3:310;
    dagger 3:278;
    deer 1:60, *61*;
    Eaton's shield 3:278;
    elkhorn 3:274;
    English hedge 3:278;
    erect sword 2:240;
    European chain 3:359;
    European oak 2:140;
    fragrant 1:125;
    gold 2:242;
    golden cloak 2:242;
    grape 2:140;
    hard 1:60, *61*;
    hardshield 3:278;
    hare's-foot 1:117, 3:278;
    hart's-tongue 3:268, *269*;
    hedge 3:278;
    holly 1:125, 3:278;
    Japanese holly 1:125;
    king 2:219;
    ladder 2:240;
    lady 1:46, *47*, 2:140;
    leather 1:10;
    leather wood 1:125;
    licorice 3:278;
    maidenhair 1:10, *10*, 2:*141*;
    male 1:125, 2:140, *141*;
    marginal shield 1:125;
    marsh 1:10, 7:884;
    mosquito 1:48;
    narrow buckler 2:140;
    necklace 1:45;
    oak 1:47, 2:140;
    ostrich 2:220;
    parsley 1:110;
    prickly shield 3:278;
    rabbit's-foot 1:118, 3:278;
    ribbon 2:*141*, 3:283;
    royal 2:256, *257*;
    rush 3:310;
    savannah 2:162, *162*;
    sensitive 2:252;
    shield 1:125, 3:278;
    silver 2:242;
    soft shield 3:278;
    squirrel's-foot 1:117;
    stag's-horn 2:140, *141*, 241, **3:274**;
    sun 2:162;
    sword 2:240;
    tree 1:*120*, 3:*342*, *342*;
    true maidenhair 1:10;
    Virginia chain 3:359;
    wall 3:278;
    wavy cotton 2:242;
    Western holly 3:278;
    whisk 1:94;
    wood 1:125;
    see also pterophytes
ferns in evolution 6:*739*
Ferocactus 2:139, 4:415
ferricretes 8:1047
fertilizers:
    and afforestation 7:880;
    and grassland 7:938, *939*, 941;
    and pollution 7:945
Ferula 2:139, 5:569, 571
ferulic acid as chemical defense 6:823
fescue 2:139;
    blue 2:139;
    creeping 2:139;
    meadow 2:149;
    red 2:139, 6:825;
    reed 2:149;
    sheep's 2:139, 149, 7:860, 862;
    tall 2:149, 7:940;
    see also Festuca
Festuca 2:139, 5:636, 638, 7:862, 863, 904, 905;
    arundinacea 7:940;
    ovina 7:860, 862;
    rubra 6:815, 825, 7:889, 921
festucoid grasses 7:862, 863

fetterbush 3:271
fever plant 2:247
feverfew 3:285
Fevillea 4:465
fiber:
    istli 2:144, **187**;
    kitul 1:77, 2:145;
    ozone 1:43, 2:144
fibers from crop plants 7:936
Fibraurea 3:401
Fibraureae 3:401
Ficus **1:52**, 2:142, 195, 3:297, 4:447, *447*, 6:825, 7:896, 897
fidelity, phytocoenal 6:729
field balm 2:162
field capacity of soils 6:804
field resistance to disease 7:933
fieldmark 7:855, 902
fig 2:142, 151, *152*, 4:446, 447, *447*, 7:897;
    Adriatic 2:142;
    climbing 2:142;
    cluster 2:142;
    common 2:142;
    devil's 1:40;
    East Indian 2:142;
    edible 2:142;
    India rubber 2:142;
    Indian 2:253, *254*;
    Maryland 3:311;
    Smyrna 2:142;
    sycamore 3:330;
    weeping 2:142;
    wild 2:142
figwort:
    Cape 3:269;
    common European water 3:311
Fijian Pacific floristic region 7:897
filaree:
    red-stemmed 2:134;
    white-stemmed 2:134
filbert 2:170, 4:409, 410;
    European 2:245;
    giant 2:245, *245*
Filipendula 2:142, 4:491, 494, 498;
    ulmaria 7:884
Filtonia 5:601
finger millet 5:640
finocchio 2:139, 3:350
fiorin 1:14
fir 1:6;
    balsam 1:6, 3:324, 341, 346;
    Alpine 7:867, 904;
    Californian red 3:341;
    cascade 3:341;
    Caucasian 1:6;
    Chinese **1:111**;
    colorado 1:6;
    common silver 1:6;
    Douglas 1:6, *123*, *124*, 6:683, 7:837, 866, 867, 942;
    Fraser 7:904;
    giant 1:6, 3:341;
    grand 1:6, 7:866;
    gray 1:124;
    Himalayan 1:6;
    Korean 1:6;
    noble 1:6, 3:341;
    Oregon 1:124;
    red 1:6, *6*, 3:341;
    Scotch 1:6;
    silver 1:6, 3:341, 6:749, 7:904;
    white 1:6, 7:866;
    see also Abies
fire 6:785, *811*, **811-2**;
    in chaparral 6:822, *822*, **7:843-4**;
    in grasslands 7:862;
    in heathlands 7:874, **874-5**;
    and weed control 7:949
fire bush 3:326, 4:520
fire thorn 4:494
fire tree, Chilean 2:130, *130*
firecracker, California 1:66
firepink 3:315
firethorn 3:285, *285*

fireweed 1:85, 2:131
Firmiana 4:442
Fisher, Ronald 6:764
fishes 9:*1206-7*, **1230-5**, *1231, 1233*;
    Cambrian 9:1154;
    Ordovician 9:1156;
    Silurian 9:1160-1;
    Devonian 9:1163-4, 1209;
    Carboniferous 9:1170;
    Jurassic 9:1184;
    Cretaceous 9:1189;
    Tertiary 9:1197
fishtail palms 1:77
Fissidens 2:143
fissility 9:1131
fissipeds 9:1246
Fittonia 2:143
Fitzroya 2:143, 7:837
fivespot 2:239
fjords 8:1056
Flacourtia 4:452
Flacourtiaceae 4:445, *451*, **451-2**, 453, 468, 510, 537
flag 2:187;
    blue 2:187;
    crimson 3:310;
    poison 2:187;
    spiral 1:106;
    sweet 1:9, *10*, 2:226;
    water 2:187;
    Western blue 2:187;
    yellow 2:187, 7:884
flag root 1:9, 2:226
Flagellaria 5:632, *633*
Flagellariaceae 5:631, **631-3**, 640
flageolets 2:169
flamboyant 1:118
flamboyant tree 4:502
flame creeper 3:345
flame flower 3:285
flame of the forest 3:321
flame vine 3:285
flamegold 2:194
flameleaf, Mexican 3:276
flaming sword 3:356
flaming trumpet 3:285, *285*
flamingo flower 1:*37*
flamingo plant 2:191
Flandrian interglacial 6:750-1
flaver 3:358
flaver drake 2:247
Flaveria 5:617
flavoring plants 2:146
flax 2:**143**, *143*, 144, *145*, 207, 208, *208*, 5:557, 558;
    blue 2:143;
    fairy 2:143;
    false 2:143;
    mountain 3:269;
    New Zealand 2:143, 144, 3:269, *269*;
    pink 2:143;
    spurge 2:143
fleabane 2:133
fleece flower 3:277
fleece vine, China 3:277
fleur-de-lis 2:187
flies and pollination 7:854
Flindersia 3:341, 5:554
flint 8:1087, 1097, 9:1135, *1190*, 1191
floating cryptogams, natant 6:725, *725*
floating fruits 6:817-8
floating hearts 2:243
floating-leaf water-herbs 6:724, *725*
Floerkea 5:560
Flood, the 9:1147, 1207, 1257, *1260*, 1265, 1275
floodplains 8:*1039*, **1039-40**, 1062
floppers 2:192
floradora 3:324
floras (descriptive) 6:*701-4*, **701-4**, 707;
    early 6:680, 688, 702

floras (living) **7:894-903**;
    distinguished from vegetation 6:708
Florida corkwood 4:407, 408
floristic composition 6:708, **727-30**
floristic districts, domains, kingdoms 7:894
floristic provinces 7:894, 898;
    Laurasian 6:741, 743;
    North American 7:898
floristic realms 7:894, **895-6**, *897*
floristic regions 7:894, **896-7**, *897*, 898
Floscopa 5:631
flour 2:143
flower of love 2:259
flowering and day-length 6:793, *795*, 795
flowering ash 5:577
flowering cherry 4:494
flowering inch-plant 3:342
flowering plants 1:32, *see also* angiosperms
flowering quince 4:494
flowering rush 1:68, *68*
flowering rush 5:619
flower-of-an-hour 2:176
fluorapatite 8:1084, 1104
fluorescence 8:1083, **1090**
fluoride pollution 7:942
fluorine 8:1084, 1100, 1109, 9:1126
fluorite (fluorspar) 8:1075, 1078, 1082, 1089, **1090**, 1104
flutes 8:1050, 9:1132
fluvial fen 7:881, 881
fly agaric 1:25
flycatcher, Australian 1:81, *82*, 4:496
flycatcher plant 1:81, *82*, 4:496
flysch 8:1035, 9:*1194*
foam of may 3:322
foam-flower 3:336
fodder crops 2:149
Foeniculum 2:139, **143**, 5:569, 571
Foetidia 3:324, 4:449
folding 8:1023, **1028-9**, *1028, 1029*, 1034, 1035, 1038, 9:*1151*, 1180, *1275*
foliage flower 3:269
foliation *see* gneissose banding
folk taxonomy 6:694
Fomes 2:143
Fontanesia 2:148, 5:577
Fontanesieae 5:577
Fontinalis 2:148, 6:725
food chains 6:*709*, 7:**941**, 946, 947
food poisoning 7:945
fool's gold *see* pyrite
foothills vegetation 7:866
footsteps-of-spring 3:306
foraminifera (forams) 8:1007, 1087, 9:*1167*, 1176, 1185, 1188, 1189, 1192, 1198, 1208, 1210, **1219**, 1220, 1227
Forbes, Edward 6:689, **7:965**
forbs 7:855
forest destruction 6:751, 7:838, 842, 862, 875, 922, 935, 937, 937-8, 958
forest limit 7:868
Forestiera 2:148
Forestry 7:935, 936, **938**;
    and peatland 7:**879-80**
forests 7:*832-3*, 832, **833-40**, *834*;
    antarctic 7:904;
    basal 7:866;
    boreal coniferous 7:838-9, 866, *903*, 938;
    camping 7:835;
    cloud 7:*866-7*, *867*;
    Colchic 7:838;
    deciduous summer 7:*831*, 838;
    dry tropical 7:836-7;
    gallery 7:835;

Man's impact on 7:937-8;
    Mediterranean 7:836-7;
    savanna 7:835-6;
    temperate rain 7:*836*, 837, 837-8;
    tropical rain 6:*692*, 709, *712*, 7:*834*, **834-5**, 878;
    Valdivian rain 7:837
forest-steppe 7:859
forget-me-not 2:237, 5:585, *586*;
    Alpine 2:237;
    Chinese 1:113;
    creeping 2:249;
    garden 2:237;
    water 7:885;
    wood 2:237
fork moss 7:884
'form' genera and species 6:*765*, 765
formations, physiognomic 6:717-8
Forrest, George 6:*685*, 685, **7:965**
Forrestia 5:629
Forskohlea 4:448, *448*
Forskohleeae 4:448
Forstera 5:607
forsterite 8:1081, 1095
Forsythia 2:148, 5:576, 577;
    viridissima 6:684
forsythia 2:148
Forsythieae 5:577
Fortune, Robert 6:684, *0*, **7:965**
Fortunella 1:91, 2:151, **194**, 5:554
fossil record 9:1149, **1206-10**, 1211, 1261
fossilization 6:730-1, 731-4, *732*
fossils 6:*730-4*, **730-5**, 8:*1086*, 1087, 1121, 9:*1123*, 1135, 1142, 1149, *1152*, 1173, 1206, *1209*, 1260, 1261, 1268, 1273;
    of *Calamites* 6:765;
    and continental drift 6:740, *743*;
    debates over nature of 9:1256-7, 1259, 1264;
    and evolution 6:765-6;
    first 6:756-8;
    of Gondwanaland flora 6:742;
    of *Lepidodendron aculeatum* 6:764;
    of *Nilssoniocladus* 6:743;
    preservation of 8:*1020*, 1021, 9:*1136*, 1207;
    of Quaternary flora 6:748;
    of *Rhynia* 6:739;
    of Tertiary flora 6:745, 745-6;
    see also stratigraphic correlation
Fothergilla 2:148, 4:406, 407
foulbrood 1:49
founder principle and genetic drift 6:775
fountain tree 3:321
Fouquieria 1:118, 4:455;
    splendens 6:*722*, 799, 7:*848*, 849, 850
Fouquieriaceae 4:455
four o'clock plant 2:231
Fox, Sidney 6:752, 753-4, 9:1202, 1203
foxglove 2:148, 227, 5:593, 595, 6:724, 761-2, 7:950;
    common 2:148;
    large yellow 2:148;
    small yellow 2:148;
    Spanish rusty 2:148
foxglove tree 2:261
foxtail 1:24;
    marsh 7:885;
    meadow 7:861
foxtail millet 5:638, 640
fractional crystallization 9:1124, 1126, 1127, 1136
fracture 8:1082
Fragaria 3:325, 4:491, *494*, 494
framboise 3:288
frame quadrats 6:716
framiré 3:341
Francoa 2:148, 4:497
Francoaceae 4:498
Francooideae 4:497

frangipani 3:275, 5:575
Frangula 1:15, 2:148, 4:537;
    alnus 7:881, 884
Frankenia 4:461, *461*, 462
Frankeniaceae 4:438, 460, *461*, **461-2**
frankincense 2:148, 5:546, *547*;
    Bible 1:62, 2:148
frankincense tree 6:*680*, 680
Franklinia 2:150, 4:432, *433*
Frasch process 8:1104
Fraser, Charles 6:687
Fraser, John 6:683
Fraxineae 5:577
fraxinella 2:150
Fraxinus 1:43, 2:219, 5:576, *576*, 577, 6:749, 7:838;
    excelsior 7:884, 896;
    nigra 7:896
Fredolia 6:722
Freemontodendron 2:150, 4:442
Freesia 2:150, 5:661, *662*
freezing 6:789, *789*
French bean 4:502; *see also* bean
French marigold 5:618
frequency 6:716
freshwater marshes 7:875, 884-5
freshwater pollution 7:**943-5**, *944-5*
fret-lip 2:168
Freycinetia 5:655, *656*, 656
friar's balsam 4:483
Friesodielsia 3:381
frijolito 3:318
fringe cup 3:334
fringebell 3:315
Frithia 4:415
Fritillaria 2:150, 5:664
fritillary, snake's head 2:150
Froelichia 4:420, *421*
Froesia 4:438
frog's bit 2:183, 5:621, 6:826
frog-spawn alga 1:53
frost shattering 8:1009, 1040, 1092, 9:*1138*
frostweed 2:171
fruit salad vine 5:659
fruits and dispersal 6:816-8
Frullania 2:150
Fuchsia 2:150, 4:512, *513*, 6:795
fuchsia 2:150;
    Californian 3:363;
    Cape 3:269;
    tree 2:179
Fuchsieae 4:512
fucoxanthin and photoreception 6:794
Fucus 2:150;
    serratus 6:828, *829*;
    spiralis 6:828, *829*;
    vesiculosus 6:828-9, *829*
Fuegian province 7:*904*, 904;
    aliens of 7:950, 952
fuelwood consumption 7:937-8
fuki 3:266
fuller's earth 9:1130
Fumana 4:458, *458*
Fumaria 2:154, 4:403, *403*, 404;
    vicia 6:724
Fumariaceae 4:*403*, 403-4
Fumarioideae 4:404
fumaroles 8:1058
fumitory 4:403, 404;
    common 2:154;
    yellow 1:106
Funaria 2:154
fundi 2:230, 5:638, 640
fungi 2:**156**, 6:*785*, 785, 7:*933*, 935;
    bootlace 1:*41*;
    honey 1:*41*, 2:156;
    saddle 3:*348*;
    slime 3:*316*;
    smut 3:*348*
Fungus 4:525
Funkia 2:179
funnel epiphytes 6:*721*, 721
Funtumia 3:297, 5:575;

africana 6:771
Furcraea 2:144, **154**, 173, 5:666
furze 3:347;
  dwarf 3:347;
  needle 2:160
Fusarium 2:154;
  solani forma *pisi* 7:957
fustic 2:126, 4:447
fusulinids 9:1176, 1177, 1219
fynbos 7:843, 874

gabbro 8:973, 1001, 1085,
  9:*1123*, 1124, **1127**, 1151;
  tholeitic 8:1092
gaboon 3:341
gage 2:151
Gagea 2:154
Gaillardia 2:154, 5:617, 618;
  aristata 6:683
Gaimardia 5:633, 7:905
Galactinia 3:266
galanga 2:191
galangal 2:154, 5:648
Galanthus 3:317, 5:664, 666;
  nivalis: ssp. *cilicicus* 6:781;
  nivalis: ssp. *nivalis* 6:781;
  nivalis: ssp. *reginae-olgae* 6:781
Galax 4:480, 481, *481*
galax, fringed 3:315
galbanum 2:139, 5:571
Galbulimima 3:378
Galearia 4:535, 537
Galega 2:154
Galegeae 4:502
galena 8:992, 1078, 1081, 1087,
  1089, **1090**, *1091*, 1099,
  1104, 1111
Galeobdolon 2:196
Galeopsis 2:154
Galeorchis 2:256
galingale 5:643;
  English 1:113
Galinsoga 2:154, 5:617
Galipea 5:552, 554
Galium 2:154, 5:607, 609, 6:723,
  825;
  aparine 6:816;
  palustre 7:876, 880, 885;
  triflorum 7:904
gallant soldier 1:50
gallery forests 7:837
gallito 3:314
gallium 8:1099, **1106**, 1107
Galton, Sir Francis 6:760, 761
Galtonia 2:154
gamalote 1:48
gambier 2:126, **154**, 5:608, 609;
  Bengal 1:112, 2:154
gamboge 2:126, **155**, 4:437
gamboge tree 2:155;
  Siamese 2:155
gametes 6:(*762*)
gamma-ray spectrometry 8:1073
Gamocarpha 5:613
gandergoose 2:256
Gangamopteris 6:742
gangue 8:*1073*, *1081*, 1097
Ganoderma 2:155
garbancillo 1:46
garbanzo 1:87
Garcinia 2:126, **155**, 194, **218**,
  4:436, 437
Garcinieae 4:436
garden egg *see* aubergine
gardener's garters 3:267, 5:640
Gardenia 2:155, 5:607, 608, 609
gardenia oil 2:136
gardens 7:959-61;
  ancient 6:680;
  Arnold Arboretum 6:685;
  Chelsea Physic 6:683, 7:963;
  experimental 6:705, 705-6;

Jardin d'Acclimatation (Leyden)
  6:684;
Jardin des Plantes (Paris) 6:683;
  Jardin du Roi 6:681;
  Kew 6:684, 687;
  medicinal 6:680, 7:959, 963;
  see also botanic gardens
gari 1:78
garigue 7:836, 843, 844
garland flower 1:116, 2:170
garlic 1:17, 2:*155*, 147, 3:350,
  351, 5:662, 664;
  wild 2:155
garlic mustard 2:174
garnet 8:973, 996, 1078, **1090-1**,
  9:1129, 1137, *1139*, 1140
garnierite 8:1105
Garrya 2:155, 4:516
Garryaceae 4:516
gas *see* natural gas
gaseous pollutants 7:942-3, *943*
Gasteria 2:155
gastropods 9:1154, 1156, 1187,
  1189, *1210*, 1224, **1226-7**
Gaultheria 2:155, 4:474, 475, *477*,
  477, 7:873, 905
Gaura 4:512
Gause, G. F. 6:691
gay feather 2:203
Gaylussacia 2:182, 7:873
Gayophytum 4:512;
  diffusum 7:915;
  eriospermum 7:915;
  heterozygum 7:915;
  oligospermum 7:915
Gazania 2:160, 5:*615*, 617, 618
geanticlines 8:1034
Geastrum 2:127, 3:284
gedu nohor 3:341
geiger tree 1:104
Geikie, A. 9:1260, **1268**, 1272
Geissois 4:487, *487*
Geissoloma 4:528
Geissolomataceae **4:528**
Gelidium 2:160, 3:289
Gelsemieae 5:572
Gelsemium 5:573
gemmules 6:760
gemstones 8:1080-1
gene banks 7:*957*, *see also* crop
  collections
gene pool 7:956
genecology 6:704-6
genecotypes 6:706
genepi 1:42
genera 6:695;
  endemic 7:913;
  and floristic units 7:894, 895;
  and isolation 7:917
genes 6:760-1, (*761*)
Genetic Code 6:761
genetic drift 6:774-5
genetic resources conservation
  7:*956-7*, **956-61**
genetic basis of evolution 6:*760-3*,
  760-1
Genista 2:160, 4:502;
  lydia 6:*721*;
  pilosa 7:873
Genisteae 4:502
Genlisea 5:*603*, 604
genotype 6:705, (*761*), 795
gentian 2:160, 5:573, 6:685;
  Alpine 2:160;
  bottle 2:160;
  Catesby's 2:160;
  closed 2:160;
  fringed 2:160;
  great yellow 2:160;
  pine-barren 2:160;
  spring 6:750;
  stemless 2:160, *160*
gentian bitter 2:160
gentian root 5:574
Gentiana 2:160, 5:*573*, 574;
  verna 6:750
Gentianaceae 5:*573*, **573-4**, 581

Gentianales 5:572-7, 592, 608
Gentianella 2:160, 5:574
geochemistry 8:995-7, 995, 996-7,
  998, 1073, 1074, 9:1268
Geococcus 4:470
geodes 8:1089
geographical distributions of plants
  6:*707*, 7:893-919
geographical isolation 6:*777*, 778
geography of plants:
  history of 6:688-9;
  methods and concepts of 6:693-
   735
Geological Record 6:738-9, *739*-
  40, *757*;
  and evidence of first life 6:756-8
Geonoma 2:160
geonomoid palms 5:654
geophone 6:991, 992
geophysics 8:990-5, *991*, *992*,
  993, *994*, 1067, 1070, 1073,
  1114
geophytes 6:*725*, 725, 727
geos 8:1056
geosynclines 8:1034, 1036, 1091,
  9:*1132*, 1151, 1158, 1166,
  1179-80, 1269
geothermal energy 8:1071
Geraniaceae 5:557, 558, **558-9**,
  560, 562
Geraniales 5:554, 556-63
Geranioideae 5:559
Geranium 2:160, 5:*558*, 558, 559;
  dissectum 6:*819*;
  sanguineum 6:706;
  wallichianum 6:686
geranium (*Pelargonium*) 2:263,
  5:558, 559;
  Alpine 2:134;
  bedding 2:263;
  fancy 2:263;
  fish 2:263;
  hanging 2:263;
  house 2:263;
  ivy-leaved 2:263;
  Martha Washington 2:263;
  regal 2:263;
  rock 2:173;
  rose 2:136;
  show 2:263;
  silver-leaved 2:161;
  strawberry 3:309;
  zonal 2:263, *263*
geranium oil 2:136, 263, 5:559
Gerbera 2:161, 5:617, 618
germander:
  tree 3:335;
  wall 3:335
germanium 8:1106-7
germination:
  and light 6:794-5;
  and temperature 6:791-2, 814;
  and water 6:799
Gerrardanthus 4:465, 467
Gesner, C. 9:1257, **1268**
Gesneria 5:596, *596*, 598
Gesneriaceae 5:579, 593, *596*,
  596-8, 603
Gesnerieae 5:596
Gesnerioideae 5:596
Gethyllis 5:664, 666
getony 2:263
Geum 2:161, 4:491, 494
Gevuina 4:519, 520
geysers 8:1058
gherkin 1:110, 2:161, 222, *223*,
  3:350, 4:465, 467;
  bur 2:222;
  West Indian 1:110, 2:222
ghost tree 1:118, 6:*684*
giant bellflower 5:606
giant cactus 1:76
giant herbs 6:*722*, **722**
giant hogweed 5:571
giant protea 4:520
Giant's Causeway 8:*1008*, 1009
Gibasis 5:*631*
gibbsite 8:1103

Gibson, John 6:686-7
Gigantopteris 9:1175, 1176
Gigartina 2:161;
  stellata 6:*829*
Gilbert, G. 8:1053, 9:1260, 1268
Gilgiodaphne 4:510
Gilgiodaphnoideae 4:510
Gilia 2:161, 5:582, 583;
  capitata 6:704
Gilieae 5:583
gill-over-the-road 2:162
Gillenia 2:161, 4:491
gillyflower 2:221
gin 1:16, 58
gingelly 3:314
ginger 1:58, 2:146, 147, **161**,
  227, 3:363, *363*, 5:647, *648*,
  648, 649, 7:880;
  butterfly 2:170;
  kahili 2:170;
  white 2:170
ginger beer 1:16
ginger lily 5:648
ginger plant 3:*363*
gingerbread plum 4:499
gingerol 2:161
Gingidia 5:569
gingili oil 3:314
gingilie 3:314
Ginkgo 2:216;
  biloba 6:683, 746, 7:*914*, 914
Ginkgoales 6:*739*, 743
ginkgophytes 6:740
ginkgo 2:216, 6:683, 746, 7:*914*,
  914, 9:1176, 1179, 1185,
  1218
ginseng 2:227, 258, 5:567, 568;
  American 2:258
Gippingian glaciation 6:749
Gironniera 4:446
Githago 1:14
Githopsis 5:604
glacial moraine successions 6:826
glacial relicts 7:912, *913*
glacial theory 9:1263, 1265
glaciation, glaciers 8:1018-20,
  1018, *1019*, **1048-50**, *1048*,
  1049, 1092, 9:*1133*, 1173,
  1175, 1193, *1262*, 1263;
  erosion by 8:1010, 1011-2,
  1012, 1037, 1051;
  see also ice, ice ages, ice sheets
glaciations 6:738-9, 748-50;
  and Boreal flora 7:903-4, 908;
  and polar distributions 7:932-3;
  and Southern Hemisphere
   distributions 7:905, 919, 920
glacier-edge vegetation 7:901
Gladioleae 5:662
Gladiolus 2:161, 5:661, 661, 662
gladiolus 2:161, *161*;
  garden 2:162
Glandularia 3:353
Glasgow Botanic Garden 6:683
glasswort 3:302, *302*, 6:*711*,
  7:886, *888*, 945
Glaucidiaceae 3:399
Glaucidium 3:399
Glaucium 2:162, 3:279, 4:*402*,
  402, 403
glauconite 8:*1082*, 1091, 9:1131,
  1191
glaucophane 8:1084, **1091**,
  9:1138
Glaux 2:162, 4:484;
  maritima 7:945
Gleason, Harold 6:709-10
Glechoma 2:162
Gleditsia 2:162, 209
Gleichenia 2:162
gley 6:805, 809-10
Glischrocolla 4:509, 509
globe amaranth 2:163
globe artichoke 5:618
globe flower 3:345, 396, 399
globe thistle 5:618
Globigerina 9:1196
globigerina ooze 8:*1059*, 1061,
  9:1191, 1219

Globigerinacea 9:1219
globigerinids 9:1189
Globularia 2:162, 5:595, 595, 596
Globulariaceae 5:593, 595, **595-6**
Gloriosa 2:162, 5:662, 664
glory bower 1:92
glory bush 3:336
glory flower, Chilean 2:127
glory vine, Japanese crimson 3:356
glory-of-the-snow 1:87
Glossopteridales 9:1217
Glossopteridophyta 9:1176
Glossopteris 6:742, 743, 743,
   8:1001, 9:1176, 1179
Gloxinia 3:316, 5:596, 598
gloxinia 2:162, 163, 3:316;
   Brazilian 3:316;
   tree 2:194;
   violet slipper 3:316
Gloxinieae 5:596
Glyceria 2:162, 5:638;
   maritima 7:889;
   maxima 7:881
Glycerieae 5:638
Glycine 2:162, 3:319, 4:502
Glycosmis 5:554
Glycyrrhiza 2:163, **203**
glycyrrhizin 2:203
Glyptodon discovered 6:760
Glyptostrobus 6:746
Gmelin, Johann Georg 6:688
Gmelin, Samuel Gottlieb 6:688
Gmelina arborea 7:936, 936
Gnaphalium 2:163, 5:617
gneisses 8:1030, 1068, 1088,
   1091, 1097, 1099, 9:1123,
   1139, 1140, 1143, 1150,
   1151;
   gray 9:1151
gneissose banding (foliation)
   9:1137
Gnetales 6:739
Gnetum 2:163
Gnidia 4:510
gnome's throne 2:254
goat's rue 2:154, 3:334
goatsbeard, false 1:45, 46
godetia 2:163, 163
Godetia 2:163, 4:512
Godoya 4:433, 434
goethite (limonite) 8:982, 1087,
   1091, 1105, 9:1131
gold 8:992, 1023, 1073, 1074,
   1075, 1078, 1081, 1082,
   1084, 1087, 1096, **1110**,
   9:1151, 1255
gold and silver flower 2:210
gold dust 1:25, 25
gold dust tree 1:47
gold flower 2:184
gold tree 5:600
golden alyssum 4:472
golden brodiaea 3:344
golden buttons 3:332
golden eardrops 1:120
golden larch 3:**282**
golden leaf spot 3:332
golden pine 4:520
golden rain tree 2:194, 195
golden rod 2:126, 3:**318**, 5:618;
   Canada 3:318;
   Leavenworth 3:318;
   sweet 3:318
golden saxifrage 4:497
golden seal 1:26
golden star 3:344
golden wattle 4:502
goldenberry 3:270
golden-chain 2:195
goldenrod 6:723, 779
golden-shower 1:78, 3:285
goldfields 2:197
Goldfussia 3:326
goldmoss 3:312
Goldschmidt, V. 9:**1268**
goldwire 2:184
Gomortega 3:383
Gomortegaceae 3:**383**

Gomphandra 4:530, 531
Gomphostemma 5:589
Gomphrena 2:163, 4:420
Gomphreneae 4:420
Gomphrenoideae 4:420
Gondwanaland 6:740, 741, 741-2,
   743, 7:919, 8:1001, 1020,
   9:1154, 1157, 1162, 1163,
   1166, **1173**, 1174, 1175,
   1176, 1177, 1179, **1181**,
   1187
Gongylocarpus 4:512
goniatites 9:1166, 1167, 1225
Gonioma 1:62
Gonium 1:20
Gonocaryum 4:530, 531
gonorrhea 1:50
Gonyaulax 2:163, 3:289
Gonypetalum 4:533
Gonystyloideae 4:510
Gonystylus 3:341, 4:445, 510, 510
gonzui zoku 5:540
goober 1:38
Good King Henry 1:86
good luck plant 1:104
Goodenia 5:607
Goodeniaceae 5:607, 618
Goodyera 2:163, 5:675;
   repens 7:903
gooseberry 2:151, 152, **163**,
   3:294, 4:497, 498;
   Barbados 3:264, 265;
   Cape 2:151, 153, 3:270;
   Chinese 1:10, 2:151;
   dwarf Cape 3:270;
   fuchsia-flowered 3:294, 294;
   Indian 3:269
gooseberry tree 3:269
goosefat 1:86, 86
goosegrass 2:154, 155, 3:280;
   European 6:816
gooseneck 2:213
Gordonia 4:432
gorgonopsids 9:1243
gorli oil 2:250
gorse 1:122, 4:499, see also *Ulex*;
   common 3:347, 347;
   Spanish 2:160
gossans 8:1074, 1091
Gossypiospermum 4:452
Gossypium 1:107, 2:163, 4:444,
   445;
   hirsutum 7:943
Gouania 4:537, 538, 538
gourd 2:163, 4:465, 467;
   ash 2:223, 3:350;
   bitter 1:91, 2:163, 232, 3:350;
   bottle 1:69, 2:163, 222, 3:350;
   calabash 1:69, 2:222, 3:350;
   club 2:223;
   dipper 2:222;
   dishcloth 2:212, 223;
   fig-leaf 1:111, 2:222;
   goareberry 2:222;
   gooseberry 2:163, 222;
   hedgehog 2:222;
   hercules'-club 2:222;
   hundredweight 3:284;
   ivy 2:223;
   knob-kerrie 2:222;
   Malabar 2:222;
   Missouri 2:222;
   ornamental 1:111;
   scallop 2:222;
   serpent 2:163, 223;
   Siamese 2:222;
   silver-seed 2:222;
   snake 2:163, 223, 3:350;
   sour 1:10;
   sponge 2:163, 212, 223;
   sugar-through 2:222;
   teasel 2:222;
   towel 2:212, 223;
   trumpet 2:222;
   viper's 2:223;
   wax 2:163, 223, 3:350;
   West Indian 2:163;
   white 2:163, 223, 3:350;

white-flowered 2:163, 222;
   wild 2:163;
   yellow-flowered 2:222, 222
gours 8:1044
goutweed 1:11
gouty stem 1:10
gowan, yellow 3:287
Grabau, A. 9:1263, **1268**
graben see rift valleys
Gracilaria 3:289
graded beds 8:1016, 1053, 9:1132
gradients:
   ecological 6:828;
   environmental 6:706, 815
gradual speciation 6:**776**;
   and schizoendemics 7:915
grain amaranth 1:83, 2:163
grain support 9:1133
grain tree 2:246
grains of paradise 3:265
gram 2:201;
   black 2:201;
   green 2:201;
   horse 1:123, 2:201;
   Madras 2:201;
   red 2:201
grama 5:638;
   black 1:62;
   blue 1:62, 2:149;
   side-oats 1:62
grama grass 7:860, 863
Gramineae 4:472, 5:633, **635-40**,
   636, 638, 641, 643, 651,
   7:862
graminoids 7:853, see also grasses
Grammatocarpus 4:464
granadilla 1:58, 2:151, 4:452,
   453;
   giant 2:151, 261;
   purple 2:261;
   red 2:261;
   sweet 2:151;
   yellow 2:151
Grand Canyon 8:1011, 9:1148,
   1175
granite 8:1009, 1036, 1083,
   1084, 1086, 1087, 1089,
   1100, 9:1123, 1124, **1125**,
   1126, 1127, 1143, 1172,
   1180
granjeno 1:81
granny's bonnet 1:38
granodiorite 8:973, 9:1125, **1126**
granulites 8:1086, 1092, 9:1137,
   1150, 1151, 1152
grape 2:151, 163, 236;
   black 3:356;
   bullace 2:151, 3:356;
   bush 2:151, 3:356;
   Cape 3:293;
   evergreen 3:293;
   fox 2:151, 3:356;
   frost 2:151, 3:356;
   mountain 3:356;
   muscadine 3:356;
   Oregon 2:215;
   river bank 3:356;
   sand 2:151, 3:356;
   sea 1:96;
   seaside 1:96;
   skunk 2:151, 3:356;
   sugar 3:356
grapefruit 1:91, 2:151, **163**, 164,
   217, 3:347, 5:552, 554
grapestone 9:1134
grapevine 2:163, 3:287, 4:538
graphite 8:992, 1089, **1091**,
   1102, 1108, 1117, 9:1138
grapple plant 5:601
graptolites 9:1154, 1156-7, 1157,
   1159, 1160, 1161-2, 1163,
   1229-30, 1263, 1270
Graptophyllum 5:601
grass 5:635, 638, 640;
   alfa 3:324;
   alkali 3:362;
   alkali rye 2:130;
   annual meadow 3:276;

bahia 2:149, 261;
   bamboo 3:308;
   Bengal 3:314;
   Bermuda 1:113, 2:149;
   bitter 2:226;
   blue-eyed 3:316;
   bristle 3:314;
   buffalo 2:149;
   buffel 2:149;
   canary 3:267;
   canary reed 2:149, 3:267, 290;
   carpet 1:48, 58, 2:149, 3:363;
   China 1:60, 2:145;
   citronella 1:113;
   coco 1:113;
   common cord 3:320;
   common quaking 1:63;
   common viper's 3:311;
   cord 3:320;
   cotton 2:133, 134;
   couch 1:113;
   creeping soft 2:177;
   dallis 2:149;
   deer 3:311;
   ditch 3:300;
   dwarf meadow 3:276;
   eel 3:349, 363;
   elephant 2:149, 3:264, 347;
   feather 3:324, 325;
   floating sweet 2:162;
   fountain 3:264, 264;
   freshwater cord 3:320;
   goose 2:129, 3:280;
   grama 1:62;
   green bristle 3:314;
   green needle 3:325;
   Guatemala 2:149;
   Guinea 2:149, 259;
   hairy crab 2:149;
   Hungarian 3:314;
   ichu 3:325;
   Japanese 3:363;
   Japanese carpet 3:363;
   Johnson 3:319;
   June 3:275;
   Kikuyu 3:264;
   knot 3:277;
   Korean 3:363;
   Korean velvet 3:363;
   kuma bamboo 3:308;
   lemon 2:136, 174;
   lyme 2:130;
   Manila 3:363;
   manna 2:162;
   marram 1:27, 70, 2:220;
   Mascarene 3:363;
   meadow 3:275, 276;
   millet 3:319;
   mondo 2:252;
   moor 2:232;
   Napier 2:149, 3:264;
   narrow-leaved cotton 2:134;
   Natal 3:264;
   needle 3:324, 325;
   nut 1:113;
   oat 2:171;
   oil 1:112;
   orchard 2:149, 1:115;
   pampas 1:105;
   pangola 2:149;
   Para 2:149, 259;
   pearl 1:66;
   pensacola bahia 2:261;
   pin 2:134;
   plume 2:132;
   porcupine 3:324;
   prairie cord 3:320;
   purple-eyed 3:316;
   quaking 1:63, 66;
   Ravenna 2:132;
   reed 2:149, 3:267, 290;
   reed sweet 2:162, 3:290;
   rescue 1:66, 2:149;
   Rhodes 1:88, 2:149;
   ribbon 3:267;
   rough bristle 3:314;
   rough meadow 3:275;
   scurvy 1:96;

sea lyme 2:130;
sea meadow 7:861;
silky 3:264;
small quaking 1:66;
soft 2:177;
smooth meadow 3:275;
Spanish 2:135;
spear 3:324;
spring 1:36;
star 2:184;
Sudan 3:319;
sugar 2:162;
sweet 2:162, 3:290;
sweet vernal 1:36;
switch 2:259;
tape 3:349;
terrell 3:301;
Texas needle 3:325;
Timothy 2:149, 3:268;
Townsend's cord 3:320;
tufted hair 1:119;
tussock 1:119;
umbrella 1:113;
Vasey 2:149;
velvet 2:177, 3:363;
vernal 1:36;
viper's 3:311;
Whitlow 1:124;
yellow bristle 3:314;
zoysia 3:363
grass nut 1:66, 3:344
grass of Parnassus 2:260, 261,
    4:497
grass oils 2:136
grass pea 2:164, 4:502
grass tree 5:666, 667;
    Australian 3:359;
    spearleaf 3:359
grass-carp and weed control 7:950
grasses 7:862-3;
    life-forms of 6:723, 723, 724;
    of meadows 7:861
grasslands 7:832, 832-3, 855-61,
    856-60;
    human influence in 7:862, 938-
    41, 939-40;
    of New Zealand 7:904-5;
    soils of 6:808, 7:862
grass-tree life-form 6:720, 720,
    7:916
grass-tundra 7:861
grass-widow 3:316
grass-wrack 3:363
grassy-bells 1:120, 2:128
gravimeter 8:991-2
gravity studies 8:991-2, 993, 1070
gravity tectonics 8:1015, 1029
Gray, Asa 6:760, 7:965
Gray, R. 6:822
gray beard 3:336
graywackes 8:1016, 9:1131,
    1132, 1150
grazing 7:862, 938-41;
    on heaths 7:875;
    intolerance to 7:861-2;
    and multiple land use 7:955;
    on prairies 7:860;
    in salt marshes 7:890;
    at timberline 7:868
Great Auk 9:1245
Great Basin province 7:898
great earthnut 5:571
Great Plains province 7:898
green bean 4:502, see also bean
green dragon 1:40
green heart 3:388
green pepper 5:579, 7:880, see also
    pepper
green revolution 7:931-4, 957
green thalloid cryptogams 6:724
greenalite 8:1074
greenbrier, laurel-leaved 3:317
greengage 2:151, 164, 3:275
greenheart 2:164, 247, 3:341;
    African 2:164;
    Surinam 2:164, 3:334
Greenland tea 7:876, see also
    Labrador tea
greenockite 8:1108

Greenovia 2:164, 4:495
greensands 8:1091, 9:1131, 1191
greenschists 8:1087, 9:1137
greenstone belts 9:1150-1, 1152
greenstones see prasinites
greenweed, Dyer's 2:126
grenadille wood, African 1:116
Grenville belt 9:1151
Grevillea 2:164, 4:519, 520, 520
grevillea 2:164
Grevilleoideae 4:520
Grewia 4:441, 441
Greyia 2:164, 5:541, 542
Greyiaceae 5:541
Grias 4:450
Grimmia 2:164
Grindelia 2:164, 5:618
grindol 2:164
Grisebach, August 6:708, 717,
    718, 7:965
Griselinia 2:164, 4:516, 517, 518
Groenlandia 5:624
gromwell, blue 2:209
Gronovioideae 4:464
Grossularia 3:294, 4:497
Grossulariaceae 4:498
grossularite 8:1090, 1091
ground elder 1:11
ground hemlock 2:173, 3:361
ground ivy 2:162
ground nut 1:38, 2:201, 201, 245,
    250, 4:472, 499, 502;
    Banbara 2:201;
    Kersting's 2:201;
ground nut oil 2:250
groundnut pea vine 2:198
ground-pine 1:14
groundsel 2:209, 3:313, 313;
    annual 6:769;
    bush 1:49;
    climbing 3:313;
    tree 1:49, 2:211
groundwater 8:992, 1009, 1034,
    1057, 1066, 1067, 1068,
    1069, 1070, 1071, 9:1135
grouse 6:814, 7:875
grouseberry 3:354
growth-forms 6:718;
    of epiphytes and lianas 6:772-3;
    of grasses 7:855;
    of tundra plants 7:853-4;
    of weeds 7:949
growth-optimum, temperature
    6:791
Grubbia 4:474
Grubbiaceae 4:474
grumulo 3:350
grumusol 6:808
Grundelia tournefortii 6:817
Gryphaea 9:1185
Guaiacum 2:167, 206, 5:554
guaiacum 2:206
guaiacum resin 2:167
guanabana 2:151
guar 2:201
guarana 1:26, 58, 5:543, 544
Guarea 1:8, 2:167, 215, 3:289,
    5:552
guava 2:126, 151, 153, 3:282,
    4:512, 7:931;
    apple 3:282;
    Chilean 2:237;
    pineapple 2:139;
    purple 3:282;
    strawberry 3:282;
    yellow 3:282
guava cheese 3:282
guayule 3:297, 5:618
guelder rose 3:354
Guettard, J.-E. 9:1268
Guettardoideae 5:608
Guibourtia 1:99
Guinea grains 3:265
Guinea plum 4:499
Guizotia 2:167, 5:617, 618
gum:
    Alpine snow 2:137;
    black 2:243;
    blue 2:135, 3:341;

cotton 2:243;
forest red 2:137;
karri 2:135;
lemon-scented 2:135;
mountain 2:137;
Murray 2:137;
red 2:137, 3:325;
river red 2:137;
silver-dollar 2:137;
silver-leaved mountain 2:137;
snow 2:137;
sour 2:243;
swamp 2:135;
Tasmanian blue 2:135;
tupelo 2:243;
water 2:243;
see also Eucalyptus
gum ammoniacum 1:123
gum arabic 1:7, 4:502
gum benjamin 4:483
gumbo 2:176, 248, 3:350
gumbo-limbo 1:68
gumtree 4:407, 512
gumweed 2:164
gumwood 7:919
Gunflint chert 6:757, 759
Gunnera 2:167, 4:504, 505, 505,
    527, 6:723, 745
Gunneraceae 4:505
Gunneroideae 4:505
Gurania 4:465, 467
gurjum 1:122, 2:250, 3:341
gurjun oil 1:122, 2:250
Gussow's Principle 8:1115
Gustavia 4:449, 450
Gutenberg, B. 9:1268
Guthriea 4:462, 462, 463
gutta sandek 2:167
gutta-percha 1:49, 2:167, 3:300,
    4:482
Guttiferae 4:432, 435-7, 436, 438,
    445
guyots 8:1060, 1063-4
Guzmania 5:646
Gyminda 4:529
Gymnacranthera 3:382
Gymnadenia 2:167, 5:675
Gymnarrhena micranthe 7:850
Gymnelaea 5:577
Gymnocalycium 2:167, 4:415
Gymnocarpium 2:140
Gymnocladus 2:167
Gymnodinium 2:167, 3:289
Gymnophyton 4:525
gymnosperms 1:100, 9:1185,
    1188, 1217-8;
    in evolution 6:739
Gymnosteris 5:583
Gymnotheca 2:182, 3:389, 389
Gynandropsis 4:469
Gynerium 5:635
Gynopleura 4:454
Gynostemma 4:467
Gynura 2:167, 5:617
Gypsophila 2:167, 4:417, 419;
    imbricata 6:722
gypsum 8:1009, 1016, 1023,
    1046, 1047, 1076, 1079,
    1080, 1082, 1083, 1084,
    1091, 1104, 9:1135
gypsyweed 3:353
Gyrocarpus 3:388
Gyromitra 2:232
Gyrostemon 4:421
Gyrostemonaceae 4:422
Gyrostemoneae 4:421, 422
gyttja 6:826, 7:881

Habranthus 5:666
Hachettea 4:526
hackberry 4:445, 446, 6:747;
    Chinese 1:81;
    common 1:81;
    European 1:81;
    Mississippi 1:81
hackmatack 3:279
Hacquetia 2:168
Hadley Cell 8:998
hadrosaurs 9:1242
Haeckel, Ernst 6:689
Haemanthus 2:168, 5:666
haematoxylin 2:210
Haematoxylon 2:126, 168, 210
Haemodoraceae 5:664, 667, 667-8
Haemodoreae 5:668
Haemodorum 5:668
Haenianthus 5:576, 577
hafnium 8:1111
hag taper 2:233
hagaed wood 1:116
Hagenbachia 5:668
Hagenia 6:721
hair grass, tufted 6:791
Hakea 2:168, 4:520, 7:874
Haldane, J. B. S. 6:752, 764
Halesia 2:168, 4:483, 484
halfa 2:135
Halgania 5:583, 584
Halimeda 2:168
Halimione 2:168, 4:423;
    portulacoides 6:711, 7:889
Halimium 4:458, 459
halite 8:1015, 1078, 1079, 1091-
    2, 1100, 1103, 1119-21,
    9:1135, see also salt
Hall, J. 9:1260, 1268-9
Hall, Sir J. 9:1260, 1261, 1268
Hall-Héroult process 8:1103
Halleria 2:178
halloysite 8:1088, 1092
Halocnemum 4:423
Halodule 5:627
halomorphic soils 6:809
Halophila 5:621, 622
Halophiloideae 5:622
halophytes 6:772, 7:885-91, 887-
    91, see also salinity
Haloragaceae 4:438, 464, 504-5,
    505, 506, 527
Haloragales 4:503-6
Halorageae 4:505
Haloragis 4:504, 505, 505
Haloragoideae 4:505
haloseres 6:826-7
Halosphaera 2:168
Haloxylon 4:423, 6:718
Hamadryas 3:399
Hamamelidaceae 4:406, 406-7,
    413, 491
Hamamelidae 4:405-13
Hamamelidales 4:405-7, 5:571
Hamamelidoideae 4:407
Hamamelis 2:168, 4:406, 406, 407
Hamelia 2:168, 5:609
Hancornia 2:169, 5:575
handkerchief tree 4:516, 6:684
hanged man 1:9
Hanguana 5:633
Hanguanaceae 5:633
Hanover salad 1:64
Haploclathra 4:433
Haplopappus 2:169, 5:618
Haplothismia 5:671
hard rush 7:885
hard-cushion plants 6:722, 722
Hardenbergia 2:169, 3:308
hardhack, golden 3:280
hardness, mineral 8:1082
hardwood consumption 7:938
Hardy, G. H. 6:774
Hardy-Weinberg Law 6:774
harebell 1:54, 57, 2:183
hare's ears 1:68
hare's tail 1:196, 7:876
haricot bean 2:169, 200, 201,
    3:267, 4:502
harmal 2:263

Harmandia 4:523, 524
harmela shrub 2:263
Harpagophytum 5:601
Harpullia 3:346
Harrisonia 5:549
Harungana 4:437
Harvard University Botanic Garden 6:683
hashish 1:74
Hatshepsut 6:680
Haug, G. 9:1263, **1269**
Hausa potato 3:275, 5:589
haustoria 6:772, *773*
Haüy, R.-J. **8**:1075-6, 1078, 1086, **9:1269**
Hauya 4:512
haw 2:169, 6:751, 800, 7:838, 940;
  black 2:227, 3:354;
  Chinese 2:170, 3:269;
  common 2:169;
  Indian 3:290;
  may 2:169, *169*;
  summer 2:169;
  swamp 3:354;
  sweet 2:227, 3:354;
  water 1:37, 2:170;
  Yedda 3:290
Hawaii 8:983, 1033, 1064, 9:1128
Hawaiian arrowroot 5:668
Hawaiian floral region 7:897, 919;
  endemics of 7:916
hawksbeard 1:108;
  beaked 1:108;
  smooth 1:108
hawkweed 2:177;
  giant 6:774;
  mouse ear 2:177;
  shaggy 2:177;
  see also Hieracium
Haworthia 2:169, 5:662
haworthia, zebra 2:169
hawthorn see haw
Haxton, John 6:684
Haylockia 5:664
haymaids 2:162
hazel 2:170, 4:409, 410;
  beaked 2:170;
  buttercup winter 1:106;
  Chinese 2:170;
  Chinese witch 2:169;
  common 2:170, *170*;
  corkscrew 2:170;
  Tibetan 2:170;
  Turkish 2:170;
  witch 2:168, *169*;
  see also Corylus
hazelnut 2:245, *245*
healing gum 4:437
healing herb 3:330
heartsease 2:258, *258*, 3:355
heartseed 1:75
heath 2:133, **170**, 4:474, 475, 477, 7:872-4, *872-5*;
  Cape 2:133;
  Cornish 2:133;
  cross-leaved 2:133, 6:829;
  fringed 2:133;
  hardy 2:133;
  Irish 1:115;
  prickly 1:8;
  St Daboec's 1:115;
  spring 2:133;
  tree 2:133
heath forest 7:835
heath rush 5:641
heather 1:71, 122, 2:133, **170**, 4:474, 475, 477, 6:786, 814, 7:872, 875, 876;
  bell 2:133, 170, *170*, 6:829;
  bog 2:133, 170;
  Christmas 2:170;
  Cornish 2:133, 170;
  cross-leaved 2:170;
  everblooming French 2:170;
  Mediterranean 2:170;
  purple 2:133, 170;

red 3:269;
  Scottish 1:71, 2:170;
  snow 2:133, 170;
  white 1:78;
  white winter 2:170
heather moor 7:880
heavy metals pollution 6:815, 7:944, 945-6, 946
Hebe 2:170, 5:593, 595, 6:721, 7:905, 920
he-cabbage 3:313
Hectorella 7:920
Hedera 2:187, 5:568, 568, 6:749;
  helix 6:750, 772, 7:838, 884, 898
hedges 6:711, *713*
Hedycarya 3:384, 384
Hedycaryopsis 3:384
Hedychium 2:170, 5:647, 648, 6:687
Hedyosmum 3:386, 386, 387
Hedyotis 2:182
Hedysareae 4:502
Hedysarum 2:171, 203
Heisteria 4:523, 523
Helenium 2:171, 5:617
Heliamphora 2:171, 4:404, *404*, 405
Heliantheae 5:617
Helianthemum 2:171, 4:458, 459;
  canum 6:787, 7:912
Helianthus 1:42, 3:329, 5:615, 617, 617, 618;
  annuus 6:724
Helichrysum 2:171, 185, 5:617, 618
Heliconia 2:171, 5:647
Heliconiaceae 5:647
Helicophila 4:470, 470
Helicophileae 4:470
Helictotrichon 2:171, 5:638, 7:861;
  pratense 7:862
Heliocereus 2:132
heliodor 8:1086
Heliophila 2:171
Heliopsis 2:172, 5:617
heliotrine 2:227
heliotrope 2:172, 227, 5:586, 8:1087;
  common 2:172;
  garden 3:349;
  summer 2:172;
  winter 3:266;
  yellow 3:326
Heliotropioideae 5:586
Heliotropium 2:172, 199, 5:586, 586;
  peruvianum 6:683
Helipterum 2:172, 5:617;
  manglesii 6:687
helium 8:971, 972, 995, 997, 1114, 9:1142
hellebore 3:396, 399;
  American white 3:353;
  green 2:172;
  stinking 2:172;
  white 3:353, *353*
hellebore powder 5:664
Helleboreae 3:399
helleborein 2:172
helleborine 1:81, 2:172;
  giant 2:131;
  marsh 2:131;
  red 1:81;
  sword-leaved 1:81;
  white 1:81
Helleboroideae 3:399
Helleborus 1:88, 2:172, 3:396, 396, 399
helmet flower 3:311
Helmholtzia 5:661
Helminthosporium maydis and blight 7:935
Helobiae 5:622, 624, 625, 627, 644
helophytes 6:725
Helosis 4:526, 526
Helvella 2:172

Helwingia 2:172, 4:517, 518
hematite 8:979, *1074*, 1080, 1091, **1092**, 1105, 9:1131, 1138, 1163
Hemerocallis 2:**172**, 5:662, 664
hemicryptophytes 6:725, *726*, 727
Hemileia 2:172
Hemiptelea 4:445
hemlock 1:26, 2:172, *172*, 227, 5:571;
  ground 2:173, 3:361;
  water 1:89
hemlock/hemlock spruce 2:126, 173, 3:341;
  Canada 2:173;
  Carolina 2:173;
  Chinese 2:173;
  common 2:173;
  Indian 2:173;
  Japanese 2:173;
  mountain 2:173;
  Western 2:173, 3:341;
  see also Tsuga
hemp 2:144, 145, *145*, **173**, 4:446, 447, 7:925;
  African 3:320;
  African bowstring 2:144, 3:307;
  bowstring 2:144, 173, 3:307;
  Ceylon bowstring 2:144, 3:307;
  Colorado River 3:314;
  Deccan 2:173, 176;
  dogbane 2:144;
  Indian 1:73, 2:144, 176;
  Indian bowstring 2:144, 3:307;
  Manila 1:6, 2:145, *145*, 173;
  Mauritius 2:144, 154, 173;
  New Zealand 3:269;
  Queensland 2:144, 3:315;
  sisal 2:173;
  sunn 1:109, 2:144, 173;
  water 2:138
hemp nettle 2:154;
  common 2:154;
  downy 2:154
hemp tree 3:355
hempseed oil 2:250
hempweed, climbing 2:229
hen-and-chickens 2:127, 182
henbane 1:26, 2:183, *183*, 226;
  black 2:183
Hendschel 6:680
henequin 1:35, 2:144, 227, 3:316;
  Salvador 3:316
hengal 1:116
henna 2:126, **173**, 4:506, 507
Hennecartia 3:384
Henry, Augustine 6:685, 687
Henslow, John 7:964
Hepatica 2:173, 3:399;
  americana 7:908;
  triloba 7:908
Hepaticeae 6:724
Heracleum 2:**173**, 5:571, 571
herb Christopher 1:10, 3:399
herb Paris 2:260
herb Robert 2:161
herb Trinity 2:259
herba militaris 1:9
herbal tea 1:58
herbals 6:680, *695*, 702
herbaria 6:680, 694, 703, 7:963
herb-cushion plants 6:722
Herbertia drummondiana 6:683
herbfields on Macquarie Island 7:920
herbicides 7:946-7, 950
herbs, life-forms of 6:722-5
hercules' club 1:39
Hercynian mountains 9:1138, 1158, 1180
Hernandia 3:388
Hernandiaceae 3:**388**
Herniaria 2:173, 4:419, 419
herniary 2:173
heron's-bill 2:133
Hesperelaea 5:576, 577
Hesperideae 4:470
Hesperis 2:173, 3:295, 4:470, 472

Hess, H. 8:1004, 1005, 9:1269
hessian 2:191
Heteranthera 5:659, *660*, 660, 661
Heterogaura 4:512
Heteropogon 4:445;
  contortus 7:940
Heteropterys 5:563, 564
Heterosmilax 5:670
Heterozostera 5:626
heterozygous individuals 6:(761)
Heuchera 2:173, 4:497
heulandite 8:1101
Hevea 1:74, 2:176, 214, 3:297, 4:535, 537;
  brasiliensis 7:925, 926
hexagonal system see crystal systems
Hexaptera 4:470
Hibbertia 2:176, 4:430, 430, 431
Hibisceae 4:445
Hibiscus 2:173, 176, 248, 4:444, 444, 445;
  cannabinus 7:936
hibiscus 2:176;
  Chinese 2:176;
  Hawaiian 2:176
hickory 3:341, 361, 5:555, 6:749, 765, 7:838, 896;
  big-bud 1:77, 77;
  mockernut 1:77;
  pignut 1:77;
  shagbark 1:77, 2:245;
  shellbark 1:77, 2:245;
  smoothbark 1:77
hiddenite 8:1099
Hiemilanosa formation-type 7:835
Hieracium 2:177, 5:617;
  umbellatum 6:705, 706, 7:908
High Arctic 7:901, 902
highbush blueberry 4:477, see also blueberry
higher plants, evolution of 6:766
high-fertility farming 7:934
high-lysine maize 7:935
higicho 4:455
Hillebrandia 4:463, 464
Hilleria 4:421
hills of snow 2:183
Himalayan explorations 6:686-7
Himalayas 8:1001, *1006*, *1035*, 1036, 1041, 9:1151, 1198
Himantandraceae 3:378-9
Himanthalia 1:18
Himantoglossum 2:177, 5:675
Hipparion 9:1197
Hippeastrum 2:177, 5:664, 666
Hippocastanaceae 5:544-5, 545, 546, 548
Hippocratea 4:528, 529, 529
Hippocrateaceae 4:529
Hippocrepis 3:354;
  comosa 7:908
Hippomane 4:535, 537
Hippophaë 2:177, 4:518, 519, 519, 6:826, 7:843;
  rhamnoides 6:706, 750, 825, 7:888
Hippuridaceae 4:504, **505-6**
Hippuris 2:177, 4:505, 506
Hiptage 5:564
Hirtella 4:498, 498
Hodgsonia 4:465, 467
Hoffmannia 2:177
hog plum 5:548
hogweed 2:173, 5:571;
  giant 2:173
Hoheria 2:177, 195, 4:445
Holarctic realm 7:892, 894, 895-6, 897
Holarrhena 5:574
Holboellia 3:399, 400
Holcus 2:177, 5:638, 7:863;
  lanatus 7:940
holcus, woody 2:177
holly 2:127, 177, 4:532;
  African 3:318;
  American 2:177;
  box 3:301;

Canary Island 2:177;
Carolina tea 2:178;
English 2:177;
European 2:177;
horned 2:177;
Japanese 2:177;
Madeira 2:177;
Oregon 2:177;
sea 2:134, 7:887;
Singapore 2:217;
Tarajo 2:177;
West Indian 3:346;
see also Ilex
hollyfern 1:114;
Japanese 1:125
hollyhock 2:178, 4:444;
figleaf 2:178;
sea 2:176
Holmes, A. 8:1002, **9:1269**
Holmskioldia 5:587
Holocene 6:*738*, 750-1, 9:1200
Holodisceae 4:491
Holodiscus 2:178, 4:491
Hololachna 4:459, 460
Holoptelea 445, 446
holosteans 9:1184, 1189, *1206*,
1234
Holosteum 1:87
Holostylis 3:391
holosymmetric class 8:1078, *1079*
holothuroids 9:1223
holotypes 6:699
Holstenian interglacial 6:749
Homalocarpus 5:569
hominids 9:1197, 1198, 1200,
1210, **1250-3**, *1251*, 1266,
1271
Homo see hominids
homologous chromosomes 6:(762)
homonyms 6:700
homozygous individuals 6:(761)
honesty 2:212, 4:469, 470, 472;
perennial 2:212
honey berry 2:224
honey flower 3:281
honey fungus 1:40, *41*
honey locust 2:162
honeydew 4:467
honeysuckle 2:178, *178*, 5:609,
610;
African 2:178;
Australian 2:178;
bush 2:210;
Cape 2:178;
common 2:210, *210*;
coral 2:210;
French 2:171;
giant 2:210;
goat-leaf 2:210;
Japanese 2:210;
native 1:52;
Tatarian 2:210;
trumpet 2:210;
winter-flowering 6:684
Honkenya 2:178, 4:417;
peploides 6:825, 7:920, *921*
Hooke, R. 9:1207, 1258, 1259,
1269
Hooker, Sir Joseph 6:679, (*679*),
682, 687, 702, 760, 7:905,
966
Hooker, Sir William 7:964, **966**
hop 1:58, 122, 2:147, **178**, *178*,
182, 4:447, 7:884;
false 2:191;
field 1:9;
Japanese 2:182;
Spanish 2:256
hop tree 3:283, *283*, 5:554
Hopea 1:122, 2:187, 4:435
horchata de Chufa 1:58, 113
Hordeum 1:53, 5:638, 640
horehound 2:220;
black 1:49, *49*;
fetid 1:49
horizons in soil 6:802, 807, *808*
horizontal structure 6:715, *see also*
pattern 6:716

Horminum **2:178**
Hormoseira **2:178**
horn silver 8:1108
horn-a-plenty 1:117, 2:226
hornbeam 2:127, **179**, *179*, 187,
4:409, 410, 6:747, 749,
7:898;
American 1:54, 2:179;
American hop 2:257;
Chinese Henry's 2:179;
common 2:179;
cordate 2:179;
European hop 2:257;
hop 2:187, **257**;
Japanese 2:179;
Oriental 2:179;
witch 2:168
hornblende 8:973, 1079, 1083,
1084, **1092**, 9:1124, 1125,
1126, 1137, 1138, 1140,
1150, 1151
Horne, J. 9:1263, **1269**, 1272
horned pondweed 5:625
horned rampion 5:604, 606
hornfels 8:1088, 9:*1123*, **1139**
hornwort 1:36, 2:234, 6:826, *827*
horse 9:1197, 1247, **1248**, *1270*,
1271
horse chestnut 1:12, 88, 5:544,
545, 6:680, 7:959;
Chinese 1:12;
common 1:12, *12*
horse nettle, Carolina 3:318
horse sugar 3:330
horseheal 2:185
horsemint 1:57
horseradish 1:65, 2:147, **179**,
4:472
horseradish tree 2:232
horse's tail 3:312
horseshoe vetch 7:908
horsetail 2:180, 6:759, 7:884;
field 2:*180*, *181*;
giant *see* Calamites;
water 2:*180*, *181*
horsetail tree 1:78
horsetails in evolution 6:*739*,
9:1175, 1176, 1179, 1185,
1209, 1216, **1217**
Horsfieldia 3:381, 382
horsts 8:1042, *1043*
hortensia 2:183
Horticultural Code 6:698
Horticultural Society 6:683, 684,
687
Hortonia 3:384
Hosta 2:179, 5:664
hot steppe 7:*832-3*, 859
hot springs 8:*1057*, 1058, 1086,
1088, 1092
hotspots 8:1063-4
Hottentot bean 2:179
Hottentot bread 3:360
Hottentot fig 4:417
Hottentot's head 3:323
Hottonia 2:179, 4:484, 6:818
Houmiria 5:556, 556
Houmiriaceae 5:556, **556**, 564
hound's tongue, common 1:113
hour-glass model of origin of life
6:752, *753*
houseleek 2:182, 4:495;
cobweb 2:182, 3:*312*;
common 2:182;
roof 2:182;
spiderweb 2:182
Houston, Dr William 6:683
Houstonia 2:182, 5:609
Houttuynia 2:182, 3:389, *389*
Hovenia 4:537, 538
How, William 6:702
Howea 2:182
Hoxnian interglacial 6:749
Hoya 2:182, 5:575, 576
Hua 4:483
Huaceae 4:483
huamuchil 3:274
huanaco 2:227

huckleberry 2:182;
bear 2:182;
black 2:182;
blue 2:182;
box 2:182;
dwarf 2:182;
hairy 2:182;
sugar 2:182
Hudsonia 4:458, 459
Hudsonian region and province
7:*897*, 898, 902
Huertea 5:540
Hugonia 5:557, *557*, 558
huisache 1:7
Hulthemia 4:494
human influence **7:923-59**;
and complexity of environment
6:786;
and dis-climaxes 6:714;
and distributions 7:909, 950-2;
on dunes 7:886, 888;
on fens 7:882-3;
on forests 6:751, 7:838, **841-2**,
875, *922*, 935, 937, **937-8**,
958;
on grasslands 7:862, 938-41, *see
also* grazing;
on heathland 7:874-5;
on islands 7:920, **921**, 952;
on marshlands 7:883, 885, 890;
on scrub 7:842, 844;
on succession 6:823;
on tundra 7:936-7, *937*
Humbertia 5:580
Humbertiaceae 5:580
Humbertieae 5:580
Humbertiodendron 5:564
humble plant 2:230
Humboldt, Baron F. H. Alexander
von 6:679, 682, *688*, 689,
708, 718, 719, 7:*966*,
9:1260, **1269**, *1270*
humid mesothermal zone,
grasslands and meadows of
7:860-1
humid microthermal zone,
grasslands of **7:861-2**
Humiria 5:556, 556
Humirianthera 4:531
Humiriastrum 5:556
hummock and hollow mosaics
6:716, 7:879
Humulus 2:178, 182, 4:446, 447;
lupulus 7:884
humus 6:*803*, 803, 804, 9:*1140*,
1140-1
hung-liang 5:540
Hunnemannia 3:279
hunting and gathering 7:927, 931
hupulone 2:147
Hura 4:537
husk tomato 5:579
Huthia 5:583
Hutton, J. 9:1148, 1258, 1259,
1260, 1261, 1262, 1264,
1268, **1269-70**, 1271, 1272
Huxley, T. 9:1260, 1262, **1270**,
1271, 1272
hyacinth 2:183, 3:311, 5:662,
6:680;
common 2:183, *183*;
Dutch 2:183;
grape 2:*183*, 236, *236*;
peacock 2:129, *129*;
Roman 2:183;
star 3:311;
starry 3:311;
summer 2:154;
water 2:129, *129*, 190, 6:*820*,
826, 7:948;
wild 1:72, 2:*182*, 183, 3:344
Hyacinthella 2:183
hyacinth-of-Peru 3:311
Hyacinthoides **2:182**
Hyacinthus 2:183, 5:664
Hyalocalyx 4:454
Hybanthus 4:450, *450*, 451
hybrid cypress 1:111

hybrids:
and crop breeding 7:932, *934*,
934, 935;
and isolation 6:*779*, *780*, 781;
and speciation 6:*697*, 776, 777,
777, 7:915
Hydatella 5:633
Hydnocarpus 1:85, 4:452;
anthelmintha 6:686
hydnocarpus oil 1:85
Hydnophytum 5:608
Hydnora 4:528
Hydnoraceae **4:527**
Hydrangea 2:183, 4:496, 497, 498
hydrangea 2:183;
climbing 1:118;
French 2:183;
wild 3:301
Hydrangeaceae 4:498
Hydrangeoideae 4:497, 5:610
Hydrastidaceae 3:399
Hydrastis 1:58, 3:399
Hydrilla 5:621, 622
hydrocarbons 8:1102, 1114,
9:*1131*;
from plants 7:936;
and pollution 7:942, 943;
see also natural gas, petroleum
Hydrocera 5:561, *561*
Hydrocharis 2:183, 5:621, *621*;
morsus-ranae 6:826
Hydrocharitaceae 5:619, *621*,
621-2
Hydrocharitales 5:621-2, 624, 644
Hydrocharitoideae 5:622
Hydrocleis 5:619
Hydrocotyle 3:264, 5:569, *571*,
571;
vulgaris 7:885
Hydrocotyleae 5:571
Hydrocotyloideae 5:569, 571
Hydrodictyon 1:20
hydrogen 8:970, 971, 972, 995,
997, 9:1202;
sulfide 8:997
hydrogen-burning 8:995
hydrogeology, hydrology 8:1045,
1069-71, *1069*, *1070*
hydrojuglone glucoside 6:823
Hydrolea 5:585
hydrologic cycle 8:*1069-70*, *1069*,
1071
hydrological gradient 8:1044
hydromorphic soils **6:809-10**
hydrophobic substances 7:844
Hydrophyllaceae 5:560, 582, 583,
584-5, *585*, 586
Hydrophyllum 5:585, *585*
hydrophytes 6:719, 725, **769-70**,
770
hydroseres 6:823, *826-7*, **826**,
7:880, *894*
Hydrostachydaceae 4:503, **5:601-2**
Hydrostachys 5:601
hydrothermal deposits 8:*1074*,
1104
Hydrothrix 5:659, 660
hydroxyapatite 8:1084
Hyenia 9:1217
hygrine 1:26
hygrochastic plants 7:850
hygromorphic evergreen shrubs
6:721
hygromorphic tuft-trees 6:720
hygromorphic tussock herbs 6:723
hygrophilous plants 6:719
Hylocarpa 5:556
Hylocomium splendens 7:884
Hymenaea 2:183, 209
Hymenanthera 4:450, 451
Hymenocallis 2:183, 5:665, 666
Hymenocardia 4:537
Hymenophyllaceae 6:724
Hymenosporum 4:488
hyolithids 9:1154
hyoscine 1:26, 117, 2:227
hyoscyamine 1:26, 117, 2:183,
227

Hyoscyamus 2:183, 5:579
Hyparrhenia 2:149, 5:638
Hypecoaceae 4:402
Hypecoideae 4:404
Hypecoum 4:402, 403, 404
Hyperbaena 3:401
Hyperbaeneae 3:401
Hypericaceae 4:436
Hypericoideae 4:436
Hypericopsis 4:461, 461, 462
Hypericum 2:183, 4:435, 436, 436, 437;
    perforatum 7:949
hypersthene 8:1085, 1089, 1092, 1097
Hyphaene 5:651, 653
Hypnum 2:184
Hypochoeris 2:184, 5:617
Hypocrea 2:184
Hypocyrta 5:596, 598
Hypodaphnideae 3:388
Hypodaphnis 3:387
Hypoxidaceae 5:666
Hypoxis 2:184, 5:665, 675
Hypsela 5:606
Hypsilophodon 9:1241, 1242
Hyptis 5:589
hyraces 9:1246, 1247
hyssop 2:174, 184, 184;
    anise 2:184;
    fragrant giant 2:184;
    giant 2:184;
    nettle-leaved 2:184;
    water 1:49
Hyssopus 2:174, 184
Hystrichospheres 9:1215

Iberis 2:184, 4:470, 470, 472
Ibervillea 4:465, 467
icacillo 1:89
Icacina 4:531
Icacinaceae 4:522, 530-1, 531, 6:747
Icacineae 4:531
icaco 1:89
ice 8:971, 972, 1011-2, 1018, 1018-20, 1092
ice ages 8:1020, 1040, 9:1263, 1264;
    Precambrian 8:1020, 9:1153, 1155, 1209;
    Paleozoic 8:1020;
    Tertiary 9:1197-8;
    Pleistocene 8:1002, 1019-20, 1047, 1051, 1052, 9:1198, 1210;
    see also glaciations
ice plant 2:184, 228, 4:417, 417
Iceland moss 1:84
Iceland poppy 4:403
Iceland spar 8:1082, 1087
icho cascarilla 3:286
ichthyosaurs 9:1181, 1189, 1205, 1211, 1236, 1237
Ichthyostega 9:1235
ichu-grass 6:723
identification of species 6:694-706
Idesia 2:184, 4:451, 452
idigbo 3:334, 341, 4:515
Idiospermum 3:385
idocrase (vesuvianite) 8:1079, 1092
Idria 4:455
igneous intrusion 8:1007, 1030-2, 1030, 1031, 1032, 1034, 1086, 1100, 1105, 9:1125, 1128, 1136, 1139
igneous rocks 8:996, 997, 1085, 1087, 1090, 1092, 1096, 1105, 9:1122-9, 1122, 1123, 1132, 1135, 1136, 1138, 1139, 1140, 1142, 1266, 1268;

extrusive (volcanic) 8:973, 9:1122;
intrusive (plutonic) 8:979, 9:1122, 1122-3, 1149;
    see also lavas
ignimbrites 8:1057, 9:1126
Iguanodon 9:1189, 1241-2
iigiri tree 2:184
ilama 1:31
Ilex 2:177, 220, 4:532, 532, 6:749, 7:838;
    aquifolium 6:791, 7:838, 898
Iljin, W. S. 7:845
Illecebraceae 4:419
illegitimate names 6:699
Illiciaceae 3:378, 379, 382, 4:405
Illiciales 3:378, 382, 399
Illicium 1:31, 2:185, 3:379, 382
Illigera 3:388
Illinoian ice advance 6:749
illipe nut oil 2:250
illite 6:802, 8:1009, 1021, 1088, 1092
illuviation 6:802
ilmenite 8:979, 1092, 1105, 1108
imbricate stacking 8:1017
imbricate structure 8:1022
immortelle 2:134, 185, 3:359;
    mountain 2:134;
    swamp 2:134
Impatiens 2:185, 5:561, 561
Impatientella 5:562
Imperata 5:638
impression fossils 6:731-2, 732
inbreeders 7:932
Inca wheat 1:27
Incarville, Pierre Nicholas le Charron d' 6:684
Incarvillea 2:185, 5:599;
    delavayi 6:684
incense tree, Chilean 2:203
inch plant 3:363;
    flowering 3:342
inchworm 2:193
incompatibility of pollen 6:780-1, 781
index species 7:898
India rubber 1:74
Indian almond 4:516
Indian bean 1:79
Indian cup 3:308
Indian floral region 7:897;
    explorations in 6:686-7
Indian grass 7:863
Indian pipe 2:232
Indian spice 3:355
Indian warrior 2:263
Indian-currant 3:330
indicator plants 6:815-6, 816
Indigenous Theory of fossil origins 6:731
indigo 2:126, 149, 185, 3:359, 4:502;
    false 1:52;
    yellow 1:52;
    Yoruba 2:210
Indigofera 2:149, 185, 3:359, 4:502
individualistic model of community 6:709-10
Indo-Malaysian dominion 7:897
induced polarization (IP) techniques 8:992-3
inert gases (noble gases) 8:971, 972
infiltration 8:1069, 1070
Inga 1:71, 4:499
ingera 2:132
inheritance, genetic basis of 6:760-1, 760-3
ink cap 1:104;
    glistening 2:157;
    magpie 1:104
inoceramids 9:1227
inorganic matter in soils 6:802, 803

insectivores 9:1246
insects 9:1228, 1229;
    Carboniferous 9:1170, 1173;
    Cretaceous 9:1189, 1219;
    development of flight 9:1163;
    and pollination 6:766, 767, 773, 780, 7:854, 905;
    and weed control 7:950
inselbergs 8:1043, 1047
insequents 8:1037-8
inset 5:647
insinde 7:863
instability in salt marshes 7:889
interglacials 6:749-51;
    and relicts 7:912
internal reproductive isolation 6:780, 781, 781
International Biological Program 7:941, 959
International Board for Plant Genetic Resources 7:959
International Code of Botanical Nomenclature 6:699-701
International Rice Research Institute 7:957
interstadials, glacial 6:750
intolerants, shade- 6:814, 7:841
intrazonal soils 6:807, 808-10
introgression 6:779-80
intrusive rocks see igneous intrusion, igneous rocks
Intsia 2:187
Inula 2:185, 4:525, 5:617
Inuleae 5:617
inundation of salt marshes 7:889
inversions in chromosomes 6:777, 819
invertebrates 9:1219-30
Iochroma 2:185
Iodeae 4:531
Iodes 4:531, 531
iodine 8:988, 1109
iolite 8:1088
Ionidium 4:450, 450
Ionopsidium 2:186
Ionotus 2:156
ions:
    nutrient 6:806;
    diffusion of 6:820;
    excluded and excreted 7:890
ipecac (ipecacuanha) 2:186, 227, 4:451, 5:608, 609;
    American 2:161;
    false 2:186
Ipheion 2:186
Ipomoea 2:186, 188, 233, 3:330, 5:580, 580, 6:770;
    batatas 7:935;
    pes-caprae 6:824, 825, 826
Ipomopsis 5:583, 6:773
Ipswichian interglacial 6:749
Irano-Turanian floristic region 7:897, 897
Iresine 2:186, 4:420
iriartoid palms 5:654
Iridaceae 5:661, 661-2, 664, 666, 670
Irideae 5:662
iridescence 8:1083, 1086
iridium 8:1099, 1110
Iris 2:186, 256, 5:661, 661, 662, 6:723, 778;
    delavayi 6:684;
    pseudacorus 7:884
iris 2:187;
    butterfly 2:187;
    crested 2:187;
    dwarf 2:187;
    English 2:187;
    lamance 2:187;
    peacock 2:232;
    Persian 2:187;
    roof 2:187;
    Spanish 2:187;
    wall 2:187;
    wild 2:187;
    yellow 2:187

Irish Deer 9:1200, 1248
Irish lace 3:331
Irish moss 3:318
iroko 2:187, 3:341
iroko-wood 4:447
iron 8:972, 979, 992, 995, 996, 997, 1009, 1010, 1021, 1074, 1081, 1082, 1083, 1085, 1087, 1088, 1092, 1094, 1099, 1105, 9:1123, 1124, 1126, 1127, 1128, 1130, 1131, 1134, 1135, 1141, 1255;
    in plant nutrition 6:806
Iron Age Man 6:751, 7:928
iron tree 2:260, 4:434
ironbark 2:187, 3:341, 4:512;
    bloodwood 2:187;
    broadleafed 2:187;
    narrowleafed 2:187;
    pink 2:187;
    red 2:137, 187;
    white 2:135
iron-nickel 8:972, 974, 979, 986, 989, 9:1122
irons 8:972, 986, 987, 988, 989, 1105
iron-sintering 7:942
ironstones 8:1074, 1087, 1092, 1099, 1105, 9:1134-5, 1134, 1186, 1187;
    banded ironstone formations 9:1134-5, 1150, 1151;
    clay 9:1134, 1135;
    oolitic 9:1134, 1135
ironweed 3:353;
    Western 3:353
ironwood 2:187, 228, 257, 6:826;
    black 2:248;
    Borneo 2:187;
    dwarf 2:187, 211;
    giant 2:187;
    Persian 2:260;
    red 2:211;
    scrub 2:187;
    sonora 2:187;
    South-sea 2:187;
    white 2:187
irradiance 6:792
isanu 3:345
Isatis 2:126, 187, 3:358, 4:470, 470
Ischnosiphon 5:650
island arcs 8:1005, 1035, 1062, 1062-3, 9:1126, 1127, 1150
islands 7:917-21, 918, 920-1;
    and endemism 7:916-7;
    habitat 7:896, 916
Ismene 2:183
isochars 7:907
Isoetes 1:94, 95, 6:725
isoflors (isopleths) 7:907
isolation 6:777, 778-81, 780, 781;
    and age of area 7:916, 917-9;
    and vicariance 7:908
Isolona 3:381
Isoplexis 2:148
Isopyrum 3:399
isostasy 8:1002, 1020, 1023, 9:1263
isostatic sea-level changes 7:909
isotherms 6:789
isotopic dating 6:735
istle (istli) 2:187, 5:666;
    jamauve 2:187;
    tula 2:187
itchweed 3:353
Itea 2:187, 4:497, 498
Iteaceae 4:498
ivory nut palm 5:664
ivory wood 3:316
ivy 2:187, 5:567, 568;
    American 2:261;
    Boston 2:261;
    Canary Island 2:188;
    Cape 3:313;
    common 2:188;
    five-leaved 2:261;

geranium 3:313;
ground 2:162;
Irish 2:188;
Japanese 2:261;
Kenilworth 1:112;
Madeira 2:188;
oakleaf poison 3:276, 294;
parlor 3:313;
Persian 2:188;
poison 3:276, *276*, 294, 7:949;
see also Hedera
Ixia **2:188**, 5:662
Ixieae 5:662
Ixora **2:188**, 5:*608*
ixtle *see* istle

jaborandi 3:271, **5:554**
jaboticaba 4:512
jaboty butter 5:565
Jacaranda **2:188**, 5:600
jacaranda 1:116, 3:341
Jacaratia 4:455
jacinth:
    Peruvian 3:311;
    Spanish 2:183
jack bean 4:502, *see also* bean
Jack in the pulpit 1:40
Jack wood 1:110
Jackfruit 1:42, 2:126, 151, 3:350, 352, 4:447
Jack-go-to-bed-at-noon 3:342
Jacks, G. V. 7:955
Jacobaea 3:313
Jacobinia 2:191
Jacob's ladder 3:276, *276*
Jacob's staff 2:233
Jacquina 4:486
jade 8:1083, 1092, 1095
jade plant 1:108
jadeite 8:*1092-3*, 1097
jaggery 1:40, 61, 77, 5:654
jalap 2:186, 231, 4:420, 5:580
Jamaica plum 5:548
jamberry 2:151, 3:270
jambolan 2:137
Jamestown weed 1:117
Jankaea 5:596
Japan wood tree 1:69
Japanese cherry 4:491, 494
Japanese date plum 4:483
Japanese explorations 6:**684-5**
japonica 1:84, 4:494
Jardin d'Acclimatation (Leyden) 6:684
Jardin des Plantes (Paris) 6:683
Jardin du Roi 6:681
Jarilla 4:455
jarrah 2:135, 3:341
Jasione **2:188**, 5:604, 606
jasmine 1:58, 2:136, 147, **188**, 5:576, 577;
    Arabian 2:188;
    bastard 1:84;
    Cape 2:155;
    Catalonian 2:188;
    Chilean 2:217;
    cinnamon 2:170;
    common white 2:188;
    crape 3:331;
    Italian 2:188;
    Madagascar 3:324;
    orange 3:308;
    primrose 2:188;
    rock 1:29;
    star 3:342;
    West Indian 3:275;
    willow-leaved 1:84;
    winter 2:188, *188*, 6:684
Jasmineae 5:577
Jasminoideae 5:577
Jasminum **2:188**, 5:576, 577;
    nudiflorum 6:684

jasper 8:1087, **1093**, 1097, 9:*1135*
Jateorhiza 3:401
Jatropha **2:188**, 3:323, 4:535, 537
Jatropheae 4:537
jawless fishes *see* Agnatha
Jeffersonia 3:395, 395, 396
Jeffry, John 6:683
jelutong 3:341
Jerusalem artichoke 1:42, 3:329, 5:618
Jerusalem cross 2:213
Jerusalem thorn 2:260
Jerusalem tree 2:258
jessamine, night-blooming 1:84
Jew bush 2:263
Jew's apple *see* aubergine
Jew's beard 3:331
Jew's ear fungus **2:188**, *189*
jimsonweed 1:117, 5:579
jobo 3:322
Job's tears 1:97, *97*
jocote 3:322
Joey Hooker 2:154
Johannesteijsmannia 5:653
Johanssen, Ivar 6:760
John-go-to-bed-at-noon 3:342
Johnny-jump-up 3:355
jointing 8:*1008*, 1008-9, **1023**, 1066
Joinvillea 5:633
Joinvilleaceae 5:633
jojoba 7:936
Joliffieae 4:465
jonquil 2:238
Joshua tree **2:188**, 3:361
Jove's fruit 2:207
Jubaea **2:189**, 5:654
Judas tree 1:82, 4:499
Juelia 4:526
Juglandaceae 4:408, 5:555, **555**
Juglandales 4:494, 5:555
Juglandicarya 6:765
Juglandites 6:765
Juglandoideae 5:555
Juglans 3:356, 5:555, 555, 6:745, 749, 765;
    regia 6:823
juglone 6:823
jujube 4:537, 538;
    Chinese 3:363;
    common 3:363;
    Indian 3:363
Juliania 5:544
Julianiaceae **5:544**, 548
jumping bean plants 2:189, 4:537
Juncaceae 5:634, **640-1**, *641*, 642, 667
Juncaginaceae **5:623**, 624
Juncales 5:640-2
Juncus **2:189**, 7:862, 905, 949, 5:*641*, 641;
    actus 7:887;
    conglomeratus 7:885;
    gerardii 7:945;
    inflexus 7:885;
    maritimus 7:889;
    trifidus 6:789, 7:910
juneberry 1:27
junico 5:641
juniper 1:54, 2:126, *146*, 147, **190**;
    Californian 2:191;
    Chinese 2:190;
    coffin 2:190;
    common 2:190;
    creeping 2:190;
    grand 2:191;
    Greek 2:191;
    needle 2:191;
    plum 2:191;
    prickly 2:190;
    sargent 2:190;
    Sierra 2:191;
    Syrian 2:191
juniper 6:750;
    dwarf 7:902
juniper tar 2:190

Juniperus 1:80, **2:190**, 3:341, 6:750;
    communis var. *depressa* 7:*902*
Jupiter 8:971, 972, 988
Jupiter's beard 1:81
Jupiter's red spot 6:*758*
Jurassic 6:*738-9*, 740, 742, 742-3, 8:1001, 1105, *1117*, 9:*1148*, *1180*, **1181-5**, *1187*, 1188, 1209, 1224, 1232, 1261;
    fauna 9:1181-3, *1184*, 1187;
    flora 9:1175, *1184*, 1185;
    geography 9:1181, *1184*;
    formation of coal in 8:1118, 9:1187;
    stratigraphic correlation 9:1184-5
Jurinea 2:191, 5:617
Jussiaeeae 4:512
Jussieu, Antoine-Laurent de 6:679
Jussieu, Bernard and Joseph de 6:683
Justicia 2:191, 5:*600*, 601
jute 2:145, *145*, **190**, 191, 3:350, 4:440, 441;
    bastard 2:176;
    China 1:87, 2:144;
    Congo 1:39, 2:144;
    tossa 2:191;
    upland 2:191;
    white 2:191
juvenile water 8:1069

Kadsura 3:382
Kaemfer, Engelbert 6:684
Kaempferia 2:191, 5:648
Kaffir beer 3:319
Kaffir boom 2:134
Kaffir bread 2:130, 3:328
Kaffir lily 1:92, 3:*310*
Kaffir plum 5:575
Kaffir potato 3:275
kahika 3:276
kajoo lahi 1:81
Kakebekia as living fossil 6:759
kaki 2:191, 3:266, 4:483
Kalanchoe 2:191, 4:495, *495*
kalanchoe:
    flame 2:192;
    pen-wiper 2:192
kale 1:63, 65, 2:149, 192, 4:472;
    borecole 2:192;
    cabbage 1:64;
    Chinese 1:64;
    cottager's 2:192;
    crimped 2:192;
    curled 1:64, *65*;
    curly 1:64, 2:192;
    flowering 1:64;
    hungry gap 1:64, 2:192;
    Indian 3:359;
    Italian 1:64;
    marrow stem 1:64, 2:192;
    Portuguese 1:64;
    ragged Jack 2:192;
    ruvo 1:64;
    Scotch 1:64;
    sea 1:*65*, 108, *108*, 3:350;
    Siberian 1:64, 2:192;
    thousand headed 2:192
Kalmia 2:192, 198, 4:477, 7:876
kalmia, bog 2:192
Kalopanax 5:568
kamacite 8:986, 989
kamenitzas 8:*1044*
Kandelia 2:218, 4:508
Kangaroo grass 7:940
kangaroo paw 1:31, 5:667, 668
kangaroo vine 1:90, *90*
Kansas glaciation 6:749
kaolin 8:*1097*
kaolin clays 6:802

kaolinite (china clay) 8:1009, 1021, 1087, 1088, 1092, **1093**, 9:1130
kapa 2:145
kapok 1:61, 2:144, **145**, *192*, *193*, 4:443, 444, 457;
    white 1:61, 2:144
kapok seed oil 2:250
kapok tree 1:80, 2:192, *193*;
    white 1:61, 2:144
kapur 3:341
Karatas 2:241
karaya gum 4:457
Kariba weed 2:192, 3:306, *306*
karo 3:274
Karoo 8:1002, 1041, 9:1187, *1211*, 1243
karren 8:1010, 1043
karri 3:341
karri tree 2:193, 261
karst 8:**1043-5**, *1044*, 1045, 1046, *1070*, 1087
kat 1:58, 2:192
katsura tree 1:82, 6:746
kauri 2:192, 3:341, 7:837;
    Queensland 2:192
kauri gum 2:192
kauri pine 2:192, 3:341, 7:837
kava 1:16, 2:126, 3:273, 388
kawaka 2:203
kaya 3:342
Kazakhstan floristic province 6:*741*, 743
keck 1:36, 2:173
Kedrostis 4:465, 467, *467*
Kegr salt 4:530
kelp 1:19, 2:192, *197*, 6:828;
    bull 1:18, 2:192, 240, *240*;
    giant 1:18, 67, 2:192, 214, 6:*782*
Kelvin, Lord 9:1262, 1263, 1265-6, 1267, 1269, **1270**
kenaf 2:144, 176, 7:936
Kentucky coffee tree 2:167
Kenyapithecus 9:1250
kerangas 7:835
kerogen 6:*758*, 8:1112, 9:*1131*
Kerr, William 6:684
Kerria 2:192, 4:491, *494*, 494
Kerrieae 4:494
Kerstingiella 2:201
keruing 1:122, 3:341
kettleholes 8:1050
Kew Gardens 6:684, 687
key, botanical 6:*704*
khair 1:7
khas-khas 2:136, **193**, 3:354
khat 1:58, 2:192
khat tree 4:529
Khaya 2:193, 215, 5:552
khesari 2:164
khus-khus 2:136, **193**, 3:354
Kibara 3:384
Kibessia 4:514
kidney bean 4:502, *see also* bean
kidney iron ore 8:*1092*
Kielmeyera 4:436
Kielmeyeroideae 4:436
Kigelia 5:600
Kilauea 8:1033-4, 1058
kimberlite 8:995, 1086, 1089, 9:*1127*, **1128-9**, *1129*
kinchpoints 8:*1039*, 1040
king nut 1:77
kingcup 1:72, 7:880, 884
kingdoms, floristic 7:894
Kingdon-Ward, Frank 6:685-6, 7:*966*, 966
Kingia 5:666, 6:720;
    australis 6:*720*
king's crown 2:191
kingwood, Brazilian 1:116
kino 2:193, 3:283;
    Bengal 1:68;
    gum 1:68;
    Malabar 2:193;
    West African 3:283

Kirengeshoma **2:**193, **4:**498
kiri wood **2:**193
Kirkia **5:**549
kirsch **1:**16
Kissenia **4:**464
Kitaibelia **4:**445
kitchingia **2:**192
Kitchinia **2:**191
kitul **5:**654
kitul fiber **1:**77
kiwi fruit **1:**10
kiwiberry **2:**151
Kleinia **2:**193, **3:**312, **5:**617, 618
Klugieae **5:**596
Kmeria **3:**378
knapweed **1:**81;
  greater **1:**81, *81*
Knautia **2:**193, **5:**611, 612
knee-roots **7:**891
Knema **3:**381, 382
Kniphofia **2:**194, **5:**662, 664
knotgrass *see Polygonum*
knotroot **3:**323
knotweed **3:**277;
  dyer's **2:**126;
  giant **3:**277
Knowltonia **3:**399
Kochia **2:**194, **4:**423, 423
Koelreuteria **2:**194, **5:**543, 544
Koenigia islandica **6:**791, **7:**909,
  910, 910
Kohleria **2:**194, **5:**596, 598
kohlrabi **1:**64, 65, **2:**194, *194*,
  4:472
kohuhu **3:**274
kokoon tree **4:**529
Kokoona **4:**529
kola **1:**58, **2:**194, *194*, 227, 245,
  245, **4:**441;
  bitter **2:**194
Kolkwitzia **2:**194
komatiite **9:**1150
komatsu-na **1:**64
kombu **1:**19
kopjes **8:**1043
korakan **2:**129
kowhai **3:**318
Krakatau, succession on **6:**824-5,
  7:920-1
Krakatoa **8:**1032, 1033, 1034,
  1058, **9:***1261*
Krameria **5:**567, *567*
Krameriaceae **5:**566-7, *567*
kratons **9:**1150, 1157
Krummholz **7:**868
krypton **8:**997
kudzu **2:**149
kummel **1:**77
kumquat **1:**91, **2:**151, 194, **5:**554;
  oval **2:**194;
  round **2:**194
Kunzea **7:**874
kunzite *see* spodumene
kurrat **2:**199
kutai **1:**39
kutira gum **4:**457
kvass **1:**16
kyanite **8:**1080, 1083, **1093**,
  1099

labdanum **1:**90
Labiatae **4:**506, **5:**587, *588*, **589**,
  590, 591, 596, **7:**919
lablab **1:**123, **2:**195, 201, *201*,
  4:502
Labrador tea **7:**903, *see also*
  Greenland tea
labradorite **8:**1096, **9:**1127
laburnine **2:**195
+ *Laburnocytisus* **2:**195
Laburnum **2:**195, **4:**502
laburnum **2:**227;

common **2:**195;
  evergreen **3:**273;
  Indian **1:**78;
  Nepal **3:**273;
  New Zealand **3:**318;
  Scotch **2:**195
labyrinthodonts **9:**1234, **1235**
lac **2:**142, **195**
lac tree **2:**195, 214
laccoliths **8:**1030, *1032*
lace bark **2:**177, 195, **4:**511
lace leaf **1:**37
lace plant **5:**623
lace shrub **3:**324
lace vine **3:**277
Lachenalia **2:**195
Lachnanthes **5:**668
Lacistema **4:**452
Lacistemataceae **4:**452, 522
lacquer **2:**195;
  Burmese **2:**195
lacquer tree **2:**195
Lactarius **2:**195
Lactobacillus **3:**308
Lactoridaceae **3:**383
Lactoris **3:**383
Lactuca **2:**195, **202**, **5:**617, 618;
  sativa **7:**943
Lactuceae **5:**613, 617
Lactucoideae **5:**617
Lacunaria **4:**438
ladanum **1:**90
lad's love **1:**42
lady of the night **1:**67, 84
lady's delight **3:**355
lady's finger **2:**176, 248, **3:**350
lady's laces **2:**207
lady's mantle **1:**15, *15*, **4:**494;
  Alpine **1:**15
lady's smock **1:**75, *75*
lady's tresses:
  autumn **3:**322;
  common **3:**322;
  slender **3:**322;
  Southern **3:**322
Laelia **2:**195, **5:**675
× *Laeliocattleya* **2:**196
Lafoensia **4:**507
Lagarosiphon **5:**621, 622
Lagascea **5:**615, 617
Lagenaria **1:**69, **2:**163, **4:**467
lager **1:**16
Lagerstroemia **2:**196, **4:**506, 507
Lagetto **2:**195, **4:**511
laggs **7:**877, *878*
Lagoecia **5:**571
Lagoecieae **5:**571
lagomorphs **9:**1249
Lagopus l. scoticus and heath **6:**814,
  7:875
Laguncularia **4:**515
Lagurus **2:**196, **5:**638
Lamanonia **4:**487
Lamarck, Jean Baptiste **6:**731, 759,
  764, **7:966**, **9:**1203, 1258,
  1266, 1270, 1271
Lambert, A. B. **6:**682
Lambertia **2:**178
lambkill **4:**477
lamb's ear **3:**323
lamb's lettuce **5:**610
lamb's quarters **3:**344
lamb's tail **3:**312
lamb's tongue **3:**323
lamellibranchs **9:**1178
Lamiaceae **5:**589
Lamiales **5:**586-91, 596, 602
Laminaria **2:**192, 196, **6:**828;
  digitata **6:**829;
  hyperborea **6:**829;
  saccharum **6:**829
Lamium **2:**196, 241, **5:**589
Lampranthus **2:**196, **4:**415, *417*,
  417
lampreys **9:**1231
lamy **3:**331
lanamar **3:**279
Lanaria **5:**668

lancewood **3:**381;
  Cuban **1:**125;
  Guianan **1:**125;
  Jamaican **1:**125
land bridges **7:**908-9, *909*
land plants, first **6:**766, *766*
land races **7:**956-7
Landolphia **2:**196, 214, **3:**297,
  5:575
Langermannia **2:**156, **3:**284
Langloisia **5:**583
langsat **5:**552
Lansium **5:**552
Lantana **2:**197, **5:**587
lantern plant, Chinese **3:**270
Lapageria **2:**197, **5:**662, *662*
Lapeirousia **2:**197, **5:**662
lapis lazuli **8:**1093, 1099, *see also*
  lazurite
Laportea **2:**241, **4:**448
Lapsana **2:**197, **5:**617
Lapworth, C. **9:**1152, 1156, 1160,
  1260, 1263, **1270**
larch **2:***196*, 197, **3:**343, 346;
  Dahurian **2:***197*, **7:**903;
  Eastern **2:**197, **3:**341;
  European **2:**197, **3:**341, **7:**904,
    912, *913*;
  golden **3:**282;
  Japanese **2:**197;
  Siberian **7:**912, *913*;
  tamarack **6:***814*, **7:**876, *902*,
    903;
  Western **2:**197, **3:**341;
  see also Larix
lard fruit **4:**467
Lardizabala **3:**399, 400
Lardizabalaceae **3:**399-400, *400*,
  401
Larix **2:**197, **3:**346, **6:**749, **7:**838,
  892, 902;
  dahurica **7:**838;
  decidua **7:**904, 912, *913*;
  eurasiatica **7:***913*;
  gmelinii **6:**781, **7:**838, 903;
  kaempferi **6:**781;
  laricina **6:***814*, **7:**876, *902*, 903;
  russica **7:**912, *913*
larkspur **1:**118, **3:**399;
  Alpine **1:**118;
  forking **1:**118;
  rocket **1:**118
Larrea **2:**197;
  divericata **6:***799*, 799, **7:**843,
    848, *849*, 850, 940
Laserpitieae **5:**571
Laserpitium **5:**571
lasiandra **3:**336
lasiocarpine **2:**227
Lasiosiphon **4:**510
Lasiospermum **5:**618
Lasthenia **2:**197
Latania **2:**197, **5:**653
laterite **6:**805, **808**, **8:**1010, 1074,
  1087, 1106, **9:**1135, 1140
lateritic soils **9:**1141
laterization **8:**1010
latex **2:**197, **3:**297
Lathraea **2:**198, **5:**598, 599;
  squamaria **6:**724
lathyrism **2:**164
Lathyrus **2:**164, **2:**198, **3:**354,
  4:502, 502;
  niger **6:**683
Latimeria **9:**1234
latitude, geographical **6:***788*
latosols **6:**805, **808**
lattice leaf **1:**37
lattices, crystal **8:**1076, 1077
lauan **3:**341
laudanoscine **1:**26
Lauraceae **3:**381, 382, 383, 384,
  387, **387-8**, **6:**744, 746, 747,
  7:896
Laurales **3:**378, 383-8
Laurasia **6:***741*, 741-2, 743, 745,
  9:1166, 1170-3, 1174, 1177,

1179, 1180-1
Laureae **3:**387, 388
laurel **2:**198, **3:**387, 388, **4:**494,
  517, **6:**746, 747;
  Alexandrian **1:**72, **2:**198;
  Australian **3:**274;
  bay **2:***146*, 147, 198, *198*,
    7:941;
  Californian **2:**198;
  Canary Island **2:**198;
  cherry **2:**198, **3:**282;
  Indian **3:**341;
  Japanese **2:**198;
  madrona **1:**39;
  maza **2:**247;
  mountain **2:**192, *192*;
  Portugal **3:**282;
  sheep **2:**192, 198;
  spotted **1:**47, **2:**198;
  spurge **1:**116, **2:**198;
  swamp **2:**198;
  Western **2:**192
laurel tree **3:**266
laurelberry fat **2:**198
Laurelia **2:**198, **3:**384, **5:**590,
  7:837
Laurembergia **4:**505
Laurentia **5:**606
Laurentide ice sheet **6:**750
Laurocerasus **2:**198, **3:**282, **4:**494
Lauroideae **3:**387-8
Laurus **2:**198, **3:**387, 388, **7:**838;
  nobilis **7:**941
laurustinus **3:**354
Lauterbachia **3:**384
Lavandula **2:**198, **199**, **5:**589,
  6:721, **7:**836
lavas **8:**978, 980, 1004, 1034,
  1042, 1057, 1089, 1093,
  9:1122, 1126, 1128, 1135,
  1149;
  aa **8:**1058;
  pahoehoe **8:***1058*;
  pillow **8:**1058, *1060*, **9:**1150;
  see also igneous rocks (extrusive)
Lavatera **2:**198, 216, **4:**444, 445
lavatera, tree **2:**198
lavender **2:**199, **5:**589;
  common **2:**198, 199;
  cotton **3:**307;
  French **2:**198;
  sea **2:**199, **207**, *207*, **6:***711*;
  Spanish **2:**198;
  spike **2:**198;
  wild **2:**199
lavender cotton **3:**307, *307*
lavender oil **2:**136, 198
laver bread **1:**19, **2:**199
laver weed **7:**945
Lawrence, G. H. M. **6:**701
Lawson cypress **6:**719
Lawsonia **2:**126, **173**, **4:**506, *507*,
  507
lawyer's wig **1:**104, *104*
layer societies **6:**729
Layia **2:**199, **5:**617
lazurite **8:**1090, **1093**
Le Gros Clark, Sir W. **9:**1271
leaching **6:**802, 806, **8:**1009,
  1046, 1074, **9:**1140, *see also*
  weathering (chemical)
lead **8:**988, 992, 997, 1023,
  1075, 1083, 1090, 1106,
  1111, 1121, **9:**1146, 1255,
  see also tetraethyl lead
lead pollution **7:**942, 944
leadwort, Cape **3:**275
leaf beet **4:**422
leaf characters and fossil study
  6:746
leaf fall:
  and drought **7:**848;
  and ethylene gas **7:**943;
  and seasonal change **6:**770
leaf rust, resistance to **7:**958
leaf-size classes **6:**725
leaf-succulents, dwarf **6:**722
leafy cryptogams **6:**724

Leakey, L. 9:1250, **1271**
leatherleaf 7:*903*, 903
leatherwood 4:474
Lebachiacaeae 6:740
Lebetanthus 4:478
Lecanora 2:219, 7:942;
  atra 6:*829*;
  conizaeoides 7:*943*
Lechea 4:458, 458, 459
Lecoq, Henri 6:689
lectin 3:347
lectotypes 6:699
Lecythidaceae 4:*449*, **449-50**
Lecythidales 4:449-50
Lecythis 2:245, 3:**307**, 4:450
Ledebouria 3:311
Ledenbergia 4:421
Ledocarpaceae 5:559
Ledum 4:477;
  groenlandicum 7:876, *902*, 903
Leea 4:539
Leeaceae 4:539
leechee 2:151, *153*, **208**, 5:*543*,
  543, 544
leek 1:17, 2:**199**, *199*, 3:*270*, 350,
  351, 5:662, 664
legitimate names 6:699
Legousia 5:604
Leguminales 4:494
Leguminosae 4:472, 473, 494,
  499-502, *502*, 525, 5:542,
  566, 567
Lehmann, J. 9:1249, 1260, **1271**
Leibniz, Gottfried 6:731
Leiophyllum 2:**199**, 4:477
Leiothrix 5:632
Leitneria 4:407, 408
Leitneriaceae 4:**407-8**
Leitneriales 4:407
Lemairocereus thurberi 6:*722*
Lemmonia 5:585
Lemna 1:**125**, 5:656, 657, *657*,
  6:691, 725, 826, *827*;
  minor 7:942
Lemnaceae 5:**656-7**, *657*, 659
lemon 1:58, 91, 2:147, 151, **199**,
  199, 5:552, *552*, 554;
  garden 2:222;
  wild 3:276
lemon balm 2:224, *224*
lemon grass 5:638, 640
lemon oil 2:136, 199
lemon verbena 5:587
lemuroids 9:1250
Lennoa 5:582
Lennoaceae 5:**582**
Lens 2:**199**, 201, 4:502
Lenten lily 2:*173*, 3:399
Lenten rose 2:172, *173*
Lentibulariaceae 5:598, *603*,
  603-4
lenticels 7:891
lentil 2:**199**, *200*, 201, 4:502
lentisc 7:898
Leonardo Da Vinci 9:1257, **1271**
Leonia 4:451
Leonotis 5:589
Leonticaceae 3:396
Leontice 3:396
Leontochir 5:666
Leontodon 2:**202**
Leontopodium 2:**128**, **202**, 5:*617*,
  617
leopard bane 1:*123*
Leopold, Aldo 7:955
Leopoldinia 3:**271**, 5:654
Lepidieae 5:470
Lepidium 1:108, 2:**202**, 4:470
lepidocaryoid palms 5:653, 654
lepidodendroid trees in evolution
  6:*739*, *740*
Lepidodendron 6:*740*, 766, 9:1216;
  aculeatum 6:*764*
Lepidodendropsis 6:743
lepidolite 8:*1082*, 1102
Lepidozamia 1:112, 2:214
Lepilaena 5:*625*, 625
Lepironia 5:643

lepospondyls 9:**1235**, 1236
Leptaspis 5:636
Leptocarpus 5:633, *634*, 634
Leptochloa 5:638
Leptodactylon 5:583
Leptolaena 4:445
Leptonycteris sanborni and
  pollination 6:*786*
leptophylls 6:725
Leptospermoideae 4:511
Leptospermum 2:**202**, 4:512, 7:874
leptotene in meiosis 6:*763*
Leptothyrsa 5:552
Lepturus 5:638
Leschenaultia 5:607
Lespedeza 2:**202**
Lesquerella 4:470
lesser celandine 3:399
lethal temperature 6:791
lettuce 2:195, **202**, 3:350, *351*,
  5:613, 615, 618, 7:*943*;
  bitter 2:202;
  cabbage 3:350;
  common 2:195, *195*, 202, *202*;
  Cos 3:350;
  lamb's 3:349, *349*;
  opium 2:202;
  poison 2:202;
  prickly 2:195, 202;
  river 3:273;
  sea 1:19, 3:**311**, *311*;
  water 3:273, *273*;
  wild 3:350;
  willow-leaved 2:202
lettuce tree 3:273, 4:420
Leucadendron 4:520
Leucaena 2:149
Leucanthemum 2:**202**, 5:618
Leuchtenbergia 4:415
leucite 8:1090, **1093**, 1104,
  9:1124
Leucobryum 2:**203**, 3:*290*;
  glaucum 6:*722*
Leucojum 2:**203**, 5:664, 665, 666
Leucospermum 4:520
Leucothoe 2:**203**, 4:477
Levenhookia 5:607
Levisticum 2:174, **211**, 5:571
levorotation 8:1112
Lewis, Merriweather 6:683
Lewisia 2:**203**, 4:424, *425*, 425
Leycesteria 2:**203**, 5:610
Liabeae 5:617
Liabum 5:617
liaison taxa 7:895
lianas 6:**720-1**, *721*, 771-2
Liatris 2:**203**, 5:615, 617
Libertia 2:**203**, 5:662
Libocedrus 2:**203**, 6:721, 7:904
Licania 2:250, 4:498, *498*, 499
lichen 2:**204**, 6:*724*, 724, 7:*853*,
  942, *943*;
  pine 1:84;
  red stone 2:126;
  snow 1:84
lichen mat 6:*724*, 724
licorice 2:146, 147, **203**, 227;
  Indian 2:203;
  wild 1:46, 2:203
licorice root 2:171, 203
Licuala 2:216, 5:651
life, origin and early history of
  6:**752-7**, 8:1034, 9:**1201-3**,
  1264
life plant 2:192
life-form 6:717, **718-27**, *719-26*
light 6:**792-5**;
  and altitude 7:869;
  competition for 6:792;
  and exposure 6:800, *801*;
  on mountains 7:866, 869;
  period of 6:*793*;
  and pollution 7:941, 944, 945;
  struggle for 6:**771-2**;
  see also day-length
light demanders 7:841-2
Lightfootia 5:604
lightning and fire 6:811, 7:843

lightwood 4:488
lignite 8:1117
lignum vitae 2:167, *167*, **206**,
  3:341, 5:554
Ligularia 2:**206**, 3:312, 5:617
Ligusticum 2:**206**, 5:571
Ligustrales 5:577
Ligustrum 3:**281**, 5:**577**;
  vulgare 6:825
lilac 2:**206**, 5:576, 577, 6:680;
  common 2:206;
  Hungarian 2:206;
  Persian 2:206, 224
Lilaea 2:**206**, 5:623, 624
Lilaeaceae 5:**623-4**
Liliaceae 5:641, 651, 659, *662*,
  662-4, 665, 666, 667, 668,
  669, 670, 675
Liliales 5:**659-70**
Liliidae 5:**659-75**
Lilium 2:**206**, 5:*662*, 664;
  giganteum 6:686
lillypilly 4:512
lily 2:**206**, 5:662, 6:683;
  African 1:12, *13*;
  Amazon 2:137;
  arum 1:**42**, *42*, 3:*361*, 362,
    362;
  atamasco 3:363;
  avalanche 2:135;
  Aztec 3:322;
  Barbados 2:177;
  belladonna 1:27;
  blood 2:168, *168*;
  blue plantain 2:179;
  boat 3:293;
  bugle 3:357;
  butterfly 2:170;
  Canada 2:206;
  corn 3:353;
  crane 3:326;
  Cuban 3:311;
  day 2:172, *173*;
  Easter 2:206;
  fire 1:114;
  flamingo 1:36;
  Formosa 2:206;
  fox-tail 2:133, *133*;
  fragrant plantain 2:179;
  ginger 1:106, 2:170;
  glory 2:162, *162*;
  golden-rayed 2:206, *207*;
  Guernsey 2:240;
  ifafa 1:114;
  Jacobean 3:322;
  Japanese toad 3:343;
  kaffir 1:92, 3:*310*;
  Kamchatka 2:150;
  Lenten 2:*173*;
  madonna 2:206, 6:680;
  martagon 2:206;
  May 2:216;
  Mount Cook 7:*915*;
  nankeen 2:206;
  narrow-leafed plantain 2:179;
  orange 2:206;
  palm 3:361;
  panther 2:206;
  paradise 2:260;
  Peruvian 1:25, *25*;
  plantain 2:179;
  prairie 2:225;
  pyjama 2:201, 1:*109*;
  resurrection 2:191;
  St Bernard's 1:36, *36*;
  St Bruno's 2:260, *260*;
  St James 3:322;
  Scarborough 3:309;
  scarlet Turk's cap 2:206;
  spear 1:*123*;
  spire 2:154;
  tiger 2:206;
  toad 3:343, *343*;
  torch 2:194;
  triplet 3:344;
  trout 2:135;
  trumpet 3:362;
  Turk's cap 2:**206**;

voodoo 3:308;
  water 6:683, 747, *798*, 826,
    827, see also water-lily;
  yellow pond 2:243
lily of the field 3:324
lily-of-the-Nile 1:*13*
lily-of-the-palace 2:177
lily-of-the-valley 2:**206**, 227;
  false 2:216;
  star-flowered 3:317;
  wild 3:285;
  see also Convallaria
lily-of-the-valley bush 3:271
lily-of-the-valley tree 1:92, 4:473,
  474
lilyturf 2:252
lima bean 2:**207**, 4:502
limba 3:341
lime 1:58, 91, 2:151, **207**, 5:552,
  554;
  key 2:207;
  mandarin 2:151;
  ogeeche 2:243;
  Persian 2:207;
  Rangpur 2:151;
  Spanish 2:224;
  Tahiti 2:207;
  West Indian 2:207
lime/linden 3:**336**, 4:440, 441,
  6:*750*, 7:*838*, 896;
  American 3:336, 341;
  Crimean 3:336;
  European 3:336, 341;
  European common 3:336;
  Japanese 3:341;
  large-leaved 3:336;
  silver 3:336;
  silver pendent 3:336;
  small-leaved 3:336;
  weeping white 3:336;
  white 3:336
lime oil 2:136
limestones 8:1021, **1043-5**, *1044*,
  1045, 1066, 1070, *1086*,
  1087, 1088, 1089, 1090,
  1104, 1114, 9:*1122*, *1123*,
  1126, 1130, *1133*, **1133-4**,
  1134, 1135, *1136*, **1138**,
  1141, 1154, 1163, *1165*,
  1170, *1171*, 1172, 1173,
  1175, 1180, 1184, *1185*,
  1186, *1213*, 1219, 1224,
  1229
Limnanthaceae 5:*560*, 563
Limnanthes 2:**207**, 5:560, 7:936
Limnocharis 5:619
Limnocharitaceae 5:619, 620
Limnophyton 5:620
limonene 2:147, 227
Limoniastrum 4:429
limonite *see* goethite
Limonium 2:199, **207**, 4:428, 429,
  429, 525, 7:889, 890;
  binervosum 6:*711*;
  vulgare 6:*711*, 7:889
limpets and seashore zonation
  6:828-9
limu eleele 2:131
Linaceae 4:429, 5:557, **557-8**,
  559, 560
linaloe oil 1:68
Linanthus 5:582, 583
Linaria 2:**207**, 3:337, 5:593, 595;
  moroccana 6:*682*
Lindemann, R. L. 6:689
linden 3:**336**, 4:440, 441, 6:*750*,
  7:*838*, 896;
  American 3:336;
  Crimean 3:336;
  European 3:336;
  European common 3:336;
  Japanese 3:341;
  large-leaved 3:336;
  silver 3:336;
  silver pendent 3:336;
  small-leaved 3:336;
  weeping white 3:336;
  white 3:336

Linden, Jean 6:683
Lindera 2:207, 3:387, 388
linen 2:144
ling 1:71, 2:170, 4:477
lingkersap 3:309
Linnaea 2:207, 5:610;
　borealis 7:894, 903
linnaeite 8:1105
Linnaeus, Carl 7:966, 9:1203;
　on Bartram 6:683;
　and binomial system 6:698,
　　699, 759;
　and *Flora Anglica* 6:702;
　in Lapland 6:688;
　and Sexual System 6:679, 759;
　and *Species Plantarum* 6:(698),
　　(701)
Linné, Carl von *see* Linnaeus, Carl
Linnean Society 6:699, 760
Linociera 5:577
linseed 2:143, 207, 250, 5:557,
　558
linseed cake 2:143
linseed oil 1:106, 2:208, 250
lint 1:107
Linum 2:143, 207, 208, 5:557,
　557, 558
lion's heart 3:270
lion's mouth 1:36
Liparophyllum 5:581, 581
Lippia 2:208, 3:353, 5:587
Lippman, Theodor 6:729
lipstick plant 1:11
Liquidambar 2:208, 3:325, 4:406,
　407, 6:748, 749
Liquidambaroideae 4:407
liquorice *see* licorice
Liriodendreae 3:378
Liriodendron 3:346, 377, 377, 378,
　6:748, 749, 7:838;
　tulipifera 6:749
Liriope 2:208, 5:664
Lissocarpa 4:483
Listera 2:208, 5:675;
　cordata 7:903
Litchi 2:208, 5:543, 543, 544
litchi 2:151, 153, 208
lithium 8:995, 1099, 1100, 1102,
　1109
Lithocarpus 4:410, 412
Lithophaga 9:1185
Lithops 2:208, 4:415, 417
lithosere 6:823, 825
lithosols 6:810
Lithospermeae 5:586
Lithospermum 2:209, 5:586
litmus 2:205
Litsea 3:388
Litseeae 3:388
Littorella 2:209, 5:591
live forever 3:312
livelong 3:312
liverleaf 2:173
liverwort 2:234
liverworts in evolution 6:739
living stone 2:208, 209, 4:415
Livistona 2:209, 5:653
lizardite 8:1099
lizards 9:1236, 1238-9
lizard's tails 3:388, 389
llanos 7:856, 859, 862, 863
Loasa 4:464
Loasaceae 4:453, 464, 465
Loasoideae 4:464
Lobaria pulmonaria 7:943
Lobb, William 6:683
Lobelia 2:209, 5:604, 604, 606,
　644;
　dortmanna 6:725
lobelia 2:209, 209;
　edging 2:209;
　giant 6:720
Lobeliaceae 5:604, 604, 606
Lobelieae 5:606
lobeline 2:209, 227
lobster plant 3:276
Lobularia 1:25, 4:472

local races *see* ecotypes
Lochneria 1:79
locust 2:209;
　African 2:260;
　black 2:209, 3:295;
　Caspian 2:162;
　honey 2:162, 209;
　water 2:162;
　West African 2:260;
　yellow 3:295
locust bean 2:209;
　West African 2:209
locust tree 2:183, 209
Loddiges nursery 6:687
lodestones 8:1094
lodging in cereal crops 6:820,
　7:949
Lodoicea 1:123, 5:653;
　maldivica 6:818
Loeselia 5:582, 583
Logan, Sir W. 9:1271
loganberry 2:151, 210, 3:300,
　4:494
Logania 5:572
Loganiaceae 5:572, 572-3, 574,
　577, 608, 610
Loganiales 5:577
Loganieae 5:572
Loganioideae 5:572, 573
logwood 2:126, 168, 210
Loiseleuria 6:722, 7:855
Lolium 3:301, 5:636, 638, 7:863;
　temulentum 7:949
Lomandra 5:633, 666
Lomatium 5:571
Lombardy poplar 4:527
Lonas 2:210, 5:618
Lonchocarpus 2:185, 210
London Clay flora 6:746, 747
London pride 2:210, 3:309
longan 2:151
long-day plants 6:795, 795
long-distance dispersal 7:905, 909,
　911, 919
long-profile 8:1038, 1038-9
Lonicera 2:178, 210, 5:609, 609,
　610;
　fragrantissima 6:684;
　maximowiczii 6:688
loofah 2:212, 212, 223, 4:467;
　angled 2:223
loosestrife 4:507, 6:818;
　garden 2:213, 213;
　purple 2:213, 213, 7:885;
　spiked 2:213, 213;
　yellow 2:213, 213
Lopezia 2:210, 4:512, 513
Lopezieae 4:512
Lophatherum 5:636
Lophiocarpus 4:421, 422
Lophiola 5:668
Lophira 2:187, 211, 4:434
Lophocolea 2:211
Lophomyrtus 2:237
Lophophora 2:211, 4:415
Lophophytum 4:526, 526
lopoliths 8:1030, 1032
loquat 2:133, 151, 153, 4:430,
　494
Loranthaceae 4:521, 524, 524-5
Lorantheae 4:525
Loranthoideae 4:524
Loranthus 2:211, 213, 4:524, 525
lords and ladies 1:42;
　American 2:239;
　Chinese 2:239;
　East Indian 3:350;
　Egyptian blue 2:243;
　Hindu 2:239;
　Indian 2:239;
　sacred 2:239, 3:350;
　white 2:243
Loropetalum 4:407
Loteae 4:502
Lotus 2:211, 3:343;
　corniculatus 6:825, 7:908;
　tenuis 7:887
lotus 3:394

lotus fruit 4:538
Loudetia 5:638
Loudonia 4:505
Louis XIV 6:681
lousewort 2:263, 5:595;
　common 2:263;
　marsh 2:263;
　swamp 2:263
lovage 2:174, 175, 211, 5:571;
　black 3:317;
　Scotch 2:206, 211
love grass 2:132, 149;
　weeping 2:132
love-in-a-mist 2:139, 241, 3:396,
　399
love-in-a-puff 1:75
love-in-idleness 2:259
love-lies-bleeding 1:25, 4:420
Lovoa 3:356, 5:552
low Arctic 7:901, 902
lowbush blueberry 4:477
Loweia 4:454
Lowestoftian glaciation 6:749
Lowia 5:647
Lowiaceae 5:647
lowland heaths, maritime
　Canadian 7:873
lowland meadows, temperate
　7:861
lows between dunes 7:887, *see also*
　slacks
Loxonia 5:596
Loxonieae 5:596
Lozania 4:452
LSD 1:26
lucerne 1:122, 2:149, 211, 211,
　221, 4:499, 502, 7:932, 948;
　common 2:211;
　wild 2:149
Lucuma 2:128, 3:307
Ludhamian phase 6:748, 749
Ludovia 5:654
Ludwigia 2:212, 4:512
Luffa 2:163, 212, 4:467
luffa *see* loofah
lulita 5:579
lulo 3:318, 5:579
Luma 2:237
Lumnitzera 4:515
Lunaria 2:212, 4:470, 470, 472
lunettes 8:1046
Lunularia 2:212
lungfish (dipnoans) 9:1164,
　1232-4
lungwort 3:284, 353
lupin 2:201, 212, 227, 4:499,
　502;
　blue 2:212;
　pearl 2:212;
　Russell 2:212;
　sundial 2:212;
　tree 2:212;
　white 2:212;
　yellow 1:26, 2:212
lupinine 1:26, 2:227
Lupinus 2:212, 4:499, 502
lupulin 2:178
lupulone 2:147
Luronium 5:620;
　natans 6:725
Lusitanian element in Britain
　7:895
Luther, Martin 6:731
Luxemburgia 4:434
Luxuriaga 7:905
Luzula 2:212, 5:641, 641;
　piperi 7:909;
　wahlenbergii 7:909
Lyallia 4:417, 7:920
Lycaste 2:212, 5:675
lychee 2:151, 153, 208, 5:544
Lychnis 2:213, 4:417, 419;
　alpina 6:816;
　flos-cuculi 6:791-2
Lycium 2:213, 5:579
Lycoperdon 2:213, 3:284
Lycopersicon 3:337, 5:579;
　esculentum 7:926, 927;

　var. *cerasiforme* 7:927
Lycopodium 1:94, 2:213, 6:764;
　selago 7:854
lycopods 9:1163, 1175, 1176,
　1216, *see also* clubmosses
Lyell, Sir Charles 6:688, 731, 760,
　7:964, 9:1147, 1148, 1191,
　1193, 1195, 1197, 1260,
　1261, 1262, 1264, 1266,
　1271, 1272
Lygeae 5:638
Lygeum 2:135, 213, 5:638, 640;
　spartium 6:723
Lygodium 2:213
lymegrass 3:301, *see also* Elymus
Lyonia 2:213, 4:477
Lysenko, Trofim 6:764
lysergic acid 1:26
Lysichiton 2:213
Lysiloma 1:71
Lysimachia 2:213, 4:484, 484;
　nummularia 6:723
Lysimachieae 4:484
lysine and maize 7:935
Lythraceae 4:438, 464, 506-7,
　507, 509, 511, 512, 5:606
Lythreae 4:507
Lythrum 2:213, 4:506, 507, 507;
　salicaria 6:818, 7:885

Maba 4:483
Macadamia 2:214, 4:520
macadamia 2:214, 245, 245;
　rough shell 2:214, 245;
　smooth shell 2:214, 245
Macaranga 4:535, 537, 6:825
Macaronesian region 7:897
macassar oil 2:214, 250, 5:544
macchia 7:843
mace 2:146, 147, 214, 226, 243,
　3:381, 382
maceration 6:732-3
Macgregoria 4:530
Macgregorioideae 4:530
Mackaya 5:601
Mackinlaya 5:568
Macleania 4:477
Macleaya 2:214, 4:402, 402, 403
Maclura 2:256, 4:447
Macrocystis 1:66, 2:192, 214
macronutrients 6:806-7
Macropeplus 3:384
macrophylls 6:725
Macropidia 5:668
Macropodium 4:470
Macroptilium 2:149
macroptilium 2:149
Macroptorus 3:384
Macrostylis 5:554
Macrotomia 1:41
Macrozamia 2:214;
　reidlei 6:720
mad apple *see* aubergine
Madagascan lace plant 5:623
Madagascan region 7:897, 897
Madagascar chaplet flower 3:324
Madagascar rubber 2:214
madar 1:72
madder 2:126, 214, 3:300, 5:608,
　609;
　field 2:214;
　Indian 2:214;
　Levant 2:214;
　wild 2:214
Madeira vine 4:425, 426
Madhuca 4:482
Madia 2:214, 5:617
madia oil 2:214
madrono 1:39
madwort 1:25
maerl 1:19

Maesa 4:486, *486*
Maesoideae 4:486
Maesopsis eminii 7:*936*
Magallana 5:562, 562
Magellanic moorland 7:873
magician's flower 3:331
magma 8:996, 1030, 1033, 1036, 1057, 1059, 1074, 1075, 1084, 1086, 1088, 9:1122, 1124, *1127*, 1128, 1136, 1142
magmatic deposits 8:1074
magnesite 8:1093-4, 1103
magnesium 8:971, 973, *995*, 996, 1086, 1089, *1093*, 1100, 1103, 9:1122, 1123, 1124, 1126, 1127, 1128, 1133, 1134, 1150;
  in plant nutrition 6:806
magnetic fields:
  lunar 8:980;
  terrestrial 8:980, 993-4, 1003-4, 1027-8, 9:1149, 1190, 1199;
  reversals in polarity 8:1003, *1004*;
  Venusian 8:981;
  see also paleomagnetism
magnetite 8:992, 993, *1074*, 1078, 1083, 1088, 1091, 1092, **1094**, 1099, 1105, 9:1151, 1202
magnetometer 8:994, 1003-4
Magnistipula 4:498, 499
Magnolia 2:198, **214**, 3:377, *377*, 378, 6:747, 766, 7:838, 866;
  grandiflora 7:837;
  wilsonii 6:744
magnolia 2:214, *214*;
  Chinese 2:215;
  great-leaved 2:215;
  saucer 2:215;
  Southern 2:215;
  star 2:215;
  umbrella 2:215
Magnoliaceae 3:377-8, *377*, 379, 381, 382, 383, 384, 385, 388, 391, 4:405
Magnoliales 3:377-82, 383, 384, 399, 4:430, 5:618, 654
Magnolieae 3:378
Magnoliidae 3:377-405
maguey 1:13, 2:144, 3:316
mahala mat 1:79
mahoe, blue 2:176
mahogany 2:215, 3:266, 341, 5:551, 552, 7:842;
  African 1:12, 2:193, 215, 3:341;
  American 3:341;
  Australian 2:127;
  bastard 2:135, 3:341;
  big-leaved 2:215;
  Borneo 1:72;
  Cape 2:215, 3:283;
  Cuban 2:215, 3:341;
  espave 1:28;
  Honduras 2:215, 3:341;
  Ivory Coast 2:215;
  Mexican 2:215, 3:341;
  Nyasaland 2:193, 215, 3:341;
  pod 1:12;
  red 2:135, 193, 215, 3:341;
  sapele 3:307;
  Senegal 2:215;
  swamp 2:135;
  true 2:215, 3:341;
  Venezuelan 2:215, 3:341;
  West Indies 2:215, 3:341
Mahonia 2:215, 3:*395*, 395, 396, 6:*789*;
  bealei 6:684, 685
Mahurea 4:436
Maianthemum 2:215
maidenhair fern 1:10, *10*
maidenhair tree 1:100, *103*, 2:216, see also Ginkgo
Maidenia 5:621

maiden's breath 2:167
maiden's tears 3:315
maiden's wreath 2:148
Maihuenia 4:413
Main, James 6:684
maiwein 2:154
maize 1:58, 83, *83*, 105, 2:149, **216**, *216*, *217*, 250, 3:328, 5:635, 638, 640, 7:883, *926*, 931, 932, 935, 948;
  high-lysine 7:935;
  Texas male sterile 7:935;
  water 3:355
Majorana 2:219, 256
malabar nightshade 4:425
malacca cane 2:216, 5:654
Malaceae 4:494
malachite 8:1085, 1089, **1094**, 1106
malacophyllous plants 7:836
Malaysian-Papuan region 7:*897*
Malcolmia 3:325
Malesherbia 4:454
Malesherbiaceae **4:454-5**, 7:896
malka 3:300
mallee 2:135, 7:842;
  brown 2:135;
  congoo 2:135
Mallotus 4:537
mallow 2:**216**, 217, 4:444;
  common European 2:216, *216*;
  curled 2:216;
  Indian 1:87, 2:144, 216;
  Jew's 2:192, 3:350;
  marsh 1:25, 2:216;
  musk 2:217;
  rose 2:176;
  sea 2:216;
  Syrian 2:248;
  tree 2:198;
  Virginia 3:315
Maloideae 4:491, 494
Malope 2:217, 4:*444*, 445
Malopeae 4:445
Malpighia 2:217, 5:*563*, 563, 564
Malpighiaceae 5:*563*, **563-4**, 7:896
Maltese mushroom 4:525
Malthus 6:760, 7:964
Malus 1:37, 89, **108**, 2:217, 4:*494*;
  sargentii 6:685
Malva 2:216, 217, 236, 4:*444*, 444, 445
Malvaceae 4:439, 441, 442, *444*, **444-5**, 537
Malvales 4:432, 439-45, 450
Malvastrum 4:445
Malvaviscus 4:444, 445
Malveae 4:445
mammal-like reptiles 9:1176, 1178-9, 1205-6, *1211*, 1236, **1243-4**, 1245
mammals 9:*1205*, 1209, 1210, 1236, 1242-3, 1244, **1245-53**;
  Permian 9:1176;
  primitive 9:1245;
  Triassic 9:1179, 1244;
  Jurassic 9:1181-2;
  Cretaceous 9:1189;
  Tertiary 9:1195, 1197, 1198
Mammea 2:151, **217**, 4:436, 437
mammee apple 2:151, **217**, 3:307, 4:435, 437
Mammillaria 2:217, 4:415, *415*
mammoths 9:1200, *1247*
mamoncillo 2:224, 5:544
Man see human influence
man root 2:258
management:
  of conservation 7:**954**, 955;
  of forests 7:842, 879-80, 938;
  of heathland 7:873, *874*, **874-5**;
  of pastures and meadows 7:938-41;
  of weeds 7:**949-50**
mancineel tree 4:535

mandarin 1:91, 2:151, **217**, 256, 5:552, 554;
  king 2:217
Mandevilla 2:217, 5:575
Mandragora 2:218, 227, 5:579;
  officinarum 6:695
mandrake 2:**218**, 226, 227, 5:579, 6:695;
  American 3:276
Manekia 3:390
Manettia 2:218, 5:609
Mangabeira rubber 2:169
manganese 8:*1083*, 1091, 1098, **1105**;
  in plant nutrition 6:807;
  nodules 8:1074, *1075*, 1105
manganite 8:1105
mangel-wurzel 2:218, 3:298, 299, 4:423
Mangifera 2:218, 5:547, 548
Mangles, Captain James 6:687
Manglietia 3:378
mango 2:151, *153*, 218, 5:547, 548
mangold 2:218, 3:298, 299
mangosteen 2:151, *153*, 155, **218**, 4:435, 437
mangrove 2:*218*, 3:**290**, 4:507, 508, 6:*712*, 7:*890*, 890-1, *891*;
  American 2:218, 3:290;
  red 2:218, 3:290;
  white 2:218
mangrove bark 2:126, **218**
mangrove fish 7:891
mangrove swamp 6:*712*, 7:886, *890-1*, **890-1**
Manihot 1:77, 2:**219**, 3:297, 4:537;
  utilissima 7:926
manihot 3:298
Manila hemp 1:6, 2:236, 3:316, 5:646, 647
Manila tamarind 3:274
Manilkara 1:49, 87, 2:**219**, 3:300, 4:483
man-in-a-boat 3:293
manioc 1:77, 83, 2:219, 3:328, 4:537
manna 2:219, 4:460
manna ash 5:577
manna plant 3:332
Mantell, G. 9:1271
mantle 8:972, **973-4**, 975, 989, 991, **996**, 997, 998, 1005, 1036, 1089, 1091, 1095, 1099, 9:1122, 1124, 1128, 1129, 9:1136;
  convection currents in 8:1002, 1007, 1063, 9:1150, 1152
manuka 2:202, 4:512
Maoutia 4:448
manzanilla 2:219
manzanilla real 2:219
manzanita:
  Eastwood 1:39;
  great berried 1:39;
  pine-mat 1:39
maple 1:8, 5:545, 546;
  Amur 1:8;
  ash-leaved 1:8;
  black 3:328;
  Cretan 1:8;
  downy Japanese 1:8;
  field 1:8, 7:838;
  great 1:8, 3:294;
  Hers's 1:8;
  hornbeam 1:8;
  Italian 1:8;
  Japanese 1:8;
  Montpelier 6:749;
  Norway 1:8;
  Oregon 1:8;
  Queensland 3:341;
  red 1:8, 6:706;
  rose 1:110;
  sugar 1:8, 3:328, *328*, 329, 7:912;

trident 1:8;
  see also Acer
maple sugar 5:546
mapping 6:*706-7*, **707-8**
maqui berry 4:440
maquis 7:836, 843
Marah 4:465
Maranta 1:41, 2:**219**, 5:*650*, 650, 651
maranta starch 5:650
Marantaceae 5:647, 648, 649, *650*, **650-1**
Maranteae 5:650
Maranthes 4:498, 499
Marantochloa 5:650
maraschino cherry 2:219
Marathrum 4:503
Marattia 2:219
marble 8:1087, 9:*1136*, 1163, 1202
marble wood 3:341
marc grappa 1:16
marcasite 8:1094, 1096
Marcgravia 4:*438*, 439
Marchantia 2:219
mare's tail 2:177, *177*, 4:505
marguerite 2:202;
  blue 2:139;
  golden 1:36
maria 8:977, 979, 9:1161
Marianthus 4:488, 489
Mariceae 5:662
Maries, Charles 6:684-5
marigold 2:219, 5:618;
  African 2:219, 3:331;
  big 3:331;
  bur 1:57, 2:219;
  Cape 1:121, 2:219;
  common 1:70, 2:219;
  corn 2:219;
  desert 2:219;
  French 2:219, 3:331, *331*;
  marsh 1:72, *72*, 2:220, 7:884, 885;
  pot 1:70, 2:174, 219;
  signet 3:331;
  striped Mexican 3:331;
  sweet scented 2:226
marijuana 1:73, 2:226
marine pollution 7:945
Mariopteris 6:*730*
Mariscus 5:643
marjoram 2:147, **220**, 5:589;
  common wild 2:154;
  pot 2:174, 220, *220*, 256;
  sweet 2:174, *175*, 220, 256
marmalade 3:314
marmalade bush 3:326
maroochy but 2:214
marram grass 6:825, 7:886, *886*, *887*
marrow 1:107, 2:**222**, 4:465, 467;
  custard 2:222, *223*;
  orange 2:222;
  vegetable 1:111, *111*, 2:222, *223*, 3:320
Marrubium 2:220
Mars 8:971, 972, 976, 977, **982-6**, *983*, *985*, 988, 989, 9:*1255*;
  'canals' 8:982;
  craters 8:982, *983*, *984*, 985, 989;
  dust storms 8:985;
  physiographic provinces 8:982-3, *984*, 985
Marsdenia 2:214, **220**, 3:297
Marsh, O. 9:1262, **1271**
marsh gas 8:1115
marsh mallow 1:25, 2:176, 216
marsh marigold 3:399, 7:884, 885
marshes, freshwater 7:875, **884-5**
marshes, salt 6:*711*, 7:886, *888-9*, **888-90**;
  succession on 6:826-7;
  tropical (mangrove) 7:890-1, 890-1
marshmallow 1:25

Marsilea 2:220
Marsippospermum 5:640-1
marsupials 9:*1205*, 1213, **1245-6**
Martin, W. Keble 6:702
Martynia 2:220, 5:*607*, 602
Martyniaceae 5:601, *602*, **602-3**
marvel of Peru 2:231, 4:420
Mascarenhasia 5:575
Maschalocephalus 5:628, 629
Masdevallia 2:220, 5:675
maskflower 1:24
mass numbers 8:997, 9:1142
mass spectrometry 8:997, *998*, 9:1143, 1146
Massenerhebung effect 7:868
Massif Central 8:1042, 1117, 9:1138, 1186, 1191
massoia bark 1:90
Masson, Francis 6:681, 683
masterwort 1:46, 5:571;
  greater 1:46, *46*;
  lesser 1:46
mastic 2:220, 3:273, 290, 5:548;
  American 2:220, 3:309;
  Bombay 2:220, 3:273;
  Chios 2:220
mastic tree:
  American 3:309;
  Peruvian 3:309
Mastixia 4:517, 518
mastodons 9:1197, 1198, 1203, 1261
mat cryptogams 6:*724*, **724**
mat grass 7:862, 940
matagouri 7:*861*
matai 2:129, 5:643
maté 1:26, 58, *58*, 2:178, 220
Mathiasella 5:569
Mathurina 4:454
Matisia 4:444
Matoniaceae 6:743
matoral 7:843
Matricaria 1:85, 2:219, 220, 5:618
matrimony vine 2:213
matrix support 9:1133
Matteniusa 4:516
Matteuccia 2:220
Matthews, D. 8:1004, 9:1269
Matthiola 2:220, 3:325, 4:470, 472
Mauna Loa 8:1057, 1058
Maundia 5:623
Mauritia 5:653, 7:896
Mauritiella 5:653
Maw, George 6:(*681*), 682
maw seed 2:253
Maxillaria 2:**221**, 5:675
Maximowicz, Carl 6:688
may 2:169, *169*;
  pink 2:169
may apple 3:395, 396
may wine 2:154
Mayaca 5:629
Mayacaceae 5:**629**, 631, 633
Mayr, Ernst 6:775
Maytenus 4:529, 7:904
mayweed 7:888, 951
mbuga 7:862
meadow grasshopper, meiosis in 6:*763*
meadows 7:860-1;
  alpine 7:*830*, 860, 868, *869*;
  arctic 7:854;
  gley soils of 6:809-10;
  shore 7:861;
  of subalpine zone 7:861, 867;
  see also pastures
meadow-steppes 7:859, 862
meadowsweet 2:142, *142*, 4:494, 7:884
mealies 2:221
meanders 8:*1038*, 1038-9, 1043
mechanical isolation 6:780
Meconopsis 2:**221**, 4:402, 6:687;
  betonicifolia 6:686;
  napaulensis 6:686
median valleys 8:*1060*, 1061

Medicago 1:92, 2:**211**, **221**, 3:314, 343, 4:499, 502;
  lupulina 6:*707*
medicinal gardening 6:680, 7:959, 963
medick 4:499;
  black 2:149, 221, 3:314, 6:*707*
Medinilla 4:513, *514*, 514
Mediterranean climate 7:836, 843
Mediterranean explorations 6:680-1
Mediterranean province 7:898
Mediterranean region 7:897
medlar 2:151, *152*, **221**, 230, 4:494;
  Japanese 2:133, 151
Medusandraceae 4:522, **522**
Megacarpaea 4:470
megachiropterans 9:1246
Megaloceros 9:1248
Megalosaurus 9:1241, 1265
megaphylls 6:725
megaplankton 7:881
Megapterium 2:248
Megatherium 6:760, 9:1248, *1266*
Megistotherium 9:1246
meiosis 6:*763*, 764
Melachodendron 3:324
Melaleuca 2:**221**, 4:511, 512
Melampsora 2:221
Melampyrum 5:593
Melandrium 3:315, 4:417
Melanodendron 7:919
Melanophylla 4:517, 518
Melanorrhoea 2:195
Melastoma 2:224, 4:514, *514*
Melastomataceae 4:511, 512, **513-4**, *514*, 5:574
Melastomatoideae 4:514
Melbourne Botanic Garden 6:687
Melegueta pepper 5:648
Melia 2:215, **224**, 5:551, 552
Meliaceae 5:551, **551-2**
Melianthaceae 5:541, **541-2**, 544, 7:896
Melianthus 5:541, *541*, 542
Melica 2:224, 5:638
Meliceae 5:638
Melicoccus 2:224, 5:544
Melicope 5:554
melilot 2:174, **224**;
  common 2:224;
  small-flowered 2:224;
  white 2:224
Melilotus 2:**224**, 4:525
Melioideae 5:551-2
Meliosma 5:544
Meliosmaceae 5:544
Melissa 2:224
Melittis 2:224
Melocactus 4:415
Melocanna 1:49, 2:144, 5:635, 636
Melochia 4:442
melon 1:110, 2:**224**, *225*, 4:465, 467;
  African horned 2:222;
  cantaloupe 2:224;
  casaba 2:222, 224;
  Chinese water 2:222;
  dudaim 2:222, 225;
  honeydew 2:178, 222, *223*, 225;
  Malabar 2:222;
  mango 2:222, 225;
  musk 1:110, 2:222, *223*, 224;
  netted 2:222, *223*, 224;
  nutmeg 2:222, *223*, 224;
  ogen 2:224;
  orange 2:222;
  Oriental pickling 2:222, 225;
  Persian 2:222;
  pomegranate 2:222;
  preserving 2:222;
  Queen Anne's pocket 2:222;
  rock 2:222;
  serpent 2:222, 225;
  snake 2:222, 225;
  stink 2:222;

sweet 2:224;
  water 2:222, *223*, 3:*357*;
  winter 2:178, 222, 224
melon shrub 3:318
melon tree 1:75, 2:**259**, 4:455
melongene 1:46
Melothrieae 4:465
Memecylaceae 4:514
Memecylanthus 5:610
Memecyloideae 4:514
Memecylon 4:514, *514*
Mendel, Gregor 6:760
Mendeléev, D. 8:1101
meni oil 2:211
meni oil tree 4:434
Menispermaceae 3:399, **400-1**, *401*, 5:544
Menispermeae 3:401
Menispermum 3:400, 401
Menodora 5:577
Mentha 2:230, 3:*265*, 5:589, 590;
  aquatica 7:876, 885
Mentzelia 2:225, 4:464
Mentzelioideae 4:464
Menyanthaceae 5:574, *581*, **581-2**
Menyanthes 2:225, 5:574, *581*, 581, 582;
  trifoliata 7:876, 880
Menziesia 2:225, 4:477
meranti 3:315, 341
merantia 7:842
Mercalli intensity scale *see* earthquakes
Mercurialis 2:225, 4:535, 537;
  perennis 6:792
mercury (metal) 8:1088, **1110**
Mercury (planet) 8:971, 976, 977, 980-1, *981*, 989
mercury (plant) 3:276;
  annual 2:225;
  dog's 2:225, *225*
merecure 4:499
Merendera 2:225
mermaids' purses 7:920
mermaid's wine glass 1:9
Merremia 2:233
Mertensia 2:225, 5:586;
  maritima 7:*921*
Merulius 2:228
Merychyppus 9:1197
mesas 8:*1013*, *1043*
mescal 5:666
mescal beans 3:318
mescal button 2:211
mescaline 1:26, 2:*210*, 211
Mesembryanthemaceae 4:417
Mesembryanthemum 2:184, **228**, 4:415, 417, *417*, 6:722
mesembryanthemum 2:228, *228*
Mesomelaena sphaerocephala 6:723
mesomorphic evergreen shrubs 6:721
mesomorphic semi-shrubs 6:721
mesophylls 5:673
mesophytes 6:719
Mesosaurus 8:1001, 9:1176
mesosiderites 8:986
Mesozoic 6:*738-9*, 740, **740-5**, *743-4*, 9:**1177-89**, 1209-10, 1214, 1216, 1236, *see also* Triassic, Jurassic, Cretaceous
Mespilus 2:**221**, 4:494
mesquite 3:281;
  honey 3:281;
  Western honey 3:281
mesquite tree 4:502
messmate 2:135
Mesua 2:228, 4:436, 437
metabasites 9:1137, 1138
metabolism:
  crassulacean acid 6:*799*, 799, 7:848;
  and drought injury 7:845;
  and temperature 6:789-92
metamorphic rocks 8:996, 1020, 1021, 1023, 1029, 1085, 9:*1122*, *1123*, 1132, **1136-40**, *1136*, *1137*, *1138*, *1139*, 1142, 1268

metamorphism 8:1036, 9:1136, 1151, 1180, 1207;
  prograde 9:1136, 1139;
  retrograde 9:1136
metaphases in meiosis 6:*763*
Metasequoia 2:228, 3:289, 6:746;
  glyptostroboides 6:746, 7:*914*, 914
metazoa, first 6:757
meteoric water 8:1069, 1074
meteorites 8:972, 974, 977, 980, 983, **986-9**, *987*, 988, 989, 995, 1086, 1089, 1092, 1094, 1095, 1096, 1097, 1105, 9:1122, 1146, 1150;
  carbonaceous 6:758
meteoroids 8:983, *987*
meteors 8:986, *987*
methane 8:971, 997, 1021, 1114, 1115, 9:1202
methoxsalen 1:27
Methysticodendron 2:226
Metrosideros 2:228
Metroxylon 2:228, 3:302, 5:651, 653, 654
Metzgeria 2:228
Mexican firecracker 2:127
Meyen, Franz 7:*966*
Meyer, Frank 6:686
mezcal 1:16, 58, *58*, 2:226, 5:666
mezereon 1:116, *116*, 2:227
Meziella 4:505
micas 8:972, 979, 996, 1029, *1082*, 1086, 1088, 1089, 1091, 1092, **1094**, 1104, 9:1124, 1129, 1131, 1136, 1137, *1138*, *1139*
micaschists 8:1086, 1095
Michaelmas daisy 1:45, 116, 2:**229**, 5:618
Michaux, Andre 6:681, 683
Michauxia 5:604, 606
Michelia 2:229, 3:378
Miconia 2:229, 4:514
Micraira 5:638
Micraireae 5:638
microchiropterans 9:1246
microclimates 6:787, *789*, 789
microcline 8:1090, **1094**, 1096, 1098, 9:*1124*, 1125
microcrinoids 9:1223
Microcycas 1:112
Microcystis 1:*50*
Microdesmis 4:535, 537
Micromelum 5:554
Micromeria 2:229, 5:589
micronutrients 6:807
micropaleontology 9:1207-8
microphyllous forest 7:835
microphylls 6:725
microscopic plant remains 6:734
microspheres, proteinoid 6:753-4, 756, 758
Microsteris 5:583
Microtea 4:421
Microteoideae 4:421, 422
mid-Atlantic ridge 8:1003, 1004
mid-ocean canyons 8:1062
mid-ocean ridges 8:994, 996, 1003-4, *1004*, *1007*, 1026, *1037*, 1040, **1059-61**, *1060*, 1063, 1064, 9:1150, 1153, 1163
Middle European province 7:898
miedra 3:276
miel de palma 2:189
migmatites 9:1139
mignonette 2:229, 4:472;
  common 2:229;
  white upright 2:229;
  wild 2:229
mignonette tree 2:173, 4:507
migration 6:816-9;
  and establishment 7:921;
  and floristic regions 7:898;
  and mapping of variability 7:907;
  and polar distributions 7:910-1

Mikania 2:229, 5:617, 618
milfoil 1:9;
　water 2:237, 6:826, *827*
Milium 2:229, 5:638
milk tree 1:66
milkweed 2:144, 5:575, 576;
　common 1:43;
　swamp 1:43, 2:144
milkwort 3:280, *277*;
　sea 2:162, 7:945
Millar, Robert 6:683
Miller, Philip 6:698
Miller, Stanley 6:752, 753
millerite 8:1105
Miller-type synthesis of protolife
　6:753, *757*
millet 1:58, 83, 2:229, 3:314,
　5:635, 638, 640, 7:948;
　African 1:83, *83*, 2:129, 230;
　bajra 1:83;
　broomcorn 2:149;
　bulrush 1:83, 2:230;
　cat-tail 2:230, 3:264;
　common 1:83, *83*, 2:229, 230,
　　259;
　finger 1:83, *83*, 2:129, 230;
　fonio 1:83;
　foxtail 1:83, *83*, 2:230, 3:314;
　fundi 1:83;
　German 1:83;
　golden 2:229;
　Italian 1:83, *83*, 2:230, 3:314;
　Japanese barnyard 1:83, 2:230;
　kodo 1:83, 2:230, 261;
　little 2:259;
　pearl 1:83, 2:149, 230, 3:264;
　proso 1:83, *83*, 2:229, 230,
　　259;
　spiked 2:230, 3:264;
　teff 1:83
Millettia 3:347;
　thonningii 6:771
Millstone Grit 9:1167
× *Miltassia* 2:230
Miltonia 2:230, 5:675
× *Miltonidium* 2:230
mimetite 8:1105
Mimosa 2:230, 3:313, 4:499, *502*,
　7:843
mimosa 1:7, 2:136;
　Bailey's 1:7;
　golden 1:7
Mimosaceae 4:499
Mimosoideae 4:499, 502
Mimulus 2:230, 236, 5:593, 595
Mimusops 2:230, 4:*482*, 483
Mindel ice advance 6:749
mind-your-own-business 3:318
mineral deficiency 7:867
mineral facies 9:1137
minerals 8:1073, 1075, 1078,
　1081-101, 9:1123, 1142
minerotrophic mire 7:880-3
mines, mining geology 8:1066,
　1071-4, *1071, 1072, 1073*
minimal area (sampling) 6:727
mining and pollution 7:944, *946*
minnie bush 2:225
mint 2:174, 175, 229, 230, 5:589,
　6:*778*;
　American apple 2:230;
　apple 2:174, 230;
　bergamot 2:174, 230;
　common 2:230;
　corn 2:224, *224*, 230;
　eau de Cologne 2:174;
　field 2:224, *224*, 230;
　ginger 2:174;
　horse 2:174;
　Japanese 2:230;
　lemon 2:174;
　orange 2:230;
　round-leafed 2:230;
　Scotch 2:174;
　water 2:174, 7:876, 885
mintbush 3:281;
　round-leaf 3:281;
　snowy 3:281

Minuartia 4:417
Miocene 6:*738, 740, 742, 747*,
　747-8, 9:1191, 1193, **1195-7**,
　1196, 1198, 1250
miogeosynclines 8:1034, 9:1158
miogypsinids 9:1195, 1196
Miquelia 4:531
mirabelle 1:116, 2:151, 3:275
Mirabilis 2:188, 230, 4:*419*, 420
miracle leaf 2:192
miracularin 2:147
miraculous berry 2:147, **231**
miraculous fruit 2:231, 3:335
mirasol 3:329
mire:
　mixed 6:716-7, 7:877;
　ombrotrophic 7:875-80, *see also*
　　bogs;
　rheotrophic 7:880-3, *see also*
　　fens
mirror of Venus 2:252
Miscanthidium violaceum 7:885
Miscanthus 2:231, 5:638
Misodendraceae 4:525
Misodendrum 4:525
missey-moosey 3:319
Mississippian 6:*738, 739, see also*
　Carboniferous
Missouri Botanical Garden 7:*960*
mist flower 2:138
mistletoe 1:17, 2:231, *231*, 4:524,
　525, 6:721, 7:898, 905, 948;
　dwarf 2:231;
　red 2:231
Mitella 2:231, 4:497, 5:596
miterwort 2:231;
　false 3:336
mitochondria 9:1204-5;
　and acquired characters 6:764;
　origin of 6:759
mitosis 6:762
Mitragyna ciliata 7:891
Mitrarioideae 5:598
Mitrastemon 4:527, 528
Mitrastemoneae 4:528
Mitrophyllum 4:415
mixed chaparral 7:843
mixed forest, evergreen 7:837
mixed mires 6:716-7, 7:877
mixosaurs 9:1237
Mkilua 3:381
mkwakwa 3:327
Mnium 2:231
mobola plum 4:499
mochi tree 2:178
mock orange 3:267, 268, 274,
　327;
　house-blooming 3:274
mockernut 1:77
Modolia 4:445
mohintli 2:191
Moho, Mohorovicic Discontinuity
　8:973
Moh's hardness scale **8:1082**
molasses 2:231, 3:329
mold:
　bakery 2:241;
　blue 3:264;
　green 3:264;
　red bread 2:241
Molinia 2:232, 5:636;
　caerulea 6:723, 829, 7:862, 883,
　　885
Mollinedia 3:384
mollusks 8:1084, 9:1154, 1160,
　1166, 1170, 1178, 1184,
　1195, 1197, *1213*, **1224-7**,
　1237
Moluccella 2:232
molybdenite 8:1108
molybdenum 8:1105, **1108**;
　in plant nutrition 6:807
mombin, yellow 3:322
Momordica 2:163, **232**, 4:465, 467
monadnocks 8:1043
Monanthes 2:232, 4:495
Monanthotaxis 3:381
monarch-of-the-east 3:308

Monarda **1:57**, 2:232, 5:589
Monardella 2:232
monazite 8:1094, 1104, 1108,
　1111
Monentes 4:435
Moneses 4:480
money tree 2:137
moneywort 2:213
Monilaria 4:415
Monimia 3:384
Monimiaceae 3:382, *384*, **384-5**,
　388, 5:590, 7:919
monkey musk 2:230
monkey nut 1:38, 2:245
monkey plant 3:301
monkey puzzle tree 1:29, *39*
monkey-bread tree 1:10
monkey-flower 2:230, *230*, 5:595;
　Allegheny 2:230
monkeypod 3:306
monkey-pot 4:450
monk's pepper tree 5:587
monkshood 1:9, *10, 26*, 3:399
moon flower 3:324
Monnina 5:566
monocarpic herbs, life-forms of
　6:719
Monochaetum 4:514
Monochoria 5:659, 660, 661
monoclimaxes 6:714
monoclinic system *see* crystal
　systems
Monococcus 4:421
Monocostus 5:648
monocotyledons 9:1218
Monodora 3:*380*, 381;
　tenuifolia 6:771
Monodoroideae 3:381
monophylectic groups 6:696
monoplacophora (cap shells)
　9:1154
monopodial crowns 7:834
Monoporandra 4:*435*
Monopsis 5:606
Monostroma 1:19, 2:232
Monotoideae 4:435
Monotrema 5:629
monotremes 9:**1245**
Monotropa 2:232, 4:477, 480, *480*
Monotropaceae 4:475, 477
Monotropoideae 4:475, 477
Monsonia 5:559
monsoon forests 7:835-6
Monstera 2:232, 5:659
montane zone 7:**866-7**;
　meadows of 7:861
Montbretia 3:344, 5:662
Montia 4:425
montmorillonite 8:1009, 1021,
　1088, **1094**, 9:1190
montmorillonite clays 6:802
Montrouziera 4:436, 437
Moon 8:976-80, 981, 989, *991*,
　998, 1008, 1097, 9:1146,
　1149, 1150, 1151, *1267*;
　asthenosphere 8:*980*;
　moonquakes 8:980, 1028;
　structure 8:*980*
moonflower 2:186
moonseed 3:401
moonstone 8:1096
moonwort 1:62, *62*, 2:140
moor grass 5:636;
　purple *see Molinia*
mooseberry 3:354
Moquila 4:494
Moquilea 4:498
mor 6:803, 807
Mora 3:341
mora 3:341
morabukea 3:341
Moraceae 4:446-7, *447*, 449
Moraea 2:232, 5:662
moraine successions 6:826
moraines 8:1018;
　lateral 8:*1019*, 1048;
　medial 8:1048;
　terminal 8:*1018*, 1050

Morchella 2:232
morel 2:232, *233*;
　false 2:232
morello 2:151
morganite 8:1086
Moricandia 4:470, *470*
Morinda 2:232
Moringa 2:232, 4:473
Moringaceae 4:472-3
Morina 5:611, *612*
Morinaceae 5:611
Morineae 5:611
Morisia 4:470
Mormodes 1:79
morning glory 2:186, *186*, 226,
　233, 5:579, 580;
　beach 2:186;
　common 2:186;
　dwarf 1:99;
　imperial Japanese 2:186
Moronobeoideae 4:436
morphine 1:26, 2:227, 253
Morrison Formation 9:1181, 1187
Morus 2:233, 4:447, *447*
mosaics, cyclic 6:716, **716-7**, *717*
mosasaurs 9:1199, 1239
Moschopsis 5:613, *613*
Moses-in-the-bulrushes 3:293
Moses-on-a-raft 3:293
moss 2:**234**;
　bog 2:235, 7:884, *see also*
　　Sphagnum;
　feather bog 7:884;
　Florida 3:336;
　fork bog 7:884;
　Iceland 1:84, 2:204, 205;
　Irish 1:77, 3:318;
　reindeer 1:91, 2:126, 204;
　rose 3:279, *279*;
　Spanish 2:144, 145, 3:336;
　stag's-horn 2:213
moss agate 8:*1083*, 1087
moss-cushion plants 6:722
mosses in evolution 6:739
mossy forest 7:866-7
Mostuea 5:583
mother of thyme 3:336
mother-in-law 2:192
mother-in-law plant 1:120
mother-in-law's armchair 2:128
mother-in-law's tongue 3:307
mother-of-thousands 3:309
moths:
　and pollination 6:773;
　and weed-control 7:950
motillo 4:440
moulded wax 2:127
Moulton, F. 9:1266
Mount Cook lily 7:915
mountain ash 1:43, 2:135, **233**,
　3:318, 319, 4:494;
　American 3:319;
　European 3:319
mountain bluet 1:81
mountain everlasting 1:31
mountain pawpaw 4:455, *see also*
　pawpaw
mountain vegetation 7:*830, 832-*
　3, 832, 863-7, **863-8**;
　glacial relics in 7:912;
　meadow grasses in 7:861
mountain-building *see* orogeny
mountain chains, ranges 8:1001,
　1002, *1007*, 1008, 1028,
　1034, **1035-7**, *1035, 1036,
　1037*, 1043, 9:1126, 1136,
　1138, 1147, 1151
Mourera 4:*503*, 503
Mouriri 4:514
mournful widow 3:309
mouse-ear **1:82**;
　Alpine 1:82
mouse-ear chickweed 4:417
Moutabeae 5:566
moutan 2:258, 4:432
Moythomasia 9:1164, *1206*
msala 3:327
mu tree 1:15, 3:346

Muchocephalus 9:*1211*
Mucor 2:**233**
Mucuna 2:**233**
mudar 1:72
mudstones 8:1016, 9:**1130**
Muehlenbeckia 2:**233**, 4:427, 428
mugwort 1:42, 6:751;
  Western 1:42;
  white 1:42
muhimbi 3:341
Muhlenbergia 1:66, 5:638
muhugu 5:618
Muiria 4:415
mulberry 2:151, **233**, 4:446, 447, *447*;
  American 2:233;
  black 2:151, *152*, 233, *233*;
  Downing 2:233;
  English 2:233, *233*;
  French 1:71;
  Indian 2:232;
  paper 1:66, 2:233;
  Persian 2:233;
  red 2:151, 233;
  Russian 2:233;
  white 2:233
mulching 7:*950, 950*
Mulgedium 2:195
Mulineae 5:**571**
mull 6:803
mullein 2:**233**, 3:353, 5:593;
  black 2:236;
  Cretan 1:81;
  dark 2:233;
  great 2:233;
  purple 2:236;
  white 2:233
Muller, Cornelius 6:822
Müller, Ferdinand Baron von 6:687
multipurpose land use 7:954
multituberculates 9:1184, 1192, 1195, 1245
mummified plant remains 6:733
mundu 2:126
mung bean 2:**236**, *236*, 4:502, *see also* bean
muninga 3:283, 341
mu-oil 3:346
Muntingia 4:**440**
Murchison, Sir R. 9:1152, 1156, 1159-60, 1161, 1163, 1173, 1260, 1261, 1262, 1270, **1271**, 1272, 1273
Murray, J. 9:1260, 1263, **1271-2**
Murraya 3:308, 5:554
murtillo 2:237
Musa 1:6, 52, 2:173, **236**, 5:646, *646, 647,* 7:896;
  acuminata 6:*722;*
  sapientum 7:*926;*
  see also banana
Musaceae 5:*646,* **646-7**, 648, 649, 650
muscadine 2:151
Muscari 2:**236**, 5:664
muscarine 1:92
muscat 2:236
muscatel 2:**236**
muscle tree 2:179
muscovite 8:*1082*, 1086, 1094, **1095**, 9:1136, 1138, *1139*
Muscovy glass 8:1095
mushroom 1:13;
  field 1:*13;*
  fool's 1:25;
  horse 1:13;
  sacred 2:226
mushroom fold 8:*1029*
musk 2:230, **236**;
  lavender water 2:230;
  monkey 2:230;
  wild 2:134
musk clover 2:134
musk plant 2:**236**
muskeg 7:*902,* 903
musquash root 1:89
Mussaenda 5:*608*

mustard 1:64, 2:147, 227, **236**, 4:469, 472, 7:932, 936;
  black 1:64, 65, 2:236, *237;*
  broad-leaved 1:64;
  brown 1:64, 2:236;
  celery 1:64;
  Chinese 1:64;
  garlic 2:174;
  Indian 1:64;
  Japanese 1:64;
  leaf 1:64;
  potherb 1:64;
  treacle 2:134;
  white 1:64, *65,* 2:236, 3:316
mustard greens 1:64
muster-John-Henry 3:331
mutagens 6:761
mutation 6:(*761*), 761, 762, 764;
  and breeding 7:934;
  and radioactive pollutants 7:947
mutationalists 6:762
Mutis, José Celestino 6:682, **7:966**
Mutisia 2:**236**, 5:*615,* 617, 618
Mutisieae 5:617, 618
mvule 3:341
mycetoma 1:44
Mycobacterium 1:51
mylonites 9:**1139**
myomorphs 9:1249
Myoporaceae 5:592, **592-3**, 596
Myoporum 5:592, *592, 593*
Myosotidium 7:920
Myosotis 2:**237**, 5:586;
  palustris 7:885
Myosoton 1:87
Myosurus 3:396, *399,* 399
Myrciaria 4:512
Myrianthus 4:448
Myrica 2:**237**, 4:408, *408,* 6:747
Myricaceae 4:**408**, *408,* 516, 7:909
Myricales 4:408
Myricaria 4:459, *459,* 460
Myriophylleae 4:505
Myriophyllum 2:**237**, 4:504, *505,* 505, 6:725, 826, *827,* 7:944;
  spicatum 7:947
Myristica 2:214, **237**, 243, 3:381, *381, 382,* 7:891
Myristicaceae 3:378, 380, **381-2**, *381,* 7:897
myristicin 2:243
Myrmecodia 5:608
myrobalan 2:126, 3:269, 334, 4:516;
  Beleric 3:334;
  black 2:126, 3:334
Myrothamnaceae 4:407
Myrothamnus 4:407
Myroxylon 2:**237**
myrrh 2:174, **237**, 5:546, *547;*
  Abyssinian 1:99;
  African 1:99
Myrrhidodendron 5:569
Myrrhis 2:174, **237**, 5:571
Myrsinaceae 4:**484-6**, *486*
Myrsinales 4:486
Myrsine 4:486, *486*
Myrsineae 4:486
Myrsinoideae 4:486
Myrtaceae 4:450, 507, *511,* **511-2**, 514, 515, 525, 7:896, 897
Myrtales 4:506-16, 528, 5:571
Myrteola 2:**237**, 7:873
myrtle 2:**237**, 3:355, 4:511, 512, 7:905;
  common 2:237;
  crape 2:196;
  Jew's 3:301;
  queen crape 2:196;
  sand 2:199;
  tarentum 2:237;
  Tasmanian 3:341;
  wax 2:237
Myrtoideae 4:511
Myrtus 2:**237**, 4:511, 512
Mystacidium 1:31
mysticetes 9:1249

Mystropetalon 4:525, 526
myxomatosis and grassland 6:*690,* 7:938, 940
Myxopyreae 5:**577**
Myxopyrum 5:**577**

Naegelia 1:30
naegelip 3:317
Najadaceae 5:*623,* **624**
Najadales 5:**622-7**, 644
Najas 2:**238**, 5:624
Nama 5:585
names:
  changes of 6:**700-1**;
  choice of 6:**699-700**;
  conserved 6:700;
  legitimate and illegitimate 6:699;
  publication of 6:699;
  scientific and cultivar 6:698;
  types of 6:**697-8**;
  vernacular 6:697-8
nanan wood 2:196
nandiflame 3:321
Nandina 2:**238**, 3:395, 396, 399
Nandinaceae 3:396
Nandineae 3:396
nanny berry 3:354
nanophylls 6:725
Napeantheae 5:596
Napeanthus 5:596
Napoleona 4:**449**, *449,* 450
Napoleonaceae 4:450
nappes 8:*1028*
naranjilla 2:**238**, *238,* 3:318, 5:579
Narcissus 1:115, 2:**238**, 5:664, *665, 665,* 666;
  pseudo-narcissus ssp. *abscissus* 7:*830*
narcissus 2:136, 238, *239;*
  poet's 2:238;
  polyanthus 2:238;
  trumpet 2:238
narcotine 1:26
nardoo 2:141
Nardostachys 2:**238**, 5:610, *611*
Nardus stricta 7:862, 940
narras 4:527
Narthecium 1:45
Narthekodes 5:569
naseberry 2:219
Nassauvia 7:920;
  latissima 7:*908;*
  magellanica 7:*908;*
  serpens 7:*908*
Nastanthus 5:*613,* 613
Nasturtium 1:108, 2:**238**, 3:*357,* 4:470, 5:562
nasturtium (*Tropaeolum*) 2:238, 3:345, 396, 5:562, *563;*
  dwarf 3:345;
  flame 3:345;
  garden 2:238, 3:345, *345;*
  tall 3:345
Natal plum 5:575
Natal tak 3:327
natant floating cryptogams 6:*725,* 725
natant water-herbs 6:725
Nathorst, Alfred 6:733
National Parks 7:952, 955, *955*
natrolite 8:1101
natural bridges 8:*1013*
natural gas 8:990, 1091, 1104, *1112, 1114,* **1114-5**, 9:1131, 1187;
  biogenic 8:1114-5
natural selection 6:**759-68**, 767-8, **769**, 9:1203, 1267
nature reserves, size of 7:**954**
Nauclea 5:608

Mystropetalon 4:525, 526
Naufraga 5:569
nautiloids 9:1156, 1164, *1210,* 1224, **1225-6**
Nautilus 9:1225, 1226
Navarretia 5:583
navelwort 3:347, *347;*
  Venus 2:249
Navia 5:644
Navicula 2:**238**
Neanderthal Man 9:1252
Nebraskan glaciation 6:749
nebular hypothesis 8:**971-2**, *972,* 9:1266
Nechamandra 5:621
Neckera 2:**238**
Neckeradelphus 2:238
Neckeropsis 2:238
Nectandra 2:164
nectarine 2:151, **239**, 4:494;
  Spanish 1:89
Nectaropetalum 5:560
Nectria 2:**239**
Neea 4:420
needle bush 2:168
needle furze 2:160
needle-leaf trees 6:*719,* 720
Negro pepper 3:381
Negro's head 3:270
Neillia 4:491
Neisseria 1:**50**
Nelumbo 2:211, **239**, 3:357, *394, 394, 395;*
  lutea 6:817
nematodes suppressed by weeds 7:949
Nemesia 2:**239**, 5:595
Nemopanthus 4:532
Nemophila 2:**239**, 5:584
Nemoral province 7:**898**
nemu tree 1:15
Neochamaelea 5:552
neodymium 8:1104
neoendemics 7:914, 915, 917
Neogene 9:1191
Neogene epoch 6:740
Neoglaziovia 2:144, 5:644
Neolithic agriculture 6:751, 7:875, 931
Neoluederitzia 5:554
Neomezia 4:486
neon 8:995, 997
Neoporteria 4:415
Neoregelia 2:**239**, 5:646
Neoschroetera 5:554
Neotropical realm 7:**895**, *896, 897*
Neottia 2:**239**, 5:*675,* 675
Neottieae 5:675
Nepenthaceae 3:**392**, *392-3,* 4:405, 490, 7:896
Nepenthes 2:**240**, 3:*392,* 392, 4:496, 7:878;
  pervillei 6:*772*
Nepeta 2:**240**, 5:589
nephelene 8:1080, 1088, 1090, **1095**, 9:1124, 1126
Nephelium 2:151, 208, 3:287, 5:544
nephrite 8:1083, 1084, **1095**, 1100
Nephrolepis 2:**240**
Nephrophyllidium 5:581
Neptune 8:971, *972*
Neptunia 4:499
Neptunism 9:1147
Nereocystis 1:66, 2:192, **240**
Nerine 2:**240**, 5:664, *666;*
  saariensis 6:683
Nerium 2:**240**, 5:574, *575,* 7:898
neroli oil 3:314
Nero's crown 3:331
Nesaea 4:507
Nesaeae 4:507
nest epiphytes 6:721
nettle 2:**241**, 4:447, 448, *449;*
  common stinging 2:241, *241,* 3:348;
  dead 2:241;
  dog 2:241;

false 2:241;
  Hawaiian false 1:60;
  hemp 2:154;
  Roman 3:348;
  small 2:241;
  stinging 2:241, *241*, 3:348,
    7:884;
  wood 2:241
nettle tree 1:81
Neurada 4:494
Neuradoideae 4:494
Neurolepis 5:635
Neurospora 2:241
Neuwiedia 5:675
New Caledonian floristic region
    7:897;
  endemics of 7:919
New Jersey tea 1:80
New Zealand bur 1:7
New Zealand flax 5:666
New Zealand floristic region 7:897,
    904;
  aliens of 7:921, 952;
  endemics of 7:916, 919;
  exploration of 6:687-8
niam fat 2:211
Nicandra 2:241, 5:579
Nicandreae 5:579
niccolite 8:1105
niche 6:786-7
nickel 8:979, 996, *1075*, **1105-6**,
    9:1151, *see also* iron-nickel
Nicobar breadfruit 5:656
Nicotiana 2:241, 3:337, 5:579,
    579;
  sylvestris 7:927;
  tabacum 7:926, 927, 943
nicotine 1:26, 2:227, 3:337,
    6:823, 7:946
Nidularium 2:241, 5:646
Niederleinia 4:461, 462
Nierembergia 2:241, 5:579, 595
Nigella 2:241, 3:396, *396*, 399;
  arvensis 6:775
niger seed 2:167, 5:618
night-blooming jessamine 1:84
nightshade 2:241, 3:317;
  Alpine enchanter's 1:90;
  black 2:241, 3:317;
  common 3:317;
  deadly 1:26, 46, 47, 2:241;
  enchanter's 1:90, 2:241;
  garden 3:317;
  silverleaf 3:317;
  woody 2:241, *241*, 3:317
Nile tree 3:321
Nilssoniales 6:*739*, 740
Nilssoniocladus 6:*743*
ningro 2:140
niobium 9:1126
Nipa 6:745, 746, *746*, 7:896;
  fruticans 6:746-7, *747*
nipplefruit 3:318
nipplewort 2:197
nispero 2:219
Nitella 2:241
Nitraria 5:554
Nitrobacter 1:51, 2:242, 6:*807*
nitrogen 8:971, 997, 1114,
    9:1143
nitrogen cycle 6:*806*, 806-7
nitronga nut 1:110
Nitrosomonas 1:51, 2:242, 6:*807*
nitta tree 2:260;
  fernleaved 2:260
noble gases *see* inert gases
nodules 8:1074, *1075*, 1096
Nolana 2:242, 5:579
Nolanaceae 5:577-9, 583
Noldeanthus 5:577
Noltea 4:538
nomenclature 6:697-701
Nomina Conservanda 6:700
Nomocharis 2:242, 5:664
none-so-pretty 3:315
nonesuch 3:314
noog 2:167
Nopalea 2:242

Nopalxochia 2:132
Norantea 4:*438*, 439
Norfolk Island pine 2:242
nori 1:19
norite 8:979
Noronhia 5:577
Northern Hemisphere heaths
    7:872-3
nosegay 3:275
Nostoc 2:242
Notelaea 5:577
Nothofagus 2:242, 4:410, *410*,
    525, 6:744, 7:837, 904, 905,
    906, 919, 920;
  antarctica 6:721, 729, *801*,
    7:838, *904*;
  ceratopetalum 7:837;
  pumilio 6:728, 729, *801*, 7:838
Notholaena 2:242
nothophylls 6:725
nothosaurs 9:1236, **1237**, 1238
Notobuxus 4:415
Notocactus 2:242
notoungulates 9:1247
nudibranchs 9:1226
nuées ardentes 9:1126
numerical analysis in plant
    sociology 6:729
numerical taxonomy 6:697
Nummulites 9:1192, 1193, 1195,
    1196
nummulitids 9:1219
nunataks 7:851, *911*, 911
Nuphar 2:243, 3:357, 394, 395;
  advena 6:683, *827*
nupharin 2:243
nut:
  Barbados 2:188;
  betel 2:245, *245*;
  Brazil 1:63, 2:245, *245*;
  butter 1:77;
  cashew 2:*244*, 245, *245*;
  curare poison 1:26, 111, 3:326;
  earth 1:38;
  French physic 2:188;
  grass 1:66, 3:344;
  ground 1:38;
  illipe 3:315;
  king 1:77;
  macadamia 2:214, 245, *245*;
  Madeira 3:356;
  maroochy 2:214;
  monkey 1:38, 2:245;
  pecan 2:262, *263*;
  pili 2:245;
  pine 2:245, *245*;
  pistachio 3:273;
  purging 2:188, *189*;
  rush 1:113;
  souari 1:77;
  tiger 1:113
nutgall tree 3:294
nutmeg 2:*146*, 147, 214, 226,
    243, 3:381, *381*, 382, 7:932;
  Brazilian 1:110;
  California 3:342;
  Peruvian 2:198
nutmeg butter 2:243
nutmeg oil 2:136
nutmeg tree 2:136, 237, 243
nutrient elements and fire 6:814
nutrient-poor water 7:875, 885
nutrient-rich water 7:875, 880,
    885
nutrition:
  and competition 6:820;
  and soils 6:806-7
Nuttall, Thomas 6:683
nux-vomica 3:326;
  water-filter 3:327
Nuytsia 4:524, *524*
Nuytsieae 4:525
Nyctagina 4:420
Nyctaginaceae 4:*419*, **419-20**, 422
Nyctanthes 5:587
Nyctanthoideae 5:587
Nymphaea 2:243, 3:357, 394, 394,

    395, 5:581, 6:724, *770*, *798*,
    826, *827*
Nymphaeaceae 3:*394*, **394-5**,
    5:619, 622, 654
Nymphaeales 3:393-5, 399
Nymphoides 2:243, 5:574, *581*,
    581, 582
Nypa 2:243, 5:651, 653, 654
nypa palm 2:243
nypoid palms 5:653
Nyssa 2:243, 4:516, 6:747;
  sylvatica 6:*747*
nyssa 2:243;
  twin-flowered 2:243
Nyssaceae 4:**516**, 518

oak 2:126, **246**, *246*, *247*, 4:410,
    412, 413, 520;
  African 2:211;
  Australian 2:135;
  black 2:246;
  blackjack 2:246;
  bull 1:78;
  bur 3:341;
  chestnut-leaved 2:246;
  cork 1:105, 2:246;
  durmast 3:341;
  English 2:235, 3:341;
  golden 2:246;
  holm 2:246, *246*;
  Hungarian 2:246;
  Italian 2:246;
  Kermes 2:246;
  live 2:246;
  Mongolian 3:341;
  Northern pin 2:246;
  pedunculate 3:341;
  pin 2:246;
  poison 3:276, 294;
  red 2:246, *246*, 3:341;
  river 1:78;
  scarlet 2:246;
  sessile 3:341;
  she 1:78;
  silk 2:164;
  Spanish red 3:341;
  swamp 1:78;
  white 2:246;
  yellow-barked 2:126, 246;
  see also Quercus
oak apple 2:247
oarweed 1:18, 2:192, **196**
oasis theory of domestication
    7:925
oat 1:83, *83*, 2:246, *246*, 5:635,
    638, 640, 7:880, 943;
  Algerian 2:247;
  animated 1:47, 2:247, 3:358;
  common wild 1:47, 2:247,
    3:358, *358*;
  cultivated 1:47, *48*;
  diploid 1:83;
  fodder 2:246;
  hexaploid 1:83;
  naked 2:247;
  potato 1:47, 2:247, 3:358;
  red 2:247;
  Tartarian 1:47, 2:247, 3:358;
  tetraploid 1:83;
  wild 1:47, 2:247, 3:**358**, *358*,
    6:822;
  wild red 1:47, 2:247, 3:358
oatgrass 2:149, 7:861;
  false 7:861, 862
oca 2:257, 3:298, *299*, 350
obeche 3:341
obedient plant 3:270
Obione 4:525
Obolaria 3:264
obsequents 8:1037
obsidian 8:1081, 1089, 9:1129
obsolete cultivars 7:958
ocean floor 8:1007, 1033, 1041,

    1055, **1059-64**, *1059*, *1060*,
    1062, *1063*, 1074, 9:1124,
    1127, 1129, 1149, 1150,
    1272
ocean trenches 8:1004-5, 1035,
    1036, 1056, *1062*, **1062-3**
oceanic heaths 7:873
oceanic islands 7:917-9;
  and endemics 7:916
Ochlandra 1:49, 2:144, 5:635
Ochna 2:247, 4:433-4, *434*
Ochnaceae 4:433-4, *434*, 435,
    438, 461
Ochradenus 4:472
Ochroma 1:49, 4:444
Ochrosia 5:574
Ocimoideae 5:589
Ocimum 1:53, 2:247, 5:589
oconee-bells 3:315
Ocotea 2:164, 247, 3:387, 388
ocotillo 1:69, 2:148, *148*, 4:455,
    6:*722*, 799, 7:848, 849
Octocorallia 9:1220
Octolepis 4:*510*, 510
Octomeles 4:464
Odontites 5:593
odontocetes 9:1249
Odontoglossum 2:247, 5:675
Odontonema 5:601
Odontostomum 5:669
Oedogonium 2:247
Oenanthe 5:571, 6:826
Oenothera 2:247, 4:512, *513*,
    6:*799*;
  lamarckiana 6:762
Oftia 5:593
oil (edible) 2:250;
  ajowan 1:77;
  argemone 3:279;
  babassu 2:250;
  balsam 1:122;
  ben 2:250;
  Brazil nut 2:250;
  cacao 2:250;
  cashew nut kernel 2:250;
  castor 2:250;
  champaca 2:229;
  chaulmoogra 2:250;
  chinawood 2:250;
  citronella 1:113;
  cocoa 2:250;
  coconut 2:250;
  cohune 2:250;
  colza 2:250;
  corn 2:250;
  cotton seed 2:250;
  croton 2:250;
  eng 1:122, 2:250;
  gingergrass 1:113, 2:250;
  groundnut 2:250;
  gurjun 2:250, 3:341;
  hempseed 2:250;
  illipe nut 2:250;
  kapok seed 2:250;
  linseed 2:250;
  lemongrass 1:113;
  macassar 2:250;
  maize 2:250;
  maw seed 2:250;
  mustard 2:250;
  Neroli 5:554;
  Niger seed 2:250;
  nitronga 1:110;
  oiticica 2:250;
  palma rosa 1:113;
  peach 2:250;
  perilla 2:250, 3:266;
  pistachio 2:250;
  rasamolo 3:288;
  walnut 2:250;
  wood 3:288
oil (mineral) 8:990, 991, 1086,
    9:1130, 1131, 1187;
  crude 8:1104;
  see also petroleum
oil flax 2:143
oil grass 1:112
oil of anise 2:185
oil of cade 2:190

oil of chamomile 1:85
oil of citronella 2:136
oil of marjoram 2:220
oil of meadowsweet 2:142
oil of Neroli 5:554
oil of sassafras 3:308
oil of savin 2:190
oil of savory 3:308
oil of terebinth 3:346
oil of vetiver 2:136, 3:354
oil palm 2:129, 250, *250*, 5:651, 653, 654, 7:932;
    American 2:129, 250
oil plant 3:314
oil pollution 7:945
oilseed rape 4:472
oiticica 4:499
Okoubaka 4:521
okoume 3:341
okra 2:176, **248**, *248*, 3:350, *352*, 4:444, 445;
    musk 2:248
okra-leaf cotton 7:924
Olacaceae 4:439, 474, 522, *523*, **523-4**, 527, 531
olas paper 1:61
Olax 4:*523*, 523
old man 1:42
old man's beard 3:348
Old Red Sandstone 9:1162-3, 1165, 1166, 1271, 1273
Olduvai Gorge 9:1198, 1252, *1253*
Olea 2:248, 5:576, 577
Oleaceae 5:576, **576-7**
oleander 5:574, 575, 7:898;
    common 2:227, 240, *240*
oleandrin 2:240
Olearia 2:248, 5:618;
    macrodonta 6:688
oleaster 2:129, 4:518, 519
Oleeae 5:577
Oleoideae 5:577
olibanum tree, Indian 1:62
Oligocene 6:*738*, 740, 742, 747, 8:1083, 9:1191, 1192, **1195**, 1229, 1250
oligoclase 8:1096
Oligomeris 4:472
Oligopithecus 9:1250
oligotrophy 7:867, 875
Olinia 4:512
Oliniaceae 4:**512-3**
olive 2:151, **248**, *249*, 250, *250*, *251*, 5:576, 577;
    Ceylon 2:249;
    Chinese 2:249;
    common 2:248;
    Indian 2:248;
    Java 2:249;
    sand 2:249;
    sweet 2:262;
    wild 2:248
olive bark tree 3:334
olive oil 2:248
olivenites 8:*1095*
olivine 8:973, 974, 975, 979, 980, 986, 989, 996, 1079, 1081, **1095**, 1099, 1103, 1105, 9:*1123*, 1124, *1127*, 1128, 1129, 1137
Olneya 2:187
olololiuqui 2:226
Olpidium 2:249
Olyra 5:636, *638*
Olyreae 5:636
ombrotrophic mire 7:875, *see also* bogs
omphacite 9:1129
Omphalodes 2:249, 5:586
omphalosaurs 9:1237
omu 3:307, 5:552
Onagraceae 4:505, 506, 507, **512**, *513*
Onagreae 4:512
Oncidium 2:249, 5:*673*, 675
Oncoba 4:451, 452
oncolites 9:1185

Oncosperma 6:747
Oncostemon 4:486
Ondinea 3:394
onion 1:17, *17*, 2:126, **249**, *249*, 3:*314*, *351*, 400, 5:662, 664, 7:932;
    bunching Japanese 2:249;
    common field 2:249;
    Gypsy 2:*155*;
    Japanese 3:400;
    sea 3:311, 348, *348*;
    spring 1:17;
    Welsh 1:17, 2:249, 3:400;
    wild 7:949
Onobrychis 2:252, 4:*502*
Onoclea 2:252
Ononis 2:252;
    repens 6:825
Onopordum 2:252, 3:335, 5:617
Onosma 2:252
Ophiocaryon 5:544
onyx 8:1083, 1087
oolites 9:1134, 1135
ooliths 8:1015, *1084*, 1087, 9:*1133*, *1134*
oozes 8:*1059*, 1061, 9:*1133*, 1191, 1215
opal 8:1010, 1081, 1089, **1095-6**, 9:1135
Oparin, Aleksandr 6:752
open vegetation 6:715
ophiacodonts 9:1243
Ophioglossum 2:252
ophiolites 9:1128
Ophiopogon 2:252, 5:664
ophiuroids 9:1223
Ophrys 2:252, 5:*675*, *675*, 6:764, *767*, 773, 780
Ophthalmophyllum 4:415
Opilia 4:523
Opiliaceae 4:523, 527
opium poppy 1:26, 2:227, **252**, 4:403
opiuma 3:274
opopanax 1:7
opportunistic species 6:827
oppossum-wood 2:168
optimum temperature 6:791
Opuntia 2:253, 4:413, 415, *415*, 6:*721*, *771*, 815, 7:843, 849, 950;
    bigelovii 6:722;
    echinocarpa 7:849;
    echinos var. *echinos* 7:917;
    stricta 6:819
opuntia 2:253, *253*;
    crested 2:254;
    little tree 2:254;
    old man 2:254
Opuntioideae 4:413
orache 1:46, 2:254, 3:350;
    sea 7:887;
    stalked 2:168
orange 1:58, 2:254, 5:552, *552*, 554, 7:926;
    acidless 2:255;
    bitter 2:151, 3:314;
    blood 2:255;
    common 2:255;
    hardy 3:279;
    house-blooming mock 3:274;
    king 6:151;
    mandarin 2:*217*, 3:308, 332;
    Mexican 1:88;
    mock 3:267, 268, 274, 327;
    Natal 3:327;
    navel 2:255;
    osage 2:126, **256**, *256*;
    pigmented 2:255;
    Seville 1:57, 91, 2:151, 3:314;
    sour 2:151, 3:314;
    sugar 2:255;
    sweet 1:91, 2:151, 217, **254**, *254*, 256;
    trifoliate 3:279;
    vegetable 2:222
orange oil 2:136
orange-fringe 2:168

orange-plum 2:168
Oratava Botanic Garden 7:963
Orbigny, A. d' 9:*1272*
Orbignya 2:**255**, 5:654
orbitolines 9:1219
orchid 2:**255**, 5:671-5, 6:683, 686, 764, *767*, 817, 7:903;
    bee 2:252;
    bird's nest 2:239, *255*;
    butterfly 2:249;
    clam-shell 2:131;
    cockle-shell 2:131, *131*;
    common spotted 1:*115*;
    dancing-doll 2:249;
    dwarf 2:255;
    early purple 2:255;
    fly 2:252, *252*;
    frog 1:97;
    giant 2:131;
    green rein 2:168;
    green woodland 2:168;
    green-winged 2:*255*, 256;
    jewel 1:*31*, 2:*163*;
    lady 2:*255*;
    lady's-slipper 1:*114*, *114*, 2:*259*;
    late spider 2:252;
    lesser butterfly 2:168;
    lily-of-the-valley 2:247;
    little club-spur 2:168;
    lizard 2:*177*;
    man 1:8, *8*;
    military 2:255, *256*;
    mirror 2:252;
    monkey 2:*255*;
    moth 3:267;
    nun 2:213;
    pansy 2:230;
    poor man's 3:310;
    purple fringeless 2:168;
    purple hooded 2:256;
    purple-spire 2:168;
    pyramidal 1:28, *28*;
    round-leaved 2:256;
    salep 2:256;
    showy 2:256;
    small round-leaved 2:256;
    spotted 1:*115*;
    woodland 2:256;
    yellow-fringed 2:168
orchid tree 1:53, *53*
Orchidaceae 5:651, **671-5**, *673*, *675*
Orchidales 5:670-5
Orchidantha 5:647
Orchideae 5:675
Orchidoideae 5:675
Orchis 2:**255**, 5:*675*, *675*
orchis, green man 1:8, *8*
order, phytocoenal 6:728
ordination 6:729-30
Ordovician 6:*738-9*, 739, 9:1152, 1154, **1156-9**, *1157*, *1159*, 1160, *1161*, 1228, 1260, 1270;
    climate 9:*1158-9*;
    fauna 9:*1156*, 1156-7, 1158-9, 1162;
    flora 9:*1156*;
    geography 9:*1156*, 1158;
    stratigraphic correlation 9:1157;
    volcanic activity 8:1034
ore deposits 8:990, 991, 992, 1023, 1031, 1071, **1072**, *1073*, **1074-5**, 1084, 1085, 9:1151
oregano 2:256, 5:589;
    wild 2:174
Oreobolus 6:722, 7:905
Oreocommunea 5:555
Oreocommuneoideae 5:555
Oreodoxa 3:328
Oreostylidium 5:607
organic matter in soils 6:*803*, 803, 804
organic wastes in water 7:944-5
organismal model of community 6:709
organized elements in meteorites 6:758

organ-pipe cactus 6:722
Orgel, Leslie 6:752
oriental poppy 4:403
Origanum 2:220, **256**, 5:589
origin, centers of 7:906-7, 927
origin of life 6:752-6, **752-6**
origins of Antarctic flora 7:905
origins of Arctic flora 7:902
origins of Boreal flora 7:903-4
origins of crop plants 7:925-9, *926*
ornithischians 9:1241-2
Ornithogalum 2:256, 5:662, 664
ornithomimids 9:1241, 1242
Ornithosuchus 9:1239
Orobanchaceae 5:593, *598*, **598-9**
Orobanche 2:256, 5:*598*, 598, 599, 6:817, 7:948
Orobus niger 6:683
orogeny (mountain-building) 8:973, 980, 989, 1036, 1066, 9:1122, 1126, 1132, 1147, 1149, 1154, 1179
Orohippus 9:1271
orpiment 8:*1098*, 1107
orpine 3:312
orris root 2:187, **256**, 5:662
orseille 2:126
ortanique 2:217, **256**
Orthilia 4:480
Orthoclada 5:636
orthoclase 8:1079, 1082, 1086, 1090, 1094, *1095*, **1096**, 1098, 9:1124, 1125, 1132
orthogenesis and determinism 6:764
Orthopterygium 5:544
orthorhombic system *see* crystal systems
Orthothylax 5:661
Oryza 1:41, 2:256, 3:294, 5:636, 640;
    bartii 7:885
Oryzeae 5:636
oryzoid grasses 7:862
Osage orange 2:126, **256**, *256*, 4:447
Osborn, H. 9:1262, **1272**
Oscillatoria 2:256
Oscularia 4:417, *417*
osier 3:305, 358, 4:468
Osmanthus 2:256
Osmunda 2:256, 6:740, 748;
    regalis 7:883, 884
Osteospermum 2:256, 5:618
ostracoderms 9:1163, 1164, 1231
ostracods 9:1160, 1162, 1185, 1207-8, **1228**
Ostrea 9:1185
Ostrowskia 5:604, 606
Ostrya 2:187, **257**, 4:409, 410
Ostryopsis 4:409
oswego tea 1:57, 2:174, 232
Osyris 4:521
Otaheite 3:322
Otaheite apple 5:548
Othonna 5:617, 618
Otozanites pulcher 6:732
otto of roses 1:46, 2:136
Ottonia 3:388
ouabain 1:9, 5:575
Oubanguia 4:439
Our Lady's lace 1:36
Our Lord's candle 3:361
Ouratea 4:434, *434*
Ourisia 2:257;
    macrophylla 6:688
outbreeders 7:932
ouzo 1:16, 31
overwinter chilling 6:793
Owen, Sir R. 9:1272, *1273*
Owenia 5:552
Oxalidaceae 5:542, 559, **559-60**
Oxalis 2:257, 3:314, 5:*559*, 559, 560, 7:838;
    sepalosa 6:722
oxalis, creeping 2:257
oxbow lakes 8:1038, 1043, *1052*
oxeye, yellow 1:68
ox-eye daisy 5:618

Oxford and Cambridge bush 3:283
Oxford University Botanic Garden
    7:951
oxlip 3:277, 280, 7:838
ox-tongues 3:271
Oxybaphus 4:420
Oxychloe 5:641
Oxydendrum 2:257, 4:477
oxygen 8:970, 971, 995, 997,
    1009, 1021, 1084, 1088,
    1097, **1102-3**, 1104, 9:1135,
    1143, 1153, 1213;
    atmospheric 6:757, 758, 766,
    7:941;
    isotopes in seawater 9:1198,
    1211-3;
    in water 7:944, 945, 946
Oxyria 4:428;
    digyna 6:749, 7:854, 909, 910
Oxyspora 4:514
Oxytropis 2:257
oyster plant 2:228, 3:293, 305,
    350;
    black 3:311
oysternut 2:245, 4:467
ozokerite 8:1112
ozone fiber 1:43

paccai 3:281
pachycephalosaurs 9:1242
Pachydiscus 9:1189
Pachylarnax 3:378
Pachyphytum 4:495, *495*
Pachypodium 4:413
Pachyrrhizus 2:204, 3:350, **360**
Pachysandra 2:258, 4:*534*, 534,
    535
pachysandra:
    Alleghany 2:258;
    Japanese 2:258
Pachystima 4:529
pachytene in meiosis 6:*763*
Pacific North American region
    7:889
Pacific South American region
    7:897
padauk 3:283;
    African 3:283, 341;
    Andaman 3:283, 341;
    brown 3:283, 341;
    Burma 3:283, 341;
    red 3:283, 341;
    sandalwood 3:283;
    vengai 3:283;
    West African 3:283, 341
paddle wood 2:258
paddy 3:294;
    hill 3:295;
    lowland 3:295;
    upland 3:295
Padopterus 4:428
padouk 3:283;
    African 3:283, 341;
    Andaman 3:283, 341;
    brown 3:283, 341;
    Burma 3:283, 341;
    red 3:283, 341;
    sandalwood 3:283;
    vengai 3:283;
    West African 3:283, 341
Padus 3:282, 4:494
Paeonia 2:258, 4:*431*, 431-2
Paeoniaceae 3:399, 4:430, *431*,
    431-2
Paepalanthus 5:*631*, 632
pagoda tree, Japanese 3:318
pahoehoe 8:*1058*
painted lady 2:127
painted leaf 3:276
painted-tongue 3:305
pak-choi 1:64, *65*, 87, *88*
paku 2:140

Palaquium 2:167, 3:300, 4:482
palas 1:68
Palaua 4:445
paleobotany 6:**730-5**
Paleocene 6:*738*, 740, 745-6, *746*,
    9:1191-2, *1192*
paleodiploids 7:914
paleoecology 9:1208, **1211-4**,
    1268
paleoendemics 7:*914*, 914, 915-6,
    916-7
Paleogene 6:740, 9:1191
paleogeography 9:1149
Paleolithic Man 6:749
paleomagnetism 6:741, 8:**993-4**,
    1002, **1003-4**, 1105, 9:1149,
    1158, 1162, 1166
paleontology 9:1266, *see also* fossil
    record, fossils,
    micropaleontology,
    paleoecology
paleopolyploids 7:914
Paleotropical realm 7:896, **896**,
    897
Paleozoic 6:*738-9*, 739-40,
    9:**1152-75**, 1209, 1210,
    1213-4, 1235, *see also*
    Cambrian, Ordovician,
    Silurian, Devonian,
    Carboniferous, Permian
paliguanids 9:1238
palissander, Javanese 1:116
Paliurus 2:258, 4:*537*, *538*
palladium 8:1110
Pallas, Peter Simon 6:688
pallasites 8:986, 988, 1096
palm 5:651-4, 6:687, *709*, *720*,
    746, 747, 7:837, 895, 896;
    American cabbage 3:328;
    American oil 2:129, 250;
    Andean wax 3:357;
    assai 2:138;
    babassu 2:255;
    bamboo 3:288;
    betel-nut 1:26, 2:227;
    blue fan 1:63;
    butterfly 1:88;
    cabbage 2:138, 3:297, 328;
    Caribbee 3:297, 328;
    Chilean wine 3:297;
    Chinese windmill 2:145, 3:342;
    coconut 3:328;
    cohune 2:255;
    coquitos 2:189;
    Cuban royal 3:297;
    curly 2:182;
    date 1:117, *117*, 3:268, 269,
        269, 328, 7:956;
    dwarf fan 2:145, *145*;
    fan 6:748;
    fishtail 1:77;
    flat 2:182;
    gebang 1:106;
    gomuti 3:302, 328;
    honey 3:328;
    India date 3:269;
    Ivory Coast raffia 3:288;
    ivory nut 2:228, 3:270;
    jaggery 3:328;
    Japanese sago 3:328;
    key 3:297;
    kitul 1:77, 3:302;
    leopard 1:27;
    nypa 2:145, 3:328;
    oil 2:129, 250, *250*, 7:932;
    palmetto 2:258, 3:335;
    palmyra 1:61, 2:145, 3:328;
    Panama hat 2:144;
    parlor 1:85;
    prickly sago 3:302;
    princess 1:120;
    raffia 3:288;
    rattan 1:70, 2:216;
    royal 3:297;
    royal palmetto 3:335;
    sago 1:77, 112, *112*, 2:*145*,
        228, 3:**302**, 328, *328*;
    South American royal 3:297;

South American wax 3:357;
    spineless sago 3:302;
    sugar 1:49, *40*, 2:145, 3:328,
        328;
    syrup 3:328;
    talipot 1:106;
    thatch-leaf 2:182;
    toddy 1:77, 3:328;
    traveller's 3:289;
    wax 1:84, 3:357;
    wild date 3:269, 328, *328*;
    wine 1:77, 2:189, 3:288
palm grass 3:314
palm hearts 2:138
palm lily 1:104
palm oil 2:129, 250, 5:654;
    American 2:129, 250, *250*
palm sugar 5:654
palm wine 1:16, 5:654
palma christi 3:295
palma de macetas 1:121
Palmae 5:633, **651-4**, *653*, 656,
    659, 7:896
palmares 7:862
palmetto 2:**258**;
    blue 2:258;
    bush 2:258;
    cabbage 2:258;
    common 2:258;
    dwarf 2:258;
    royal 3:335;
    scrub 2:258;
    Texan 2:258
palmetto thatch 3:335
palmiet 3:281, 5:641
palmita 1:75
palmyra palm 1:61
palo campechio 2:168
palo muerto 1:12
palo negro 1:116
palo verde, Mexican 2:260
palsas 7:903
palta 3:266
palynology 6:734
Pamianthe 5:666
pampas 7:832, 859
pampas grass 1:105, 5:638
PAN (peroxyacetyl nitrate) 7:942,
    943
pan 6:*805*, 805
Panaeolus 2:226
Panama hat plant 1:75, 5:654,
    655
Panama rubber 4:447
panaquillon 2:258
Panax 2:258, 5:568
Pancheria 4:487, *487*
Pancratium 2:258, 5:664, 665,
    6:723
Panda 4:535, 537
panda plant 2:192, 3:268
Pandaceae 4:535
Pandanaceae 5:654, **655-6**, *656*,
    7:896
Pandanales 5:655-6
pandang 2:258
Pandanus 2:258, 5:655, 656, *656*,
    6:*720*, 826
Pandorea 2:259, 3:334, 5:600
Pandorina 1:20
Pangaea 6:741, 742-3, 8:1001,
    1002, 9:1154, 1173, 1174,
    1179, 1181, 1241, 1275
pangenesis 6:760
Paniceae 5:638
panicoid grasses 7:862, 863
Panicoideae 5:636, 638, 640
Panicum 2:230, **259**, 5:638, 640,
    6:723;
    atrosanguineum 7:863
panning 8:*1081*
pansy 2:259, 3:355, 4:450, 451;
    European wild 2:259, *259*,
        3:355;
    field 2:259, 3:355;
    garden 2:259, 3:355;
    miniature 3:355;
    Shirley 2:259;

show 3:355;
    tricolor 2:259;
    tufted 3:355;
    yellow mountain 2:259
panther cap 1:25
pantotheres 9:1245
pantropical distributions 7:896
papain 2:259
Papaver 2:252, 259, 3:279, 4:*402*,
    402, 403, 6:691;
    alpinum 6:750;
    dubium 6:781;
    orientale 6:681;
    rhoeas 6:781, *821*
Papaveraceae 3:396, 4:*402*, **402-
    3**, 404, 459, 469
Papaverales 3:399, 4:402-4
papaverine 1:26, 2:227
papaya 1:75, *75*, 2:151, *153*, 259,
    259, 4:455, 7:880;
    American 2:259;
    mountain 1:75
paper 2:144
paper plant 2:139
paper reed 1:113, 5:643
paperback tree 2:221
Paphiopedilum 2:259, 5:*673*, 675
Papilionaceae 4:499
Papilionoideae 4:499, 502
paprika 1:74, 2:260, 5:579
papyrus 1:113, *113*, 2:144, 5:643,
    6:*724*, 826, 7:883, *885*, 885
papyrus swamp 6:*724*
Para nut 2:245, 4:450, *see also*
    Brazil nut
Para rubber tree 1:74, 4:537
parachute diaspores 6:*817*, 817
paradise flower 1:69, 3:317
paradise nut 4:450
paradise plant 2:191
paradise tree 3:315
Paradisea 2:260
Paraguay tea 2:178
Parahebe 2:170
paralic coals 8:1116-7
parallelism 6:696
Paramecium 6:691
Paramichelia 3:378
paramo 7:861
paramomyids 9:1249-50
Parano-Amazonian floral region
    7:897
paranut 2:245, 4:450, *see also*
    Brazil nut
para-para 3:273
parapithecids 9:1250
parapsids 9:1236, 1237
paraquat 7:947
Parasemionotus 9:*1206*
parasites:
    adaptations of 6:*772*, *773*;
    annual and root 6:724;
    weed 7:948
parathion 7:946
parchment-bark 4:488, 489, 7:897
pareiasaurs 9:1236
Pariana 5:636
Parianeae 5:636
Parietaria 4:448, *448*
Parietarieae 4:448
Parinari 4:498, 499
Pariophthalmus 7:891
Paris 2:260
Parkinson, Sydney 6:(*687*)
Parkinsonia 2:260
parkland 7:838-9;
    savanna 7:856
Parks, National 7:952, 955, 955
Parmelia 2:260, 7:942
Parmentiera 5:599
Parnassia 2:260, 4:497, *497*
Parnassioideae 4:497
Parodia 4:415
Paronychia 2:260, 4:419
Paronychieae 4:419
Paronychioideae 4:417, 419
Parrotia 2:268, 4:407

parrot's beak 2:211
parrot's bill 1:92
parrot's claws 2:171
parrot's flower 2:171
parsley 2:147, 174, 175, **260**,
    5:569, 571;
  cow 1:36, 37;
  Hamburg 3:350;
  horse 3:317;
  turnip-rooted 2:261, 3:350
parsnip 2:261, 3:298, 350, 5:569,
    571;
  common cow 2:173;
  Peruvian 1:41
Parthenium 3:297, 5:617, 618;
  argentatum 6:822
Parthenocissus 2:261, 4:538, 539;
  quinquefolia 6:772
partridge berry 2:155
Parvatia 3:400
Paspalum 2:230, **261**, 5:638,
    6:723, 7:856, 863
paspalum, ribbed 2:261
pasque flower 3:284, 399
Passiflora 2:261, 4:452, 453, 453
Passifloraceae 4:452-3, 453, 454,
    455, 463, 465
passion flower 4:452;
  blue 2:261;
  red 2:261
passion fruit 1:50, 2:151, 153,
    4:452, 453;
  yellow 2:261
pasta althaea 1:25
Pasteur point 6:766
Pastinaca 2:261, 3:350, 5:571
pastis 1:31
Pastonian phase 6:748-9
pastures 6:718, 7:860;
  alpine 7:863;
  grasses of 7:862-3, 958;
  management of 7:938-41, 939;
  on peatland 7:880;
  see also meadows
Patagonian region and province
    7:904
Patagonula 5:583, 584, 584
patchouli 2:136, 3:276, 5:589
patchouli oil 3:276
Patella and seashore zonation
    6:829
Patrinia 5:610, 611
patristics 6:696
patroendemics 7:914, 917
patronite 8:1105
pattern 6:716, 716-7, 717
patterned bog 7:902-3
Paullinia 1:58, 69, 5:543, 543,
    544
Paulownia 2:193, **261**
Pausinystalia 1:26
Pavon y Jiménez, José 6:682
Pavonia 2:261, 4:445
pawpaw 1:75, 75, 2:151, 153,
    259, 259, 4:455, 7:880;
  American 2:259;
  mountain 1:75
Payena 2:167
Paypayrola 4:451
PE ratio 7:866
pea 2:261, 4:499, 502, 5:599,
    7:957;
  asparagus 1:44, 107, 2:200,
    201, 262;
  Australian 1:123;
  black-eyed 2:201;
  butterfly 1:92, 2:149, 262;
  chick 1:87, 2:201, 201, 262;
  chickling 2:164, 199;
  common 2:261, 3:306;
  Congo 2:201;
  culinary 2:261, 3:273;
  cultivated 2:262;
  Darlington River 3:330;
  earthnut 2:198;
  everlasting 2:199, 199;
  field 2:201, 261, 3:273;
  flame 1:88, 2:262;

garden 2:200, 201, 261;
  glory 1:92;
  grain 1:87;
  grass 2:164, 199, 262;
  heart 1:75;
  Hindu 1:107;
  hoary 3:334;
  Jerusalem 1:107;
  kaffir 2:201;
  kordofan 1:92;
  perennial 2:198;
  pigeon 2:201, 201, 262, 3:271,
    271;
  poison 3:330;
  rabbit's 3:334;
  rosary 1:6, 2:262;
  sea 2:198;
  snow 2:261;
  Sturt's desert 1:92, 93;
  sugar 2:261;
  sweet 2:199, 262;
  Tangier 2:199;
  winged 2:201, 211;
  winter sweet 3:330
pea shrub 1:74;
  Russian 1:75;
  Siberian 1:74
peach 1:17, 2:151, 152, 262, 262,
    3:282, 4:491, 494, 6:823;
  Chinese cling 2:262;
  freestone 2:262;
  vine 2:222
Peach, B. 9:1263, 1269, **1272**
peach leaf curl 3:332
peach wood 1:69
peacock flower 1:69, 118
peacock ore *see* bornite
peacock plant 2:191
peanut 1:38, 2:245, 250
pear 2:151, 152, **262**, 263, 4:491,
    494;
  alligator 1:47, 2:151, 3:266,
    350;
  balsam 2:232;
  Chinese 3:285;
  common 2:262;
  European 2:262;
  melon 3:265, 318;
  paper-spined 2:254;
  prickly 2:242, 254;
  sand 3:285;
  willow-leaf 3:285
pearl barley 2:262
pearl bush 2:138, 4:494
pearl millet 5:640
pearl plant 2:169
pearlspar *see* dolomite
pearly everlasting flower 1:29
Pearson, Karl 6:761
peat 6:810, 810, 8:1115-9, 1117,
    9:1141, 1170, 1171;
  and bogs 7:875-80, 877-80;
  and fens 7:880, 881-2, 883;
  and muskeg 7:903
peavine, grass 2:164
pebble plant 2:208, 4:415, 6:722
pebble-phosphate 9:1135
pecan nut 2:245, 245, 262, 263,
    5:555
Pecora 9:1248
Pectis 5:617
Pedaliaceae 5:601, 603
Pedalium 5:601
Pediastrum 2:263
Pedicularis 2:263, 5:593, 595,
    6:780, 7:853, 854
Pedilanthus 2:263
pedimentation 8:1011
pediments 8:1047
pediplain *see* peneplain
pedalfers 9:1141
pedocals 9:1141
pedogenesis 6:802-3
peepal tree 2:142
peepul 2:142
Peganum 2:226, **263**, 5:554
pegass 7:879
pegmatites 8:1030, 1031, 1084,

1086, 1089, 1109
pelagic sediments 8:1060, 1061,
    1062
Pelargonium 2:160, **263**, 5:558,
    559, 6:722
Pelea 5:554
Pelecyphora 4:415
Pelée, Mont 8:1058
pelican flower 1:40, 40, 3:392
pelites 8:1084, 1093, 1099,
    9:1136, 1137, 1138
Pellia 2:263
Pellicieraceae 4:432
Pellionia 4:448
pellitory 1:28
Pelomyxa 9:1205
Peltigera 2:263, 6:825
Peltiphyllum 4:497
Peltophorum 1:118
Peltostigma 5:552
Pelvetia 3:264;
  canaliculata 6:828, 829
pelyosaurs 9:1176, **1243**
Penaea 4:509, 509
Penaeaceae 4:508-9, 509, 528
Penaeeae 4:509
Penck, A. 9:1263, **1272**
pendulous bellflower 5:604, 606
peneplain (pediplain) 8:1014,
    1042, 1043, 1047, 9:1267
Peniantheae 3:401
Penianthus 3:401
penicillin 3:264
Penicillium 3:264
Pennisetum 2:230, 3:264, 5:638,
    640;
  mezianum 7:856, 863
pennisetum, Chinese 3:264
Pennsylvanian 6:738, 739-40, *see*
  also Carboniferous
penny flower 2:212
pennyroyal 2:174
pennywort 3:264, 347, 347,
    7:885;
  American 3:264;
  Asiatic 3:264;
  marsh 3:264;
  wall 3:264
Penstemon 3:264, 5:593, 595, 595;
  centranthifolius 6:777, 7:915;
  grinnellii 6:777, 7:915;
  jeffreyanus 6:683;
  spectabilis 6:777, 7:915
Pentadesma 3:331, 4:436, 437
Pentaglottis 1:15
Pentaphragma 5:604, 606
Pentaphragmataceae 5:604
Pentaphylaceae 4:432
Pentaschistis 5:636
pentlandite 8:1105
peony 2:258, 4:431, 6:680;
  Chinese 2:258;
  common garden 2:258;
  tree 2:258
Peperomia 3:264, 388, 390, 390
peperomia:
  emerald-ripple 3:264;
  fantasy 3:264;
  green-ripple 3:264;
  ivy-leaf 3:265;
  platinum 3:265;
  silver-leaf 3:265
Peperomiaceae 3:388, 390, 390
pepino 3:265, 318, 5:579
Peplis 4:507
Peponaspis 4:465
Peponium 4:465
pepper 1:26, 2:146, 147, 227,
    3:265, 265, 388;
  African 3:265;
  baby 3:295;
  bell 3:265;
  betel 1:57, 3:273;
  black 3:265;
  cayenne 1:79, 3:265;
  chili 1:74, 74, 3:265;
  cubeb 3:265;
  green 1:74, 2:164, 3:265,
    7:880;

1086, 1089, 1109
  Jamaican 1:17, 3:265;
  Japan 1:31, 3:362, 363;
  kava 3:273;
  melagueta 3:265;
  negro 3:265;
  Nepal 3:265;
  paprika 2:260, 3:265;
  red 1:74, 3:265, **289**;
  sweet 1:74, 3:265, 330, 350,
    5:579;
  tabasco 1:74;
  Trinidad devil 3:289;
  white 3:265
pepper elder 3:390
pepper face 3:265
pepper oil 3:265
pepper plant 3:265, 273
pepper tree 2:220, 227, 3:309,
    309, 5:548;
  Australian 3:309, 309;
  Brazilian 3:309;
  California 3:309, 309;
  monk's 3:355
pepper vine 1:28
pepperbush 7:906;
  sweet 1:92
peppercorn 1:17, 3:265, 265
pepperidge 2:243
peppermint 2:136, 147, 174, 175,
    227, 230, 3:265;
  broadleaved 2:135;
  peppermint oil 2:136, 3:265
Pera 4:537
Peracarpa 5:604
percolation 8:1070
peregrina 2:188
perennating buds and life-forms
    6:725, 725-7, 726
perennial-herb life-forms 6:719,
    722-4
perennials and breeding 7:932,
    933
Pereskia 3:265, 4:413
Pereskioideae 4:413
Pereskiopsis 4:413
Perezia 5:617
periclase 8:974, 1103
Pericopsis 1:12, 3:341
Peridinium 3:265
peridot 8:1095, **1096**
peridotite 8:973, 979, 1001, 1085,
    1099, 9:1123, 1124, **1128**,
    1129, 1137
periglacial pan 6:805
Perilepta 3:326
Perilla 3:265, 5:589
Periodic Table 8:1101, 1102
periodicity 6:717
Periomphale 5:610
Periploca 5:575
Periplocoideae 5:576
perissodactyls 9:1195, **1247-8**
periwinkle 5:574, 575;
  common 3:355;
  greater 3:355;
  lesser 3:355;
  Madagascar 1:79, 2:227;
  rose 1:79
permafrost 6:807, 7:851, 901,
    901, 936, 8:999, 1050, 1051
permeability 8:1065, **1066**, 1070,
    9:1131
Permian 6:738-9, 740, 741-2,
    742, 743, 8:1118, 9:1152,
    1154, **1173-7**, 1178, 1205,
    1209, 1236;
  climate 9:1174-5;
  fauna 9:1174, 1176-7;
  flora 9:1174, 1175-6;
  geography 9:1174;
  stratigraphic correlation
    9:1173-4
Pernettya 3:266, 4:477, 7:873
Peronospora 3:266
Perotis 5:638
Perovskia 3:266
peroxyacetyl nitrate 7:942, 943
Persea 1:47, 3:266, 387, 388

Perseeae 3:388
Persica 4:494
persimmon 1:121, 2:126, 151, 153, 3:266, 4:483;
American 1:121, 3:266;
common 1:121, 3:266;
kaki 2:191
perthite 8:1094, 1096, 9:1124, 1125
pesticides 7:946, 950
pests, weed vectors of 7:949
Petagnia 5:569, 571
petalite 8:1102
Petalonyx 4:464
Petasites 3:266, 5:617
Petitia 5:587
Petiveria 4:421, 422
Petiveriaceae 4:422
Petrea 3:266, 5:587
petrified plant remains 6:733, 733-4
Petrocosmea 5:596
petroleum 8:1021, 1028, 1062, 1073, 1086, 1091, 1111-4, 1114, 1118, 1119, 1121, 9:1130, 1214, 1260;
substitutes 7:936;
traps 8:1113, 1121
Petroselinum 2:147, 174, 260, 3:350, 5:571, 571
pe-tsai 1:65, 87
petty whin 2:160
Petunia 3:266, 5:579, 6:795
petunia 3:266, 266;
large white 3:266;
violet-flowered 3:266
Peucedaneae 5:571
Peucedanum 5:571, 7:876
Peumus 3:384, 385
peyote 2:210, 211
peyote button 2:226
Peziza 3:266
peziza, orange-peel 2:156
Pfaffia 4:420
pH 6:805
Phacelia 3:267, 5:584, 585
Phacellaria 4:521
Phacocapnos 4:403
phacoliths 8:1030, 1032
Phaedranassa 5:666
Phalaenopsis 2:207, 3:267, 5:675
Phalaris 3:267, 5:638, 640;
arundinacea 7:885
Phallus 3:284, 324
Phanerophlebia 1:114
phanerophytes 6:725, 725-7, 726
Phanerozoic period 6:739-40
Phareae 5:636
Pharus 5:636
Phaseoleae 4:502
Phaseolus 2:169, 207, 236, 3:267, 4:502, 502;
vulgaris 7:943
Phaulothamnus 4:421
pheasant's-eye 1:10, 2:227
Phebalium 5:554
Phellinaceae 4:532
Phelline 4:532
Phellodendron 3:267, 5:652, 654
Phenakospermum 5:647
phenecotypes 6:706
phenetic classification 6:696
phenetic similarity tables 6:696
phenocrysts 9:1126
phenogram 6:696
phenolics 6:822, 823
phenology 6:717
phenotype 6:704, (761), 769
Philadelphaceae 4:498
Philadelphus 3:267, 4:498;
lewisii 6:683
Phillyrea 3:268, 5:576, 577, 6:721
Philodendron 3:268, 5:659, 659
philodendron 3:268;
blushing 3:268;
giant 3:268;
heart-leaf 3:268, 268;
horsehead 3:268;
red-leaf 3:268;

spade-leaf 3:268
Philonotis 3:268
Philydraceae 5:660, 661
Philydrella 5:661
Philydrum 5:661
Phinaea 5:596
Phlebocarya 5:668
Phlebodium 3:278
Phleum 3:268, 5:636, 638, 7:863;
alpinum 7:861, 910, 910;
pratense 7:861
phlogopite 8:1082, 1086, 1094, 9:1129
Phlomis 3:268, 5:589
Phlox 3:268, 5:582, 583
phlox 3:268, 268;
fall 3:268;
moss 3:268;
mountain 3:268;
perennial 3:268;
summer 3:268
Phobos 8:985-6, 986
phoenicoid palms 5:653
Phoenix 1:117, 3:268, 5:651, 653, 653, 7:896;
theophrasti 7:956
Pholisma 5:582
phonolite 9:1126
Phoradendreae 4:525
Phoradendron 2:231, 4:525
Phormium 3:269, 5:666
phosphates 8:1101, 1104
phosphorites 9:1135
phosphorus 8:995, 1084, 1088, 1104, 1106, 9:1126, 1135;
in plant nutrition 6:806-7
Photinia 3:269, 4:494
photinia, Japanese 3:269
photochemical pollution 7:943
photoperiodism 6:793, 794
photoreceptors 6:794
photosynthesis 6:794, 8:997, 1102, 9:1153;
and fossil plants 6:759;
and light 6:792, 794, 7:869;
and temperature 6:789-91;
and water conservation 6:795, 799, 799
phototropism 6:794
Phoxanthus 5:544
Phragmidium 3:269
Phragmites 3:269, 289, 5:638, 6:810, 7:862, 885;
australis 6:724, 826, 7:876, 880, 881-2, 884, 885, 893;
communis 6:827
phreatic caves 8:1044
phreatic surface 8:1070
phrygana 7:844
Phryma 5:591
Phrymaceae 5:591
Phrynieae 5:650
Phrynium 5:650
phycobilins 6:794
Phygelius 3:269
Phylica 4:537, 538, 538, 7:874
Phyllachne 5:606, 607;
clavigera 7:908;
uliginosa 7:908
Phyllantheae 4:537
Phyllanthus 3:269, 4:535, 537, 537
phyllites 9:1138, 1151
Phyllitis 3:269
phyllocarids 9:1156
Phyllodoce 3:269, 4:477;
caerulea 7:873;
empetriformis 7:873;
glanduliflora 7:873
Phylloglossum 1:94
phyllophane 6:785
Phyllospadix 5:626
phyllosphere 6:789
Phyllostachys 3:269, 5:636
Phyllostylon 1:62
Phyllothamnus 4:477
Phyllotheca 6:743
phylogenetic classification 6:696, 697

Phymatotrichum 1:26
Physalis 3:270, 5:579, 579
physic gardens 7:963
physic, Indian 2:161
physic nut 4:537;
French 2:188
physiognomy 6:717-27, 718
Physocalymma 4:507
Physocarpus 4:491
Physoderma 3:270
Physostegia 3:270
Physostigma 6:818
phytelephantoid palms 5:654
Phytelephas 3:270, 5:653
Phyteuma 3:270, 5:604, 604, 606
phytochoria 7:894-8
phytochrome 6:794, 795
phytocoena 6:709, 727-30, 728
phytocoenose 6:709
Phytocrene 4:531, 531, 6:747
Phytocreneae 4:531
Phytolacca 3:270, 4:421, 422, 422
Phytolaccaceae 4:415, 417, 419, 421-2, 422, 469
Phytolacceae 4:421
Phytolaccoideae 4:421
phytomass 6:709, 715
Phytophthora 3:270
phytoplankton 1:20, 3:274
phytosaurs 9:1239
phytosociology 6:727-30
phytotoxins 7:844, 941, 942, see also herbicides
phytotrons 6:691, 706
piassava 5:654
piassava fiber 3:271
Picconia 5:577
Picea 3:272, 6:748, 826, 7:838, 879, 902;
abies 6:791, 7:903, 941;
engelmannii 7:867, 904;
glauca 7:866, 903;
mariana 7:876, 903;
obovata 7:903;
rubens 7:904;
sitchensis 7:938
pickaback plant 3:337
pickerel weed 3:279, 5:659
Picramnia 5:549
Picrasma 5:549
Picris 3:271, 5:617
picrodontids 9:1249
pie plant 3:293
Pieris 3:271, 4:477;
japonica 6:684
Pierrine 4:439
piezometric surface 8:1070
pig-a-back plant 3:337
Pigafettia 5:653
pigeon berry 3:270
pigeon pea 2:262, 3:271, 271, 4:502
pigeon-foot 3:302
pigeonite 8:1092
pigeon's blood 8:1098
pigments, light-absorbing 6:794
pignons 3:272
pignut 1:99, 5:571
pig's ear 1:107
Pilea 3:271, 4:448, 448
pilea, watermelon 3:271
pili nut 2:245
pillow lavas 8:1058, 1060
pillwort 3:271, 271
Pilobolus 3:271
pilocarpine 1:26, 3:271
Pilocarpus 3:271, 5:554
Pilostyles 4:527, 528
Piltdown Man 9:1271
Pilularia 3:271, 6:725
pimbina 3:354
Pimelea 3:271, 4:510, 510
Pimenta 1:17, 53, 3:265, 272, 4:511
pimenta 1:17, 3:272
pimenta (Capsicum) 1:74, 3:272, 5:579
pimento see pimenta
pimiento see pimenta

pimpernel 1:28;
bog 1:28;
scarlet 1:28, 29;
wood 2:213;
yellow 2:213
Pimpinella 1:31, 5:571
Pinaceae 6:743
Pinacopodium 5:560
pincushion flower 2:168, 3:309, 4:520
pine 2:145, 3:272, 4:413, 520;
aleppo 7:836;
Austrian 3:272;
black cypress 3:306;
bristlecone 6:734, 735, 7:868;
Buddhist 3:276;
Chile 1:39, 3:341;
Cuban 7:938;
cypress 1:71, 3:272, 306;
Eastern white 3:324;
giant 3:272;
golden 2:164;
ground 1:14;
hoop 1:39, 7:837;
Huon 1:115, 3:272;
Italian stone 3:272;
Japanese umbrella 3:310;
Japanese white 3:272;
kauri 7:837, see also kauri;
lace bark 2:195;
lodgepole 7:942;
longleaf 3:272, 296, 341;
mahogany 3:276;
maritime 3:272, 346;
Mexican stone 2:245;
Monterey 1:100, 3:272, 7:938;
Moreton Bay 1:39;
mountain 1:115;
Norfolk Island 1:39, 2:242;
Parana 1:39, 3:341;
parasol 3:310;
pitch 3:296;
ponderosa 7:866, 942;
red 1:115, 3:272;
Rottnest Island 1:71;
Scots 1:6, 39, 3:272, 273, 296, 341, 6:719, 7:841, 894, 941;
screw 2:258, 6:720, 826, 7:896;
Southern 3:272;
Southern yellow 3:272, 296, 341;
stone 2:245, 3:272, 346;
sugar 3:272;
Swiss stone 2:245;
thatchscrew 2:258;
timber 7:942;
totara 3:276;
Western white 3:272, 341;
Western yellow 3:341, 7:866, 942;
white 3:272, 276, 324, 341;
see also Pinus
pine kernel 2:245
pine resin 1:58
pineapple 1:58, 2:126, 144, 145, 151, 153, 3:272, 272, 5:644, 644, 646, 7:880, 926, 950, 950;
wild 3:336
pineapple flower 2:137
pineapple guava 2:139
pineapple weed 7:951
pinene 1:73
Pinguicula 3:272, 5:603, 603, 604
pink 1:119, 4:417, 419;
California Indian 3:315;
Cheddar 1:119;
clove 1:119;
cluster-head 1:119;
cottage 1:119;
grass 1:119;
kirtle 2:256;
maiden 1:119, 119;
rainbow 1:119;
sea 6:750, 750;
spotted kirtle 2:256;
wild 3:315
pinnipeds 9:1246
Pinus 2:195, 3:272, 296, 346,

6:747, 748, 826, 7:837, 838,
841, 842, 876, 879, 884,
885, 895, 902;
aristata 6:734, 735, 7:868;
balfouricana 6:683;
banksiana 6:814, 7:903;
caribaea 7:938;
contorta var. latifolia 7:942;
flexilis 7:942;
halepensis 7:836;
mugo 7:868;
ponderosa 7:866, 942;
radiata 7:938;
sabiniana 6:730;
serotina 6:814;
strobus 7:841;
sylvestris 6:719, 7:841, 894,
903, 941
pioneer vegetation 6:817, 823,
7:841-2, 887
Piper 3:265, 272, 388
Piperaceae 3:386, 388, 389, 390
Piperales 3:378, 388-90
Piperanthera 3:390
piperidine 1:26, 2:227
piperine 1:26
pipe-rot 3:324
pipes 8:1030, 1089, 9:1128-9
Piptanthus 3:273, 4:502
Piptocalyx 3:384
Piqueria 3:273, 5:617
Pirie, Norman 6:752
Piriqueta 4:454
pisco 1:16
pisolites 9:1134
Pisonia 3:273, 4:419, 420
pistachio 2:245, 245, 3:273,
5:548
Pistacia 2:220, 3:273, 334, 5:548,
548;
lentiscus 7:898
Pistia 3:273, 5:657, 659, 659;
stratiotes 6:770
pistol plant 3:271
Pisum 2:261, 3:273, 4:499, 502
pita 2:144, 5:644
pitanga 2:137
Pitcairnia 3:273, 5:644, 644, 646
Pitcairnioideae 5:644
pitchblende see uraninite
pitcher plant 1:81, 82, 2:171, 240,
240, 3:272, 273, 308, 392,
4:404, 496, 6:772, 7:878,
878, 896, 903;
Californian 1:117, 117
pitchstone 8:1081
pith plant 1:11
Pithecanthropus erectus 9:1252
Pithecellobium 3:273, 4:499
Pithecoctenium 5:599
Pittosporaceae 4:488, 488-9,
5:564, 618, 7:897
Pittosporeae 4:488
Pittosporum 3:274, 4:488, 488,
489, 7:897
placentals 9:1205, 1245, 1247-53
placers 8:1074
placoderms 9:1163-4, 1232
placodonts 9:1236, 1237-8
plagioclase 8:979, 986, 996,
1080, 1083, 1090, 1096,
9:1124, 1125, 1126, 1127,
1129, 1137, 1140
Plagiorhegma 3:395, 396
plagioseres 6:823
Plagiothecium 3:274
Plains province 7:898
Planchonia 4:449
plane 3:274, 4:405, 406;
American 3:274, 330;
London 3:274, 274, 6:777;
Oriental 3:274;
see also Platanus
Planera 4:445, 446
planetesimal hypothesis 9:1266
Planitorae 5:563
plankton 3:274, 9:1134, 1135,
1198

planosols 6:805
plant ecology:
history of 6:689-91;
methods and concepts of 6:693-
735
plant explorations 6:680-8, 680-8
plant geography:
history of 6:688-9;
methods and concepts of 6:693-
735
plant nutrition:
and competition 6:820;
and soils 6:806-7
plant resources, future 7:935-6
plant sociology 6:727-30
Plantaginaceae 5:591, 602
Plantaginales 5:591, 602
Plantago 3:274, 5:591, 6:691, 723,
7:905;
coronopus 6:769, 7:887;
cretica 7:850;
lanceolata 7:928;
major 6:704, 794;
maritima 6:706, 750, 769,
7:889, 890
plantain 3:274, 5:591;
buck's horn 3:274;
common 3:274;
crowfoot 3:274;
edible 2:151, 236;
grass 3:274;
hoary 3:274;
narrow-leaved 3:274;
rattlesnake 2:163;
ribwort 3:274, 274, 7:928;
sea 3:274, 6:706, 750, 769;
stag's horn 7:887;
water 1:15;
wild 2:171;
see also Plantago
plantations, tree 7:842, 879-80,
936, 936, 938
plant-available water 6:804
plants in evolution 9:1163,
1214-9
Plasmodiophora 3:274
plasmolysis 6:799, see also drought
injury
Platanaceae 4:405-6
Platanthera 1:115
Platanus 3:274, 330, 4:405, 406,
6:744, 746;
acerifolia 6:777;
kerri 6:776;
occidentalis 6:776, 777;
orientalis 6:776, 777
plate margins 8:1032-3, 1062-3;
constructive 8:1033, 1059-61,
1063;
destructive (subduction zones)
8:997, 1004-5, 1005, 1006,
1007, 1008, 1031, 1033,
1034, 1091, 1093, 9:1127,
1138, 1140, 1154, 1162,
1163, 1180, 1187
plate tectonics 6:741-3, 741, 742,
8:972, 973, 989, 990, 997,
1001, 1002, 1003-8, 1005,
1006, 1020, 1023, 1029,
1031, 1035, 1055-6, 1059,
1062-3, 1105, 9:1130, 1138,
1149, 1152, 1158, 1163,
1174, 1205, 1208, 1263,
1269, 1275;
earthquakes and 8:1005, 1006,
1024, 1025-6, 1033, 1034,
1040;
paleomagnetic evidence for
8:993, 994, 1002, 1003-4;
paleontological evidence for
8:1001, 1002;
rift valleys and 8:1040-1;
vulcanicity and 8:1003, 1005,
1007, 1032-3, 1033, 1034;
see also continental drift, plate
margins, sea-floor spreading
plateaux 8:1012, 1013, 1034,
1035, 1041-3, 1042, 1043,
1047, 1057, 1064, 9:1126,
1128, 1181

platinum 8:979, 1110
Platonia 4:437
Platycarya 5:555, 6:747
Platycerium 2:240, 3:274, 6:721;
bifurcatum 6:687
Platycodinae 5:604
Platycodon 3:275, 5:604, 606
Platyspermatica 5:554
Platystemon 4:402, 402
Platytheca 5:564
playas 8:1047
Playfair, J. 9:1260, 1261, 1272
Plectranthus 3:275, 5:589
Pleioblastus 7:861
Pleione 3:275, 5:675
Pleiospilos 4:417
Pleistocene 6:738, 740, 742, 749,
9:1191, 1197, 1200
pleochroism 8:1099
Pleodendron 3:379
pleroma 3:336
plesiadapids 9:1249-50
plesiosaurs 9:1181, 1189, 1236,
1237
pleurisy root 1:43
Pleurophyllum 7:920;
hookeri 7:920
Pleurozium schreberi 7:884
Pliny 6:680, 7:952
Pliocene 6:738, 740, 742, 748,
9:1191, 1197-8, 1197, 1216
plow pan 6:805
plugs, volcanic 8:1030, 1032,
1057
plum 1:58, 2:151, 152, 3:275,
282, 4:491, 494;
American 2:151, 3:275;
cherry 2:151, 3:275, 282;
Chinese date 2:191;
coco 1:89;
damson 1:116, 2:164, 3:275,
282;
date 2:191;
European 2:164, 3:275, 282;
hog 3:322;
Jamaica 3:322;
Japanese 2:151, 3:275, 282;
Japanese date 2:191;
Java 2:137;
marmalade 2:219, 3:307;
ogeeche 2:243;
Oriental 3:275;
pigeon 1:96;
red 3:322;
Spanish 3:322;
Victoria 3:275
plum brandy 3:275
plum yew 1:81;
Chinese 1:81;
Japanese 1:81
Plumbaginaceae 4:428-9, 429,
525, 5:558
Plumbaginales 4:428-9
Plumbago 3:275, 4:429, 429
plume flower 2:191
plume poppy 4:403
plumed diaspores 6:817
Plumeria 3:275, 5:574, 575
Plumerioideae 5:575
plush plant 2:192
Pluto 8:971
plutonic rock see igneous rocks
Plutonism 9:1147
plutons 8:1030, 1031
Pluviilignosa formation-type 7:834
pneumatophores 7:891, 891
Poa 3:275, 5:636, 638, 6:723,
816, 7:854, 863, 904, 905;
flabellata 6:723, 7:861, 862;
himalensis 7:861;
pratensis 7:861;
trivialis 7:861;
sispitosa 7:861
Poaceae 5:635
poached egg flower 2:207, 5:560
Poales 5:635-40
pocket handkerchief tree 1:118,
118
Podalyrieae 4:502

Podandrogyne 4:468
podgrass, shore 3:343
Podocarpaceae 6:743
Podocarpus 3:276, 6:744, 7:837,
904
podocarpus:
fern 3:276;
weeping 3:276
podococoid palms 5:654
Podophyllaceae 3:396, 399
Podophylloideae 3:396
Podophyllum 2:188, 3:276, 3:395,
396
Podostemaceae 4:502-3, 503,
5:602, 7:896
Podostemales 4:502-3
Podranea 3:334, 4:503, 503
podsols 6:807, 808
podzol 9:1140, 1141
Poeae 5:638
Pogostemon 3:276, 5:589
pohutukawa 2:228
Poinciana 1:118, 4:502
poinciana:
dwarf 1:69;
royal 1:118;
yellow 1:118
Poinsettia 2:138
poinsettia 2:138, 138, 3:276, 276,
4:535, 537, 6:768;
Japanese 2:263
point quadrats 6:714, 716
poison berry 3:317
poison bulb, Asiatic 1:109
poison ivy 3:276, 276, 294,
5:547, 7:949;
oakleaf 3:276, 294
poison nut, curare 1:26, 111,
3:326
poisons:
in food 7:945;
in inland waters 7:944;
in weeds 7:949;
see also phytotoxins, toxins
poke, Indian 2:210, 226, 3:353
pokeberry 3:270
pokeweed 3:270, 4:421, 422;
Virginia 3:270
Polakowskia 4:465
Polanisia 5:549
polar deserts 7:845, 902
polar distributions 7:909-10, 910
polar plant 3:315
polar wandering 8:994
Polemoniaceae 4:455, 5:560, 580,
582, 583, 584, 586, 591
Polemoniales 5:577-86, 602
Polemonieae 5:583
Polemonium 3:276, 5:583
Polianthes 3:277
poljes 8:1044, 1045
pollen 9:1149
pollen analysis 6:734, 9:1146,
1207-8;
and early agriculture 7:928-9;
of Quaternary vegetation 6:748,
748
pollen incompatibility 6:780-1,
781
pollination:
artificial 7:934;
by bats 6:786;
by insects 6:766, 767, 773, 777,
780, 7:854, 905;
and reproductive isolation 6:780
pollucite 8:1109
pollution 7:941-7, 942-6
Polyalthia 3:381
polyanthus 3:277
Polycarpeae 4:419
Polycarpon 4:419
polychores 7:895
polyclimaxes 6:714
Polygala 3:277, 5:565, 566, 566
polygala, fringed 3:277
Polygalaceae 4:533, 5:564, 565-6,
566, 567
Polygalales 5:554, 563-7
Polygaleae 5:566

Polygenes 7:925
Polygonaceae 3:389, **4:427-8**, *428*, 429
Polygonales **4:427-8**
Polygonatum **3:277**, 6:723
Polygonum **3:277**, 389, 4:427, 428, *428*, 6:751, 816, 7:949;
  amphibium 6:826, 7:947;
  convolvulus 6:724;
  viviparum 7:854
polygonum, Japanese 3:277
polyhalite **8:1096**
Polylepis 6:721
Polymnia 5:617
polymorphism 8:1081, 1084, 1088, 1093, 1099
Polynesian Pacific region 7:*897*, 897
polyploidy and rapid speciation 6:776
Polypodium **3:277**;
  pellucidum 6:*823*
polypody 2:141;
  European 3:278;
  golden 3:278;
  rock 3:278;
  wall 3:278
Polypompholyx 5:603
Polyporus **3:278**
Polyscias 5:568
Polysiphonia **3:278**
Polystachya **3:278**, 5:675
Polystichum **3:278**
polytopy **7:907-8**
Polytrichum **3:278**, 7:854;
  commune 6:722
Pomaderris **3:278**, 4:538
pombe 1:16
pomegranate 2:151, *153*, **3:278**, *278*, 284, 4:506, 512;
  dwarf 3:278
pomelo 1:91, 2:151, 164, **3:278**, 314, 332
Pomoideae 4:491, 494
pompom **3:278**
Poncirus **3:279**, 5:552, 554
pondweed **3:279**, 5:624, 625;
  broad-leaved 6:826;
  Cape 1:37;
  curled 7:947;
  horned 3:361;
  see also Potamogeton
pongids 9:1250
Pontederia **3:279**, 5:659, *660*, 660, 661
Pontederiaceae **5:659-61**, *660*
Pontic province 7:898
Pooideae 5:638, 640
poor man's weather glass 1:28
popinac 1:7;
  white 2:149
poplar 2:145, **3:279**, 4:467, *467*, 468, 6:750;
  balsam 3:279, 341;
  black 3:279, 341;
  Carolina 3:279;
  Chinese necklace 3:279;
  cottonwood 6:826;
  gray 3:279;
  Lombardy 3:279;
  silver-leaved 3:279;
  Western 3:279;
  white 3:279, 341;
  yellow 3:346
popolo, yellow 3:317
poppy 2:147, **3:279**, 4:402, 403, 6:750;
  Alpine 3:*279*;
  Arctic 2:259;
  blue 2:221;
  bush 1:119;
  California tree **3:296**;
  California 2:135, 3:*279*, 7:*951*;
  common 2:259, *259*;
  corn 2:259, *259*;
  crested 1:40;
  Flanders 2:259, *259*;
  Hawaiian 3:279;

Himalayan **2:221**, *221*;
  horned 2:162;
  Iceland 2:259;
  Mexican 3:279;
  opium 1:26, 2:227, **252**, 259;
  Oriental 2:259;
  plume 2:214;
  prickly Mexican 1:40;
  red horned 2:162;
  sea 2:162;
  Tibetan 2:221;
  tulip 2:259;
  Welsh 2:221;
  yellow Chinese 2:221;
  yellow horned 2:162;
  see also Papaver
population pressure and domestication 7:927
Populus 1:44, **3:279**, 4:467, *467*, 468, 6:750;
  deltoides 6:826
Poraqueiba 4:530, 531
pore space in soil 6:*803-4*, 804-5
porosity **8:1070**, 9:1131
Porphyra **3:199**, 3:279, 289;
  umbilicalis 7:945
porphyroblasts 8:1099, 9:1137, *1139*
porphyry deposits 8:1073, 1074, 1106, 1108
Portugal laurel 4:494
Portulaca **3:279**, 4:424, *425*, 425
portulaca, kitchen garden 3:279
Portulacaceae **4:415**, **424-5**, *425*, 426, 504
Portulacaria 4:425
Posidonia **3:279**, 5:626, 627, 7:885
posidonia fiber 3:279
Posidoniaceae 5:625, **626-7**
Poskea 5:595, 595
possum apple 1:121
possum wood 1:121
Post, Hampus von 6:689
postclimaxes 6:714
Potaliaceae 5:572
Potalieae 5:572
Potamogeton **3:279**, 5:624, 625, 6:725, 816, 826, *827*;
  crispus 7:947;
  densus 7:944;
  natans 6:724, 826, 7:944, 945;
  pectinatus 7:944
Potamogetonaceae 5:623, **624-5**, 626, 627
potassium 8:972, 973, 974, 979, 988, 996, 997, 1007, 1074, 1090, 1091, **1104**, 1109, 1121, 9:*1122*, 1142, 1143, 1149, 1152, 1270;
  in plant nutrition 6:*806-7*
potassium-argon dating 8:1091, 9:1143, 1199
potato **3:279**, *280*, 298, *298*, 318, 328, 5:579, 6:*778*, 789, *790-1*, 7:*897*, 926, 931, 932, 933;
  air 3:328;
  chosui 2:201;
  duck 3:302;
  Hausa 1:98, 3:275, 350;
  Irish 3:318;
  kaffir 3:275, 350;
  prairie 3:283;
  Sudan 1:98;
  swan 3:302;
  sweet 2:186, *186*, 3:298, 299, *299*, *330*, *330*;
  telingo 1:27;
  Tennessee sweet 2:222;
  white 3:318
potato blight 3:270, *270*, 7:933
potato creeper, giant 3:317
potato tree, Chilean 3:318
Potentilla **3:280**, 325, 4:*464*, 494;
  anserina 6:723, 774;
  glandulosa ssp. *tyica* 6:704
Potentilleae 4:494
Poterium 1:7, 3:306, 4:491, 494

potholes 8:1011, 1043
Pothomorphe 3:388
pottery tree 4:494
poui 5:600;
  pink 3:331;
  yellow 3:331
Pouteria 2:128, 151, 3:307
powderpuff, red 1:71
Powell, J. 9:1260, 1268, **1272**
Praecitrullus 4:467
prairie flower 2:154
prairie rocket 2:134
prairies 7:832, 859, **860**;
  grasses of 7:863;
  overgrazing of 7:940
prase 8:1087
prasinites 9:1137
Pratia 5:604, 606
prayer plant 2:219
prebiotic soup 6:*752*, 752, 753, 756
Pre-Boreal phase 6:*750*, 750
Precambrian 6:*738-9*, 756, **9:1149-52**, *1150*, *1151*, *1152*, 1157, 1158, 1201, 1220, 1224, 1230;
  fossils 9:*1152*;
  geography 9:*1150*;
  ice ages in 8:1020, 9:1153, 1155, 1198;
  ironstones 8:*1074*, 1087, 1092, 1105, 9:*1134-5*, 1150, 1151;
  rocks 8:980, 9:1142, 1146, *1151*, *1152*, 1154
precipitation/evaporation ratio and mountain vegetation 6:866
prediction, ecological 6:*689-90*
predictive value 6:695
predictivity 6:695
preferential species 6:729
Premna 5:587
Prenanthes 5:617
presence, phytocoenal 6:727
preservation:
  of crop collections 7:*958-9*;
  of land races 7:957;
  of plant remains 6:*731-3*, *732*, *733*, 7:928;
  see also fossilization
pressure waves *see* seismic waves
preventive weed control **7:949**
Prichardia 7:908
prickly ash 1:39
prickly elder 1:39
prickly pear 2:242, 254, 4:415, *see also Opuntia*
pretty-face 3:344
pride of Barbados 1:69
pride of India 2:194, 224
pride-of-the-peak 2:168
Primary rocks 9:1259
primary succession 6:823
primates 9:1192, **1249-50**
primitive cultivars 7:*927*, *956-7*, **956-7**
primitive mammals **9:1245**
primrose **3:280**, 4:484, 6:769, *781*, 7:838;
  baby 3:280;
  common 3:277;
  common evening 2:248;
  drumstick 3:280;
  English 3:*281*;
  evening 2:247, 6:762, 799;
  fairy 3:280;
  German 3:280;
  Japanese 3:280;
  poison 3:280;
  water 6:818
Primula 1:47, **3:277**, 280, 4:484, *484*, 6:685, 687, 723;
  vulgaris 6:769, *781*
Primulaceae **4:429**, **484**, *484*, 486
Primulales 4:432, **484-6**
Primuleae 4:484
Prince Albert yew 3:308
princess flower 3:336
princess tree 2:193, 261

principal components analysis 6:730
Pringelia 7:920
Pringlea 4:470
Pringleeae 4:470
Prionium **3:281**, 5:640, *641*, 641
Prionoteae 4:478
Prionotes 4:478
priority in publication of names **6:699**
Pripet marshes 7:885
prisere 6:823
Priva 5:587
privet 2:148, *206*, **3:281**, 5:577, 6:825;
  Chinese 3:281;
  common 3:281;
  glossy 3:281;
  golden 3:281;
  ibota 3:281;
  Japanese 3:281;
  mock 3:268;
  Nepal 3:281;
  swamp 2:148;
  wax-leaf 3:281
Proboscidea 5:*602*, 602
procolophonids 9:*1204*, 1236
Proconsul 9:*1250*, 1271
Procrideae 4:448
Pronaya 4:489
prophase in meiosis 6:*763*
prophet flower 1:41
Propliopithecus 9:1250
prop-roots 7:891
prosauropods 9:1241
Proserpinaca 4:505
prosimians 9:1192, 1195, 1249
proso 2:230, 5:638, 640
Prosopanche 4:528
Prosopis **3:281**, 4:499, 502, 6:721
prostrate grasses 7:855
Prostanthera **3:281**, 7:874
Protea **3:281**, 4:519, 520
protea:
  giant 3:281;
  king 3:281;
  peach 3:281
Proteaceae **4:519-20**, *520*, 6:744, 7:837, 896, 897, 919, 964
Proteales **4:518-20**
proteinoids 6:*753-4*, *756*, *see also* protocells 6:758
Proteoideae 4:520
proterochampsids 9:1239
Proterosuchus 9:1239
proterotheres 9:1205
Proterozoic 6:*738*, 756, 9:1150, **1151-2**
Protieae 5:547
Protium 2:129, 5:546, 547, *547*
proto-Atlantic 9:1154, **1158**, 1159, 1160, 1162
protocells 6:756, 757, 758, *see also* microspheres 6:753, *756*
protolife 6:*752-5*, *752-6*, **758**
Protosuchus 9:1243
proustite 8:1108
provinces:
  floristic 7:894, **898**;
  Laurasian 6:*741*, 743;
  North American 7:*898*
prunasin as chemical defense 6:823
prune **3:282**
Prunella 1:17, **3:282**, 4:490
Prunoideae 4:491, 494
Prunophora **3:282**
Prunus 1:17, 38, 60, 86, **116**, 2:164, 198, 219, 239, 262, **3:275**, **282**, 316, 324, 4:491, 494, *494*, 6:685
psammites 9:1136
Psammogeton 5:571
psammosere 6:*825*, **825-6**
Pseudananas 5:644
Pseudobaeckera 4:491
Pseudobeaconia 9:1206

pseudocopulation 6:767, 773, 780
Pseudolarix 3:282
Pseudolmedia 4:447
Pseudoludovia 5:654
Pseudomonas 3:282
pseudomorphs 6:758, 9:1179
Pseudophoenix 5:653, 654
Pseudosmilax 5:670
Pseudosolaneae 5:593
pseudotachylites 9:1139
Pseudotsuga 1:123;
    menziesii 6:814, 7:837, 866, 867, 942
Pseudowintera 1:125, 3:378
Pseudowolffia 5:657
Psidium 3:282, 4:512
psilocin 3:283
Psilocybe 3:282
psilocybin 3:283
psilomelane 8:1105
psilophytes 1:94;
    in evolution 6:739
Psilophyton 6:739, 766
psilopsids 9:1163, 1216
Psilotum 1:94, 95
Psittacanthus 2:231
Psophocarpus 1:44, 3:283
Psoralea 3:283
Psorospermum 4:437
Psychotria 1:26, 2:186
Psylliostachys 2:207
Ptaeroxylon 2:215, 3:283
Ptelea 3:283, 343, 5:552, 554
Pteranodon 9:1189, 1239
Pteridium 1:62, 2:126, 3:283, 6:825;
    aquilinium 6:801
Pteridophyllaceae 4:402
Pteridophyllum 4:402, 403, 404
pteridophytes in evolution 6:739
pteridosperms in evolution 6:739
Pteris 3:283, 6:825
Pterisanthes 4:539
Pterocactus 4:413
Pterocarpus 2:193, 3:283, 289
Pterocarya 3:283, 5:555
Pteroceltis 4:445
Pterocephalus 5:611, 612, 612
Pterocladia 3:289
Pterodactylus 9:1239
pterophytes 9:1216, 1217, 1218,
    see also ferns
pterosaurs 9:1181, 1189, 1236,
    1239
Pterospermum 4:442
Ptilotus 4:420
publication of names 6:699
Puccinella 7:861, 901;
    maritima 7:889, 921
Puccinia 3:283
Puccinia recondita resistance 7:958
puccoon 2:209;
    red 3:306
Pueraria 2:149
puffball 2:157, 213, 3:284;
    giant 2:156
Pulmonaria 3:284, 5:586
pulp for paper 7:935, 935-6, 938
pulque 1:13, 16, 5:666
Pulsatilla 3:284, 396, 399;
    vulgaris 6:786
pummelo 1:91, 2:151, 164, 3:278,
    314, 332
'pump-action' of glaciers 7:920
pumpkin 1:111, 2:222, 3:284,
    4:465, 7:925;
    American 2:222;
    autumn 2:222;
    Brazilian 2:222;
    Canada 2:222;
    cushaw 2:222, 3:284;
    fetid wild 2:222;
    summer 2:222;
    wild 2:222;
    winter 2:222
puna (puno) 7:868
puncture vine 6:816
Punica 3:278, 284, 4:512

Punicaceae 4:506, 507, 512
Purdiaea 4:474, 475
Purdom, William 6:686
Purdy, Carl 6:683
Purgatorius 9:1249
purging nut 4:537
purple arrowroot 5:648, 649
purple loosestrife 4:507
purslane 4:425;
    rock 1:70;
    sea 1:46, 2:168, 6:711
Puschkinia 3:284, 5:664
pussy-ears 2:192
putty 2:207
Puya 3:285, 5:644, 6:720
P-waves *see* seismic waves
Pycnanthus 3:382
Pycnarrhena 3:401
Pygaster 9:1185
Pyracantha 3:285, 4:494
Pyramidotorae 5:563
pyrargyrite 8:1108, 1109
Pyrenacantha 4:531, 531
Pyrenees 9:1193
pyrethrin 3:285
Pyrethrum 3:285
pyrethrum 3:284, 285, 5:615,
    618, 7:946;
    Dalmatian 3:285;
    garden 1:89
pyrite (fool's gold) 8:992, 1021,
    1074, 1078, 1081, 1082,
    1084, 1087, 1091, 1093,
    1094, 1096, 1104, 1105,
    9:1131
pyroclastic rocks 8:1034, 9:1122
Pyrola 3:285, 4:480, 480, 7:903
Pyrolaceae 4:477, 479-80, 480
Pyroloideae 4:477
pyrolusite 8:1105
pyrope 8:1090, 1091
Pyrostegia 3:285, 5:600
pyroxenes 8:973, 974, 979, 980,
    986, 989, 996, 1084, 1085,
    1088, 1089, 1092, 1097,
    9:1124, 1125, 1126, 1127,
    1128, 1129, 1136, 1137,
    1139, 1140
pyroxenoids 8:1098
pyrrhotite 8:1097, 1105
Pyrrorhiza 5:668
Pyrus 2:262, 3:285, 4:494
Pythium 3:285
Pyxidanthera 4:480, 481

qat 1:58, 2:192
quack-grass 1:13, 14
quadrats 6:714, 715, 716
quaking grass:
    common 1:63;
    small 1:66
Qualea 5:564, 565
quality in crops 7:932, 949
quamash 1:72
quanta of light energy 6:792
quarrying and pollution 7:944,
    946
quartz 8:973, 1009, 1021, 1023,
    1031, 1080, 1082, 1083,
    1084, 1085, 1086, 1087,
    1088, 1089, 1091, 1094,
    1097, 1097-8, 1104, 9:1122,
    1124, 1125, 1126, 1127,
    1130, 1131, 1132, 1136,
    1137, 1138, 1139, 1140,
    1151
quartz sandstones *see* sandstones
quartzites 8:1021, 1068, 1097,
    9:1136, 1137
quass 1:16
Quassia 3:286, 5:549, 549
quassia 3:286

quassia root 3:286
Quaternary 6:738-9, 740, 742,
    748-51, 8:1001, 9:1149,
    1191, 1198-200;
    climate 9:1198, 1199;
    fauna 9:1199-200;
    flora 9:1198, 1199;
    geography 9:1198;
    see also ice ages
quebracho 2:126, 3:286, 5:548;
    red 3:286
Queen Anne's lace 1:36
queen of the meadow 2:142
queen of the night 2:227, 3:312
queen of the prairie 2:142
Queensland arrowroot 5:648, 649
Queensland nut 2:245
Quercoideae 4:410
Quercophyllum 6:765
Quercus 1:105, 2:246, 4:410, 410,
    527, 6:711, 727, 745, 747,
    748, 765, 826, 826, 7:837,
    838, 841, 843, 866, 884;
    alba 6:791;
    engelmannii 7:836;
    falcata 6:823;
    ilex 6:719, 7:836;
    robur 6:826, 7:896
quetchalalatl 5:544
Quetzalcoatlus 9:1239
Quiabentia 4:413
quickbeam 3:319
quickthorn 6:169
quihuicha 1:27, 2:163
Quiina 4:438
Quiinaceae 4:438
Quillaja 3:286, 4:494
quillwort 1:94;
    sand 1:94, 95
quince 2:151, 152, 262, 3:286,
    4:494;
    Bengal 1:11;
    common 1:84, 112, 3:286;
    flowering 1:84, 3:286, 286;
    Japanese 1:84, 84;
    Maules 1:84
Quinchamalium 4:521, 521
quinidine 2:227
quinine 1:26, 2:227, 3:286,
    5:607, 608, 609, 7:925
quinoa 1:86, 4:423
quinones 1:58
Quisqualis 3:286, 4:514, 515, 516

rabbit ears 2:254
rabbits and grassland 6:690,
    7:920, 938, 940
races:
    land 7:956-7;
    local *see* ecotypes
radiation:
    adaptive 6:773-4, 774, 7:908;
    atomic 7:947;
    solar 6:785, 787, 792-3, 800,
    7:866, 869
Radiola 5:557
radiolaria 8:1007, 1061, 9:1135,
    1163, 1185, 1189, 1190,
    1191, 1219, 1220
radiolarites 9:1220
radiometric dating (radioisotope
    dating) 6:735, 9:1142-3,
    1146, 1149, 1152
radish 1:64, 65, 3:286, 287, 350,
    4:472, 6:680, 780, 781,
    7:934;
    Chinese 3:286;
    Italian 3:286;
    wild 3:288;
    winter 3:350
radium 8:1100, 1111
radon 8:1073

raffia 2:145, 145, 3:286, 288,
    5:651, 654, 7:896
raffia palm 5:651
Rafflesia 3:286, 4:527, 527, 528,
    7:834;
    arnoldii 6:724
Rafflesiaceae 4:527, 527, 7:896
Rafflesiales 4:527-8
Rafflesieae 4:528
ragged cup 3:315
ragged robin 2:212, 213
ragi 1:129
ragweed 1:27, 5:618
ragwort 1:26, 3:313, 313;
    common 3:312;
    Oxford 3:313, 7:951-2;
    purple 3:313;
    see also Senecio
railroad road 2:186
rain ballast dispersal 6:818
rain forests:
    montane (cloud) 7:866-7, 867;
    temperate 7:832-3, 836, 837,
    837-8;
    tropical 6:692, 709, 712, 7:832-
    3, 834, 834-5, 878, *see also*
    mangrove swamp;
    Valdivian 7:837;
    see also forest destruction
rain tree 3:306
rainborne solubles 7:943-4
rain-green shrubs 6:721
rain-green trees 6:719
rain-shadow deserts 7:845
rain-splash dispersal 6:818, 818
rainwater 8:1009, 1010-1, 1021,
    1043, 1044, 1074, 1087,
    9:1135, *see also* meteoric water
raised beaches 9:1200
raised bogs 7:877, 878, 878, 879,
    903
raisin 2:236, 3:287, 4:538, 539;
    Malaga 3:287;
    muscatel 3:287;
    wild 3:354
Rajania 5:670
raki 1:16, 31
rakkyo 1:17
Ramapithecus 9:1250
rambutan 2:151, 153, 3:287,
    5:543, 544
Ramelina 2:205
ramie 1:60, 2:145, 145, 7:936
ramie fibre 4:447, 448, 449
ramin 3:341
Ramonda 3:287, 5:596, 596, 598
rampion 1:54, 3:270, 287, 5:604,
    606;
    spiked 3:270
ram's horn 2:220
ramsons 2:155
Ranales 3:399
Ranalisma 5:620
rand plant 3:355
Randia 3:287, 5:609
Randonia 4:473
Rangoon creeper 3:286
rank (of coals) 8:1117-8
Ranunculaceae 3:395, 396-9,
    396, 399, 400, 4:405, 431,
    494, 5:620
Ranunculales 3:395-401, 4:530,
    5:544, 654
Ranunculeae 3:399
Ranunculoideae 3:399
Ranunculus 1:68, 3:287, 3:396,
    399, 399, 6:680, 691, 826,
    7:905;
    alpestris 6:698;
    aquatilis 6:764, 7:944;
    biternatus 7:908;
    enysii 6:779;
    ficaria 6:723, 816;
    flammula 7:876, 880, 885;
    insignis 6:776, 779;
    lyalii 7:915;
    nivalis 7:854, 854;
    nivicola 6:776;

penicillatus 6:725;
repens 7:950;
verticillata 6:776
ranunculus, garden 3:287
Raoulia 3:288, 6:722, 5:617;
eximia 7:919
Rapanea 4:486
Rapatea 5:628, 628
Rapateaceae 5:628, 628-9, 632
Rapateoideae 5:629
rape 1:64, 2:149, 236, 250,
3:288, 4:472;
British 3:288;
Continental 3:288;
Indian 1:64, 3:288;
oilseed 1:64, 65;
swede 3:330;
turnip 1:64, 3:288;
Raphanobrassica 7:934
Raphanus 3:286, 288, 350, 4:470,
see also radish
Raphia 3:271, 286, 288, 5:651,
653, 653, 654, 7:896
Raphiolepis 4:494
rapid speciation 6:776-7
Rapistrum 4:470
rare earth elements 8:979, 1104-
5, 1111, 1121, 9:1126
rasamala 3:288, 4:407
rasamala resin 3:288
Raspalia 4:491
raspberry 2:151, 152, 3:288, 289,
4:491, 494;
American red 2:151, 3:288,
300;
Arctic 3:289;
black 2:151, 3:288, 300;
European red 2:210, 3:288,
300;
flowering 3:300;
purple 3:288;
purple flowering 3:300;
wine 3:358
rati 1:6
Ratibida 5:617
rattan 1:115, 115, 3:289
rattan cane 5:653, 654
rattan palm 1:70
rattle, yellow 3:290, 343
rattle bell 1:109
rattle box 1:109
rattle weed 1:52
rattlesnake-master 2:134
rauli 3:341
Raunkiaer, Christen 6:717, 719,
725, 7:966
Rauvolfia 3:289, 5:574, 575
Rauwolf, Leonhardt 6:680
Ravenala 3:289, 5:647
Ravenia 5:554
Ravensara 3:388
raw table (sampling) 6:727
real community 6:709
realgar 8:1098, 1107
realms, floristic 7:894, 895-6, 898
Reaumuria 4:459, 459
Reaumurieae 4:459
Rebutia 4:415
Recent rocks 9:1259
reclamation of salt marsh 7:883,
885, 890
recombination of genes 6:761,
763, 764
red algae 3:289
red beefwood 4:413
red bud 1:82
red currant 4:498
red elf cup fungus 3:266
red gum 4:407
red hot poker 2:194
red ink plant 4:422
red iron tree 4:434
red lady ultisol 6:809
red pepper 3:289, 5:579
red robin 2:161
red root 2:209
red tide 1:19, 3:289
red valerian 5:610

redbark 3:286
redgram 2:201
redoul 5:550
red-top 1:14;
Western 1:14
redwood 3:289, 313, 341;
Andaman 3:283, 289;
Brazil 1:66;
coast 3:313;
dawn 2:228, 3:289, 6:746,
7:914, 914;
giant 3:289, 7:837, 914;
Sierra 3:289, 313;
West Indian 3:289;
see also Sequoia
reed 3:289, 5:635, 638, 642;
common 3:269;
giant 1:43;
narrow small 3:290;
paper 1:113;
purple small 3:290;
small wood 3:290;
Spanish 1:43;
totora 3:310;
see also Phragmites
reed fen 7:881
reed grass 1:43, 7:862, 881, 885
reedmace:
great 3:347;
lesser 1:68;
small 3:347
reedmace bulrush 5:643
reedswamp 6:826, 7:883, 884
reef thatches 3:335
reefs 8:1056, 1064, 9:1132, 1134,
1215, 1221, 1259, 1267
Reevesia 4:442, 443
refugia 7:910, 911
regions, floristic 7:894, 896-7,
897, 898
regosols 6:810
reindeer moss 1:91
Reinwardtia 5:557, 557, 558
Reiter, H. 6:719
relative dating 6:734-5
relative evolutionary age 7:914
relevés 6:727, 728
relicts 7:912, 912, 913, 914
rendzinas 6:810
replication of genes 6:761
reproduction:
asexual 6:777-8;
and isolation 6:778, 780-1,
780-1;
sexual 6:753;
of tundra plants 7:854;
vegetative 6:777, 778, 816
reptiles 9:1166, 1205, 1206,
1236-44, 1236, 1240;
Carboniferous 9:1170, 1173,
1235;
Permian 9:1176, 1209;
Triassic 9:1178, 1238;
Jurassic 9:1181, 1187;
Cretaceous 9:1188, 1189, 1191
rescinnamine 5:575
rescue grass 1:66
Reseda 2:126, 229, 3:295, 4:472,
473
Resedaceae 4:403, 451, 469, 472,
473
Resedeae 4:472
reserpine 2:227, 5:575
resins 3:290
resistance:
to diseases 7:932, 933, 934,
935, 957, 958;
to herbicides 7:950
resources:
critical 6:820;
environmental 6:784, 7:953;
genetic 7:956-7, 956-61;
plant 7:935-6
restharrow 2:252, 6:825;
spiny 2:252
Restio 5:634, 634
Restionaceae 5:633-4, 634, 641,
6:773, 7:896, 897

Restionales 5:632-4
restoration of forests 7:938
restricted distributions 7:912-21
resurrection plant 3:290, 290
retama 2:260
retsina 1:58
Reussia 5:659, 660, 661
Reynosia 2:187
Rhabdodendroideae 5:554
Rhabdodendron 5:554
Rhabdothamnus 5:596
Rhacomitrium 3:290
Rhacopteris 6:743
Rhamnaceae 4:519, 537-8, 538,
539
Rhamnales 4:537-40, 5:571
Rhamnidium 2:187
Rhamnus 1:67, 77, 4:537-8;
catharticus 4:769
rhamphorhynchoids 9:1239
Rhaphiolepis 3:290
Rhaptopetalum 4:439
rheotropic mire 7:878, 880-3, see
also fen
Rheum 3:290, 293, 4:428, 6:723,
7:941
rheumatic fever 1:51
Rhinanthoideae 5:593, 595
Rhinanthus 3:290, 5:593, 595,
595
rhinoceroses 9:1247-8
rhipidistians 9:1232, 1235
Rhipogonum 5:670
Rhipsalidopsis 3:290
Rhipsalis 3:290, 4:413, 415, 415
Rhizanthes 4:528
Rhizobium 1:59, 3:290, 4:499,
6:807
Rhizocarpon 2:205;
geographicum 6:724
rhizome herbs 6:723
rhizome of iris 6:778
Rhizophora 2:218, 3:290, 4:508,
7:891
Rhizophoraceae 7:896, 4:440,
507-8, 508
Rhizopus 3:290
Rhodanthe 2:172
Rhodiola 3:312
rhodium 8:1110
rhodochrosite 8:1098, 1105
Rhododendroideae 4:477
Rhododendron 1:48, 3:290, 4:474,
475, 477, 477, 6:678, 681,
683, 685, 687, 7:838;
catawbiense 6:683;
formosum 6:686;
speciosum 6:683
rhododendron 3:293;
tree 3:290
Rhodoleia 4:406, 407
Rhodoleioideae 4:407
rhodonite 8:1097, 1098, 1105
Rhodotypos 3:293, 4:494
Rhodymenia 1:19, 3:289;
palmata 6:829
Rhoeadales 4:403
Rhoeo 3:293, 5:629, 631, 631
Rhoicissus 3:293
Rhoideae 5:548
Rhoiptelea 5:555
Rhoipteleaceae 5:555
Rhopalocarpaceae 4:445
Rhopalocarpus 4:445
rhourds 8:1046
rhubarb 3:293, 2:227, 228, 3:350,
351, 4:427, 428;
bog 3:266;
Chile 2:167;
China 3:293;
currant 3:293;
garden 3:290, 293, 350;
medicinal 3:290, 293;
Sikkim 3:290;
see also Rheum
rhubarb-herbs 6:723
Rhus 2:195, 3:276, 293, 5:544,
547, 548, 548;

radicans 7:949
rhynchocephalians 9:1238
Rhynchoglossum 5:596
Rhyncholacis 4:503
Rhynchospora 3:312, 5:643, 7:876
Rhynchosporoideae 5:643
Rhynchotheca 5:559
Rhynia 6:739, 739
Rhyniophytales 9:1216
rhyodacites 9:1126, 1127
rhyolite 8:1057, 1058, 1089,
9:1123, 1126, 1127, 1180
Rhytidophyllum 5:596
Rhytisma 3:294
rias 8:1056
Ribes 1:112, 2:163, 3:294, 4:497,
498
Ribesoideae 4:497
Riccia 3:294;
fluitans 6:725
rice 1:58, 83, 83, 105, 2:256,
257, 3:294, 295, 328, 5:635,
636, 640, 7:863, 931, 933,
934, 950, 957;
African 1:83, 3:294;
annual wild 3:363;
dee-gee-woo-gen 7:934;
Indian 3:363;
wild 3:363, 7:885
rice paper 5:568
rice spirit 1:41
rice tree, Formosa 2:139
riceflowers 3:272
rice-grass 7:862
Richardia 3:361
Richea 4:478, 478
Richter, C. 9:1268
Richter magnitude see earthquakes
Ricineae 4:537
ricinine 1:26
Ricinodendron 4:537
Ricinus 1:78, 3:295, 4:535, 537
Rickettsia 1:51
riebeckite 8:1084, 1085, 1089,
1098
rift valleys 8:1040-1, 1042, 1043,
1062;
East African (Great) 8:1003,
1023, 1040, 1041, 9:1126;
Rhinegraben 8:1023, 1040
Rigidella 5:662
Rindera 5:586
Ring of Fire 8:1036, 9:1127
Rinorea 4:450, 451
ripple drift 8:1016-7, 1017
ripple marks 9:1129, 1134, 1136
ripples 8:1062, 9:1213
Riss ice advance 6:749
river oak 4:412, 413
river tea tree 2:221
river valleys 8:1037-40, 1038,
1039, 1056, 9:1267
Rivina 1:60, 3:295, 4:421, 422
Rivineae 4:421, 422
Rivularia 1:51
roads and plant-life 7:936, 937
Robinia 2:209, 3:295, 4:499
robustic acid 2:164
Roccella 2:126, 205
Rochea 3:295, 4:495
Rochefortia 5:583
roches moutonnées 8:1012, 1048
Rock, Joseph 6:686
rock cress 1:38, 4:472;
hairy 1:39
rock crystal 8:1097, 1097-8
rock jasmine 1:29
rock nettle 4:464
rock purslane 1:70
rock salt see halite
rock surfaces, succession on 6:825
rockberry 2:130
Rockefeller Foundation and dwarf
wheats 7:934
rocket 2:174, 3:295, 4:472;
American sea 1:69;
dame's 3:295;
dyer's 2:229, 3:295;

garden 3:295;
prairie 2:134, 3:295;
sea 1:69, 70, 7:887, 920;
sweet 2:173, 3:295;
wall 2:174;
yellow 3:295
rock-rose 1:90, 91, 2:171, 171,
4:458;
hoary 7:912;
white 2:171;
see also desert roses
rocks 8:1081, 9:1122-41, 1259;
oldest known terrestrial 8:972,
9:1146, 1149, 1202;
see also igneous rocks,
metamorphic rocks,
sedimentary rocks
Rocky Mountains 8:1041, 9:1155,
1166, 1171, 1175, 1186,
1190
rod, silver 1:45
rodents 9:1195, 1198, 1249
Rodgersia 3:296, 4:497
Roella 5:604, 7:874
Roezl, Benedict 6:683
roman candle 3:361
Romneya 3:296
Romulea 3:296, 5:662
Rondeletia 3:296, 5:609
root cells 6:795
root crops and early agriculture
7:925, 928
root parasites and saprophytes
6:724
root rot of peas 7:957
rooted frequency 6:716
Roquefort cheese 3:264
Roridula 4:490
Roridulaceae 4:490
Rorippa 2:238, 3:296, 4:470
Rosa 1:46, 3:296, 4:491, 494,
494;
banksiae 6:684
rosa de montaña 4:428
Rosaceae 4:432, 491-4, 494, 498,
502
Rosales 3:393, 4:405, 407, 487-
99, 503, 533, 5:571, 592
Roscoea 3:296, 5:648
rose 3:296, 296, 4:491, 494,
6:680, 7:945;
brier 3:296;
cabbage 1:46, 2:136;
California 1:72;
Champney 3:296;
China 3:296;
Christmas 1:88, 2:227;
damask 1:46, 2:136, 3:296;
dog 3:296, 296;
Egyptian 3:309;
floribunda 3:296;
French 1:46;
guelder 3:354;
hoary rock 7:912;
hybrid tea 3:296;
Japanese 3:296;
Lenten 2:172, 173;
musk 1:46, 2:136, 3:296;
noisette 3:296;
sweet 3:296;
tea 3:296;
Turkestan 3:296
rose bay 2:240
rose elder 3:354
rose geranium 2:136
rose hip syrup 3:296
rose imperial 4:456, 457
rose moss 3:279, 279
rose of China 2:176
rose of heaven 3:315
rose of Jericho 3:290, 4:470
rose of Sharon 2:176, 184
rose pink 5:574
Roseae 4:494
rosebay:
broad-leaved 3:331;
East Indian 3:331
rosebay willowherb 1:85, 85,
2:131

roselle 2:144, 147, 176
rosemary 2:174, 175, 3:297;
bog 1:29, 29
Rosenbusch, K. 9:1265, 1272,
1273, 1275
roseroot 3:312, 312
rosette annuals 6:724
rosette-herbs 6:723
rosewood 2:127, 3:296;
Bengal 3:283;
black 1:116;
Bombay 1:116;
Brazilian 1:116, 3:341;
East Indian 1:116, 3:341;
Honduras 1:116, 3:341;
Malabar 1:116, 3:341;
Nicaragua 1:116, 3:341;
Rio 1:116;
Senegal 2:193, 3:283;
Thailand 1:116, 3:341
Rosidae 4:487-571
rosin 1:6, 3:272, 296
rosinweed 3:315
Rosmarinus 3:297, 5:589, 589,
7:836
Rosoideae 4:491
Ross, James Clark 6:679
Rostkovia 5:640
Rotala 4:507
rotenone 1:119, 2:210, 7:946
Roucheria 5:557
rouge plant 1:60, 3:295, 4:422
roundwood 3:319
roundwood consumption 7:937
Rourea 5:542, 542, 543
rowan 3:318, 319, 4:494;
Japanese 3:319;
Kashmir 3:319;
Vilmarin's 3:319
royal fern 6:748, 7:883, 884
royal palm 5:654
Royal Society 6:759
Roystonea 3:297, 5:653, 654
rubber 3:297, 7:925, 926, 932;
African 2:196;
ceara 1:74, 2:219, 3:297;
India 1:74, 3:297;
Jequie 2:219, 3:297;
Lagos 3:297;
landolphia 3:297;
Madagascar 2:196, 214, 3:297;
Mangabeira 2:169;
Manicoba 3:297;
Panama 3:297;
Para 1:74, 2:176, 176, 3:297,
297
rubber plant 2:142, 3:297;
American 3:265;
baby 3:265
rubber tree 3:309, 4:535, 537
rubbish heap theory of
domestication 7:925
rubbish tip 7:946
Rubel, Eduard 7:966
Rubia 2:126, 214, 3:300, 5:609
Rubiaceae 5:573, 607-9, 608,
610, 618
Rubiales 5:607-9
rubidium 8:979, 988, 997,
9:1126, 1142, 1143, 1149
rubidium-strontium dating 9:1143,
1146, 1152
Rubioideae 5:608
Rubus 1:60, 63, 2:210, 3:288,
300, 358, 4:491, 494, 494,
6:690, 721, 826;
fruticosus 6:772
ruby 8:1081, 1088, 1098, 1099
rudaceous rocks 9:1130, 1131,
1132-3, 1133
Rudbeckia 3:300, 5:617
ruderal species 6:794, see also
weeds
rudistids 9:1227
rue 2:147, 174, 3:300, 5:552,
554;
Alpine meadow 3:335, 6:750;
goat's 2:154, 3:334;

meadow 3:300, 335;
Syrian 2:226;
yellow meadow 3:300, 335
Ruellia 3:300, 5:600
Ruiz Lopez, Hipolito 6:682
rum 1:58
Rumex 3:301,4:428, 428, 6:751;
acetosella 6:723;
crispus 7:888
runch 3:288
runner in strawberry 6:778
Ruppia 3:301, 5:624, 626
Ruppiaceae 5:624, 626
rupturewort 2:173
Ruschia 4:417, 417
Ruschioideae 4:415, 417
Ruscus 3:301
rush 2:189, 3:301, 5:640, 641,
6:789, 7:862, 885, 887, 910,
949;
chairmaker's 3:301, 311;
comb 3:310;
corkscrew 2:190;
floating mud 3:311;
flowering 1:68, 68, 3:301;
hard 2:190, 7:885;
Japanese-mat 2:189;
mud 7:945;
scouring 2:180, 3:301;
sharp 2:189;
soft 2:189, 191;
spike 3:129
rush nut 5:643
Russian explorations 6:688
rust:
brown 3:283;
flax 2:221
rusting 8:1009, 1010
Ruta 3:300, 301, 5:552, 552, 554
rutabaga 1:64, 3:298, 301
Rutaceae 5:547, 549, 552, 552-4,
564, 618
Ruteae 5:554
ruthenium 8:1110
rutile 8:1079, 1098, 1105, 1108
Rutoideae 5:554
Ruyschia 4:438, 439
rye 1:58, 83, 83, 2:149, 3:301,
301, 311, 344, 5:638, 640,
7:932, 934;
wild 2:130, 149;
winter 7:880
ryegrass 2:149, 3:301, 5:638,
640, 6:718, 7:932, 940;
Australian 3:301;
bearded 3:301;
Italian 3:301;
perennial 3:301, 301

Saale ice advance 6:749
Sabal 2:145, 258, 6:748, 7:896
Sabatia 5:573, 574
saber-toothed tigers 9:1200, 1205,
1246
Sabia 5:544
Sabiaceae 4:534
sabkhas 8:1119, 9:1135
Sabrenia 6:747
sacaline 3:277
Saccellium 5:583, 584
Saccharomyces 3:302
Saccharum 2:231, 3:302, 327,
5:636, 638, 640;
officinarum 7:926;
spontaneum 6:825
Sacoglottis 5:556, 556
sacred bamboo 3:395, 396
sacred bark 4:538
sacred lotus 3:394
saddle fungi 2:172
safflower 1:77, 2:126, 5:618
saffron 1:109, 2:126, 146, 147,
5:662;

meadow 1:98
safrole 2:227
sage 2:174, 175, 229, 3:302,
5:589;
Bethlehem 3:284;
black 1:41, 3:302;
blue 3:302;
clary 1:91;
coastal 7:843;
common 3:302;
garden 3:302;
green 3:302;
Jerusalem 3:268, 284, 302;
linden-leaf 3:302;
lyre-leafed 3:302;
meadow 3:302;
pineapple-scented 3:302;
scarlet 3:302, 305;
silver 3:302;
yellow 2:197, 3:302
sage tree 3:355
sagebrush 6:822, 822, 7:843;
common 1:41
sagé-leaved semi-shrubs 6:721
Sageretia 3:302
Sagina 4:417
Sagittaria 3:302, 5:619, 620, 620
sago 1:40, 77, 112, 2:228, 3:302,
7:880;
Portland 1:42;
queen 3:328
sago cycas 3:361
sago palm 1:112, 3:302, 5:651,
653, 654;
prickly 3:302;
spineless 3:302
saguaro 1:69, 6:722, 7:843, 849,
850
Sahara Desert 6:791, 7:842, 844,
845, 8:1046
Saharo-Arabian region 7:897
Sahel 7:859
sainfoin 2:252
St Anthony's fire 1:26, 2:132
St Helena:
endemics 7:916;
extinctions 7:921
St Helena ebony 7:921
St John's bread 1:76, 2:201
St John's wort 2:183, 7:949;
creeping 2:184;
perforated 2:184
St Julien 1:110
St Martha wood 1:69
St Peter's wort 2:184
St Petersburg Botanic Garden
6:688
St Thomas tree 1:53
Saint-Hilaire, G. 9:1266
Saintpaulia 3:302, 5:596, 598
saki 1:16
sal 7:835
sal tree 4:407, 3:341
Salacia 4:528, 529
salep 5:675
Salicaceae 4:467, 467-8, 516
Salicales 4:467-8
salicin 3:358
Salicornia 3:302, 4:422, 423, 423,
6:828, 7:886, 889, 945;
bigelowii 7:945;
europaea 7:888, 889;
herbacea 6:711, 7:889
salicylic acid as chemical defense
6:823
saligna 3:341
saline soils 6:809
salinity:
in coastal habitats 7:885-6, 890,
891;
in desert soil 7:845
Salix 3:305, 358, 4:467, 467, 468,
6:826, 827, 7:838, 841, 855,
869, 882, 901, 901, 902;
arctica 7:854, 854, 855;
atrocinerea 7:881, 884;
herbacea 6:722, 722, 749, 750,
7:912;

polaris **6**:749, 750;
repens **7**:887
sallow **3**:305, 358, **7**:881, 882, 884;
  white **1**:7
salmonberry **3**:300
Salmonella **1**:51
Salpiglossideae **5**:579
Salpiglossis **3**:305, **5**:579, 579
salsify **1**:85, **3**:298, **305**, 342, 350, **5**:618;
  black **3**:305, 311, 350;
  Spanish **3**:305, 311
Salsola **3**:305, **4**:*423*, 423, 525;
  kali **6**:825
salt **8**:1081, 1103, *1113*, *1118-9*, **1119-21**, **9**:*1179*, see also halite
salt domes **8**:1091, *1113*, 1121
salt marshes **6**:*711*, **7**:886, *888-9*, **888-90**;
  succession on **6**:826-7;
  tropical (mangrove) **7**:*890-1*, **890-1**
salt pans **8**:*1119*
salt weathering **8**:1009, 1046
saltation **8**:1012, **9**:1129
saltbush **2**:194, **3**:**305**, **4**:530;
  four-wing **3**:305;
  Mediterranean **3**:305;
  spiny **3**:305
Saltera **4**:509
saltwort **4**:*426*, 427, 427, **6**:825;
  black **2**:162;
  prickly **3**:305
Salvadora **4**:530
Salvadoraceae **4**:**530**
Salvertia **5**:564, *565*, 565
Salvia **1**:91, **3**:302, 305, **5**:589, *589*, **6**:721, **7**:843;
  leucophylla **6**:822;
  splendens **6**:*793*
Salvinia **2**:192, **3**:306;
  cuculata **6**:*725*;
  natans **6**:725
saman **3**:306
Samanea **3**:306
samara dispersal **6**:817
sambong **1**:60
Sambucus **3**:306, **5**:610;
  nigra × *racemosa* **6**:781
Samoleae **4**:484
Samolus **4**:484, *484*
samphire **1**:109, **3**:302;
  golden **2**:185, *185*;
  marsh **3**:302, *302*
sampling **6**:714-5;
  and chorology **6**:707;
  and phytosociology **6**:727-9
San Andreas Fault **8**:1023, 1025-6, *1027*, 1056
Sanchezia **5**:601
sand dunes **7**:886-8;
  succession on **6**:*824-5*, **825-6**, **7**:*886-7*
sand in soil **6**:*802*, 803
sand myrtle **2**:199
sandalwood **4**:520, 521;
  white **3**:307
sandalwood tree **3**:306
sandalwood oil **2**:136
sandarac **3**:**306**
sandbox tree **4**:537
sanderswood, red **3**:283
Sandoricum **5**:552
sandpaper plant **4**:464
sands **8**:1067, *1068*, 1081, 1097;
  as carriers for petroleum **8**:1113
sandstones **8**:1021, 1029, 1097, **9**:*1122*, 1129, 1131, *1132*, 1162, 1170, 1171, *1172*, 1180, 1186, *1189*, 1191, **9**:*1123*, **1131-2**, 1136, see also arenaceous rocks
sandwort **1**:40, **6**:825;
  sea **2**:178, *178*, **6**:825
Sangamon interglacial **6**:749
Sanguinaria **3**:306, **4**:402

Sanguisorba **3**:**306**, **4**:491, *494*, 494
Sanguisorbeae **4**:491, 494
sanicle:
  purple **3**:306;
  wood **3**:306
Sanicula **3**:306, **5**:569, *571*, 571
Saniculeae **5**:571
Saniculoideae **5**:569, 571
sanidine **8**:1090, 1094, 1096, **1098**, **9**:1124
Sanseverinia **2**:173, **3**:**306**, **5**:664, 666
Sansevieria **2**:173, **3**:**306**, **5**:664, 666
Santalaceae **4**:474, **520-1**, *521*, 525, 527
Santalales **4**:520-7
Santaleae **4**:521
Santalum **3**:**306**, 307, **4**:*521*, 521
Santiria **5**:546, 547
santol **5**:552
Santolina **3**:**307**, **5**:618
santonin **5**:618
Sanvitalia **3**:**307**, **5**:617
sapele **3**:**307**, 341, **5**:552;
  heavy **3**:307, 341
sap-green **1**:67, **4**:537
Saphronitis **5**:*673*
sapida **1**:14
Sapindaceae **5**:541, *543*, **543-4**, 545, 546, 548, 552, 563, 564
Sapindales **4**:530, **5**:540-54, 571
Sapindus **5**:544
Sapium **2**:126, **3**:331, **4**:537
sapodilla **1**:87, **2**:151, 219, **4**:482
sapodilla plum **4**:482, 483
Saponaria **3**:**307**, **4**:419
saponin **2**:227, **7**:925
Sapotaceae **4**:482, **482-3**
sapote **2**:128, **3**:**307**, **4**:482, 483;
  black **1**:121, **3**:307;
  Colorado **3**:307;
  white **3**:307
sapote borracho **2**:128
Sapria **4**:528
Saprolegnia **3**:307
saprolite **8**:1010
saprophytes, root **6**:724
sapu **2**:229, **3**:378
sapucaia **2**:245, **3**:307
sapucaia nut **4**:449, 450
Saracha **5**:579
saranta, black **2**:150
Sararanga **5**:655
Sarcandra **3**:386
Sarcocaulon **5**:558, 559
Sarcococca **3**:**307**, **4**:534, 535
sarcocolla **4**:509
Sarcodes **4**:480
Sarcolaena **4**:445
Sarcolaenaceae **4**:440, **445**
Sarcophyta **4**:526
Sarcorhachis **3**:388
Sarcosperma **4**:482
Sarcospermataceae **4**:482
Sarcostigma **4**:531
Sarcostigmateae **4**:531
sard **8**:1087
sardonyx **8**:1083
Sargassum **3**:307
Sargent, Professor Charles Sprague **6**:685
Sargentodoxa **3**:399, *400*, 400
Sargentodoxaceae **3**:400
Sarmienta **5**:596
Sarothamnus **1**:114
Sarracenia **3**:**308**, **4**:404, *404*, 405, 496, **7**:*878*;
  purpurea **7**:*903*
Sarraceniaceae **3**:393, **4**:*404*, **404-5**, 490
Sarraceniales **3**:393, **4**:404-5, 490
sarsaparilla **1**:58, **2**:147, **3**:308, 317, **5**:670;
  false **3**:308;

German **1**:75;
  Jamaican **3**:317;
  Mexican **3**:317;
  tampico **3**:317;
  wild **3**:308, 310, 317
sarson **1**:64
Saruma **3**:391
Sarumeae **3**:391
Sasa **3**:308, **5**:636, **7**:861
Sassafras **3**:308, 387, 388
sassafras **2**:147, 227, **3**:308;
  Chinese **3**:308
sassafras oil **2**:136
satal **2**:155
Satan's bolete **1**:61
satin-spar **8**:1091
satinwood **1**:88, **3**:308, 341;
  Brazilian **3**:308;
  Ceylon **3**:341;
  East Indian **3**:308, 341;
  scented **3**:308;
  West Indian **3**:308, 341, 363
satsuma **2**:151, 217, **3**:308, **5**:554
Satureja **2**:151, 217, **3**:308, **5**:554
Satureja **3**:308
Saturn **8**:971, *989*, **9**:1255
Satyrium **3**:308, **5**:675
Sauer, Carl **7**:925
sauerkraut **1**:51, **3**:308
saurischians **9**:1241
Sauromatum **3**:308
sauropods **9**:1189, 1241
Saururaceae **3**:**388-9**
Saururus **3**:388, 389, *389*
sausage tree **5**:600
Saussurea **5**:617
Sauvagesia **4**:434
savanna **1**:48, **6**:*710*, **7**:832, *856-7*, **856-7**;
  forest **7**:835-6;
  soils of **6**:*803*, 808, *808*
savin **2**:190
savory:
  summer **2**:174, *175*, **3**:308;
  winter **2**:174, **3**:296
saw grass **5**:643
sawbrier **3**:317
Saxegothaea **3**:308
Saxifraga **2**:210, **3**:308, **4**:497, **6**:*723*, 749, **7**:869, 902;
  cernua **7**:854;
  maweana **6**:*682*;
  oppositifolia **6**:750, **7**:854, 909
Saxifragaceae **4**:407, 487, 489, 494, 495, **496-8**, *497*, 503, **5**:609, 610
saxifrage **3**:308, **4**:496, 497, 498;
  magic-carpet **3**:309;
  meadow **6**:309, *308*;
  mossy **3**:309;
  opposite-leaved **6**:750, **7**:854, 909;
  purple mountain **3**:309
Saxifragoideae **4**:497
Saxofridericia **5**:629
Saxofridericioideae **5**:629
scab **3**:353
Scabiosa **3**:309, **5**:611, *612*, 612
scabious **3**:309, **5**:611, 612;
  devil's bit **3**:*309*;
  Red Indian **3**:309;
  sweet **2**:133, **3**:309
scabwort **2**:185
Scaevola **5**:607;
  taccada **6**:*824*
scale-leaf trees **6**:*719*, 720
Scaligeria **5**:571
scallops **2**:222
scammony **1**:99, **5**:580
Scandiceae **5**:571
Scandinavian Shield **9**:1162
scandium **8**:1104
Scandix **5**:571
Scapania **3**:309
scapes **7**:850
scapolite **8**:1090, **1098**
Scarborough lily **3**:309
scarlet bush **2**:168
scarlet fever **1**:51

scarlet runner **4**:502
scarlet-bugler **3**:*265*
Scenedesmus **1**:20
Schaefferia **1**:62
scheelite **8**:1110
Schefflera **3**:309
Scheuchzeria **5**:623
Scheuchzeriaceae **5**:*623*, 624
Schickendantzia **5**:666
Schiekia **5**:668
Schimper, Andreas **6**:719, **7**:967
Schinopsis **3**:286, **5**:548
Schinus **2**:220, **3**:309, **5**:548
Schisandra **3**:308, 310, 382
Schisandraceae **3**:378, **382**, 400
schistosity **9**:1137, **1138-9**
Schistostemon **5**:556
schists **8**:1036, 1083, 1086, 1088, 1089, 1090-1, 1092, 1093, 1099, **9**:*1137*, **1138-9**, *1138*, *1139*, 1202;
  blue **8**:1036, **9**:1137;
  green **8**:1087, **9**:1137;
  see also micaschists
Schizaea **3**:310
Schizanthus **3**:310, **5**:579
Schizeilema **5**:569
Schizocapsa **5**:668
Schizocodon **3**:315, **4**:481, *481*
schizoendemics **7**:915
Schizolaena **4**:445
Schizoneura **6**:*743*
Schizopepon **4**:465
Schizopeponeae **4**:465
Schizopetaleae **4**:470
Schizopetalum **4**:470
Schizophragma **3**:310
Schizostylis **3**:310
Schleichera **2**:195, 214, 250, **5**:544
Schlumbergera **3**:310, **4**:415
Schmithüsen, Josef **6**:719
schnappes **3**:333
Schoenocephalium **5**:*628*, 629
Schoenoplectus **6**:826
Schoepfia **4**:*523*
scholar tree, Chinese **3**:318
Scholleropsis **5**:659, 660
Schotia **2**:179
Schouw, Joachim **6**:708
Schrameckia **3**:384
Schrebera **5**:577
Schrebereae **5**:577
schreibersite **8**:989
Schubertia grandiflora **6**:*703*
Schultesiophytum **5**:654
Sciadopitys **3**:310
Sciaphila **5**:627
scientific nomenclature **6**:698
scientific taxonomy **6**:694-5
Scilla **3**:311, 323, **5**:664
Scilleae **5**:664
scintillometers **8**:1073
Scirpodendron **5**:643
Scirpoideae **5**:643
Scirpus **1**:68, **3**:311, **5**:643, **7**:885, 931;
  caespitosus **6**:829
sciuromorphs **9**:1249
Scleractinia see corals
Scleria **5**:643
Scleroderma **2**:127, **3**:284
scleromorphic evergreen shrubs **6**:721, **7**:843
sclerophyll trees **6**:719
sclerophyllous forests **7**:836-7, 874
Scleropyrum **4**:*521*
Sclerotinia **3**:311
Scolopendrium **3**:269
Scolopia **4**:452
Scolymus **5**:617
scopolamine **1**:26, 117, **2**:227
Scopolia **1**:26, **5**:579
Scorodocarpus **4**:*523*
Scorzonera **3**:305, 311, 333, 350, **5**:617, 618
scouring rush **2**:180
scree **6**:802, **8**:*1009*, 1048, **9**:1132

screw-augur 3:322
screw-pine 2:258, 5:655, 656,
    6:720, 826, 7:896;
    thatch 2:258
screw-pine life-form 6:720
Scrope, G. 9:1260, 1262, **1272-3**
Scrophularia 3:311, 5:593, 595
Scrophulariaceae 4:506, 5:573,
    579, 590, 591, **593-5**, 595,
    596, 598, 599, 600, 601, 603
Scrophulariales 4:503, 5:591-604
Scrophularioideae 5:593
scrub 6:*718*, 7:*832-3*, 832, 836,
    842, **842-4**
scuppernong 3:356
scurvy grass 1:96, 7:920;
    common 1:96;
    early 1:96
Scutellaria 3:311, 5:589, 589
Scybalium 4:526
Scytonema 1:51
Scytopetalaceae 4:439
Scytopetalum 4:439
sea buckthorn 4:518, 519
sea coral 2:254
sea eryngium 2:134
sea holly 2:134, 5:600, 601
sea holm 2:134
sea kale 1:108, *108*, 3:350, 4:472
sea kale beet 1:85
sea lavender 4:428, 429
sea lettuce 1:19, 3:311, *311*
sea pink 1:40, 4:429
sea rocket 1:69, *69*;
    American 1:69
sea rush 5:641
sea urchin 2:168
sea whistles 1:43
seablite 6:750, 7:945
sea-dispersed fruits 6:*818*, 818,
    7:905
sea-floor spreading 8:973, **1003-4**,
    1007, 1025, 1026, *1033*,
    1036, 1040, **1059-61**, 1062,
    1064, 9:1181, 1269
sea-grass 3:363, 5:627
sea-level changes 7:909
seamounts 8:*1060*, 1063-4
Sears, Paul 7:955
seas, pollution of 7:945
seashores:
    meadows of 7:861;
    succession on 6:*824-5*, 825-6,
    7:*886-7*;
    zonation of 6:828, 829;
    see also coastal vegetation 7:*885-
    91*
seaside grape 4:428
seasonal change 6:717, *788*;
    adaptations to 6:770-1, *771*,
    793
seasonal forests 7:*832-3*;
    deciduous summer 7:831, *838*,
    838;
    dry tropical 7:**835-6**
seaware 2:150
seawater 9:1154
seaweed 3:311
Sebaea 5:574
Sebastiana 2:189, 4:537
sebil 2:226
Secale 3:301, 311, 5:638, 640
Secamoneae 5:576
Sechium 1:85, 2:222, 3:350,
    4:465, 467, 467
Secondary rocks 9:1259
secondary succession 6:823
Securidaca 5:566, 566
sedge 1:75, 2:149, 3:312, 5:642,
    643;
    beak 7:876;
    bottle 1:75, 7:876;
    deer 6:829;
    fen 3:312;
    few-flowered 7:876;
    great 6:750;
    lesser pond 1:75;
    mud 7:876;

panicled 7:882, *883*, 884;
    pendulous 1:75;
    sand 1:75, 6:825;
    slender 7:876;
    spring 1:*75*;
    tufted 7:876;
    tussock 1:75;
    see also Carex, Cladium
Sedgwick, Adam 7:964, 9:1152,
    1156, 1159-60, 1163, 1261,
    1262, 1266, 1270, 1271,
    1272, **1273**
sedimentary deposits 8:1074
sedimentary rocks 8:996, 997,
    1014, 1020-1, 9:1122, *1123*,
    1127, **1129-35**, *1130*, *1131*,
    1132, *1133*, *1134*, *1135*,
    1136, 1142, 1264, 1268
sedimentation 8:989, *see also*
    diagenesis
Sedum 2:184, 3:312, 4:495, 6:722,
    815, 825, 7:843, 869, *887*
seed dispersal 6:816-9, *817-9*;
    and aliens 7:950-2;
    of desert annuals 7:850;
    long-distance 7:905, 909, 911,
    919
seed ferns 9:1163, 1176
seed flax 2:143
seeds, first 6:766, *766*
Seguieria 4:421, *422*
seiches 8:1027
seifs 8:1046
seismic waves 8:972-4, 1003,
    1024, **1024-5**, 1026, 1027;
    body waves 8:990-1, 1024;
    Love waves (L-waves) 8:*1024*;
    pressure waves (P-waves) 8:973,
    991, *1024*;
    Rayleigh waves (R-waves)
    8:*1024*, 1024-5;
    shear waves (S-waves) 8:*1024*;
    surface waves 8:990-1, **1024-5**
seismograms 8:991, 1024
seismology, seismic studies 8:972,
    980, **990-1**, *991*, 992, 1005,
    1067, 1071, 1073
seismometers 8:991, *1024*
Selaginaceae 5:593, 596
Selagineae 5:593, 596
Selaginella 1:94, 3:290
Selangan batu 3:315
selection:
    directional 6:769;
    disruptive 6:769;
    natural 6:759-64, 767-8, **769**;
    stabilizing 6:769
selective species 6:729
Selenicereus 3:312
selenite 8:1091
self-dispersal 6:818-9, *819*
self-heal 1:17, 3:282
Selliara 5:607
Semecarpeae 5:548
Semecarpus 5:548
Semeiocardium 5:562
Semibegoniella 4:463
semidesert scrub 6:*718*, 7:842-3
seminole-bread 3:361
semiparasitic epiphytes 6:721
semi-rosette herbs 6:723
semi-shrubs 6:721
semiwoody life-forms 6:719
Sempervivum 2:182, 4:495, 6:722
Senecio 3:312, 5:617, 618, 6:722,
    769, 825, 7:893;
    heritieri 6:*775*;
    jacobea 7:887, 949;
    johnstonii ssp. *barbatipes* 7:896;
    kleinia 6:769;
    squalidus 7:951-2;
    vulgaris 6:769
senecio, tree 3:313
Senecioneae 5:615, 617
senecionine 1:26
senna 1:78, 2:227, 4:502;
    Aden 1:78;
    Alexandrian 1:78, 2:227;

American 1:78;
    bladder 1:98;
    coffee 1:78;
    common bladder 1:98, 99;
    dog 1:78;
    Indian 1:78;
    Italian 1:78;
    ringworm 1:78;
    scorpion 1:105;
    sickle 1:78;
    smooth 1:78;
    Tinnevelly 1:78
sensitive plant 2:230, *230*, 3:313;
    giant 2:230;
    wild 3:313
sentry 2:182
Septoria 3:313
Sequoia 3:289, 313, 6:746, 747,
    7:867;
    sempervirens 7:*837*, *914*, 914
sequoia, giant 3:289, 313, 341
Sequoiadendron 3:289, 313;
    giganteum 6:747, 7:*837*, 914
seraya 3:341
Serenoa 5:651
seres 6:823-7
Serjania 5:543, 543
Sernander, Rutger 6:729, 7:967
serotinous cones 6:814
serpentine 8:972, *1085*, **1099**,
    1100, 1105, 9:1129, 1137
serpentine soils 6:*(704)*
serpentinites 8:1099, 9:1128,
    1137, 1138
Serpula 3:314
serradella 2:149
service berry 1:27
service tree 3:318;
    bastard 3:319;
    true 3:319;
    wild 3:319
sesame 2:147, 250, *250*, 3:314,
    314, 5:601
sesame oil 4:406
Sesamoides 4:472, *473*
Sesamum 3:314, 5:601
sesban 2:149, 3:314
Sesbania 3:314
Seseli 5:571
Sesuvium 4:417
Setaria 2:230, 3:314, 5:638, 640,
    7:931
sevenbark 2:183
Seville orange 3:314, 5:554
sewage 7:944, 944-5, 945, **945-6**
sewage fungus 7:944
sex, origin of 6:753, 757
Seychellaria 5:627
Seymouria 9:1235
seymouriamorphs 9:1235
Seyrigia 4:465, 467
shadblow 1:27
shadbush 1:27
shaddock 1:91, 2:151, 164, 3:278,
    314, 332
shade bearers (tolerants) 7:841
shade-intolerants 6:*814*, 7:841
shaggy cap 1:104, *104*
shaggy mane 1:104, *104*
shales 8:1016, 1029, 1067, 1114,
    9:1130-1, *1131*, *1132*, 1135,
    1137, *1138*, *1157*, *1161*,
    1170, 1171, *1172*, 1180,
    1184, 1186, 1229, 1230
shallon 2:155
shallot 1:17, 3:314, 350, *351*,
    5:664
shame plant 2:230
shamrock 2:257, 3:314
shank, red 3:277
sharks 9:1163-4, 1232;
    cartilaginous 9:1189;
    spiny *see* acanthodians
she cabbage 3:313
she oak 1:78, 4:412, 413
shea butter tree 4:483
sheep berry 3:354
shell flower 2:232

shellac 2:142, **195**
shellbark, big 1:77
Shepherdia 3:314, 4:518, *519*, 519
shepherd's club 2:233
shepherd's purse 1:74, 4:470
Sherbournia 5:608
Shetler, Stanwyn 6:701
she-to 2:226
Shigella 1:51
shinleaf 3:285
shoe flower 2:176
shola 1:11
shoot frequency 6:716
shooting star 1:122
shore *see* seashore
shore podgrass 3:343
Shorea 1:116, 3:315, 4:434, 435,
    435, 7:842;
    robusta 7:835
shoreweed 2:209
short-day plants 6:795
Shortia 3:315, 4:480, 481
shot, Indian 1:73
shrimp plant 2:*190*, 191;
    Mexican 2:191
shrub tundra 7:902
shrubby dwarf succulents 6:721
shrubby succulents 6:721, *722*
shrubland *see* scrub
shrubs 6:*721*, 721
Sibiraea 4:491
Sibthorpia 5:595
Sicana 2:222, 4:467
sickle medick 2:211
Sicyoeae 4:465
Sicyos 4:465
Sida 3:315, 4:445
Sidalcea 3:315, 4:445
sideoats 2:149
siderite (chalybite) 8:1021, *1074*,
    1084, 1087, 1089, **1099**,
    1102, 1105, 9:1135
Sideroxylon 2:187, 4:482
Sideritis 5:589
side-saddle flower 3:308
Siebold, Franz von 6:684
sierozem 6:808
Sierra Leone butter 3:331
Sierra Nevada 9:1138, *1199*,
    1264
Sigillaria 6:*740*, 743
silage and pollution 7:946
silcrete 6:805, 8:1047
Silene 3:315, 4:417, *419*, 419,
    6:781;
    acaulis 6:722, 7:855;
    maritima 6:750;
    secundiflora 6:791;
    viscosa 6:791-2
Silenoideae 4:417
silica 8:996, 1087, 1088-9, 1090,
    1102, 9:*1122*, *1123*, 1124,
    1126, 1127, 1128, 1130,
    1141, 1220
silicate minerals, silicates 8:972,
    973, 974, 975, 996, 1081,
    1084, 1090, 1103, 1104,
    9:1122, 1126
silicon 8:971, 973, 974, 980, 995,
    996, 1084, 1097, **1104**,
    1107, 9:1122
silk cotton tree 1:61, 80, 2:144,
    192, 4:443;
    Indian 1:61, 2:144;
    red 1:61, 2:144
silk oak 4:520
silk plant, Chinese 1:60
silk tree 1:15
silk-tassel bush 2:155
silkweed 1:43
sillimanite 8:1084, 1093, **1099**,
    9:1137
sills 8:1030, 1034
Silphium 3:315, 5:617
silt 9:*1131*;
    in soil 6:*802*, 803
siltstones 9:1230
Silurian 6:*738-9*, 739, 743, 766,

9:1152, 1154, 1156, **1159-63**, *1161*, 1164, 1231, 1260, 1261, 1271, 1272;
climate 9:1162-3;
fauna 9:*1160*, 1160-1;
flora 9:*1160*;
geography 9:*1160*, 1162-3;
stratigraphic correlation 9:1161-2
silver 8:1023, 1075, *1078*, 1090, **1108**, *1109*, 1110, 9:1151
silver bell 2:168;
mountain 2:168
silver buffalo 3:314
silver dollar 2:212
silver rod 1:45
silverbell tree 4:483, 484
silverberry 2:129
silverweed 3:280, see also Potentilla
Silvianthus 5:610
Silybum 3:335, 5:617
Simarouba 3:315
Simaroubaceae 4:490, 5:547, 549, **549-50**, 552
simazine 7:946
similarity tables, phenetic 6:*696*
Simmondsia 4:534, 7:936
Simmondsiaceae 4:534
simpoh 4:431
Sinapis 1:85, 2:236, 3:316, 4:470, 472;
arvensis 7:948
sinigrin as chemical defense 6:823
sinkholes 8:1043, *1044*
Sinningia 2:162, 3:316, 5:596, 598
Sinofranchetia 3:400
Sino-Japanese region 7:*897*
Sinomenium 3:401
Siparuna 3:384
Siphocampylus 5:606
Siphonodon 3:316
Siphonosmanthus 5:577
siris tree 1:14;
pink 1:15
sisal 2:144, 145, 3:316, *316*
sisal agave 3:316
sisal hemp 3:316, 5:666
sissoo wood, Indian 1:116
Sisymbrieae 4:470
Sisymbrium 4:470
Sisyrinchieae 5:662
Sisyrinchium 3:316, 5:661, 662
skeleton weed 5:618
Skimmia 3:316, 5:552, 554;
reevesiana 6:684
Skoltsberg, Carl 7:**967**
skullcap, common 3:311
skullcap flower 3:311
slacks between dunes 7:886, *887*, 888
slash-and-burn agriculture 7:935, 952
Slater, Gilbert 6:684
slates 8:1087, *1110*, 9:*1137*, **1138**, 1139
slime fungi 3:*316*
slipper flower 1:70, 2:263, 5:595
slipperwort 1:70
slippery elm 4:446
slivovitz 1:16, 58, 3:275
Sloane, Sir Hans 6:682
Sloanea 4:440, 440
sloe 1:60, *60*, 3:275, **316**
sloe gin 1:60
slope and exposure 6:800-1, 7:863
smaltite 8:1105, 1107
smartweed 3:277;
water 3:277
Smeathmannia 4:453
smelting 7:936-7, 942
Smilacaceae 5:670
Smilacina 3:317
Smilax 3:308, 317, 5:670
smilax 1:43, 44, 3:317
Smith, W. 9:*1147-8*, 1207, 1260-1, **1273**
Smithiantha 3:317, 5:596, 598
smithsonite 8:1106

smoke 7:941, *942*
smoke tree 1:106, 3:317, 5:548;
American 3:317
smother crops 7:950
smut fungi 3:348, *348*
Smyrnieae 5:571
Smyrnium 3:317, 5:571
snail flower 3:267
snake bark 1:8
snake gourd 4:467
snake plant 2:144, 3:307
snake wood 1:66
snakeroot 3:392;
black 1:10, 89, 3:306;
button 2:134, **203**;
Indian 2:227, 3:289;
Sampson's 2:160;
seneca 3:277;
Virginia 1:40
snakes 9:1236, **1238**
snakeweed 3:277
snap bean 4:502
snapdragon 1:36, 5:595;
chaparral 1:36;
common 1:36, *37*;
withered 1:36
Snider-Pellegrini, A. 8:1001
snow, red 3:289
snow on the mountain 2:138
snowball cushion 2:217
snow-bed communities 7:901-2
snowbell, fragrant 3:327
snowbell tree 4:483, 484
snowberry 3:330, 5:610
snowdrop 3:317, *317*, 5:664, 666, 6:*781*;
common 3:317;
giant 3:317
snowdrop tree 2:168, 4:484
snowflake 2:203, 5:666;
spring 2:203;
summer 2:203;
water 2:243
snowflower 3:320
snow-in-summer 1:82, *82*
soap root 3:307
soap tree 2:167
soapbark tree 3:286, 4:494
soapberry 3:314
soapweed 3:361
soapwort 3:307, *307*, 4:419;
rock 3:307
sociability 6:727
sociations 6:729
societies 6:710, 729
sociological amplitude 6:710
sociology of plants 6:**727-30**
soda-apple 3:317
sodalite 8:1090, **1099**, 9:*1124*, 1126
sodium 8:979, 995, 996, 1090, **1103**, 1121, 9:*1122*, 1128;
in plant nutrition 6:807
soft chaparral 7:843
soft rush 5:641
soil erosion 8:1048
soil mechanics 8:1066
soil profile 9:1141
soils 6:785, **801-10**, *802-11*, 8:1010, 1021, 1045, 1051, 1066, 9:*1122*, **1140-1**, *1140*, *1141*, 1165, 1171;
ahumic 8:1051;
of Australian heathland 7:874;
of grasslands 7:856-7, 859-60, **862**;
of marshland 7:884;
serpentine 6:(*704*);
and sewage sludge 7:*945-6*;
and tropical mires 7:878
Solanaceae 4:506, 5:*579*, *579*, 580, 583, 593, 602, 7:897
Solander, Daniel 6:(*687*)
Solandra 5:579
Solaneae 5:579
solanine 1:26, 3:318
Solanum 1:46, 2:128, **238**, 241, 3:265, 279, **317**, 5:*579*, *579*;

dulcamara 7:884;
tuberosum 6:789, *790-1*, 7:*926*
solar radiation 6:785, 787, **792-3**, 800, 7:866, 869, see also light
Solar System 8:977, 998;
composition of 8:980;
origin and formation of 8:971-2, *972*, 988, 995, 996, 9:1146;
scale of 8:*974-5*
solasodine 3:318
Soldanella 3:318, 4:484, *484*
Soleirolia 3:318
Solfatara 8:1058
solid solution series 8:1081
Solidago 3:318, 5:618;
× *asperula* 6:*779*;
rugosa 6:779;
sempervivens 6:779
solifluction 7:851
Sollya 4:*488*, 488, 489
Solomon's seal 3:277
Solomon's zigzag 3:317
solonchak and solonetz soils 6:809
soluble airborne pollutants 7:*943-4*
Sonchus 3:318, 335, 5:617, 618, 7:*915*;
abbreviatus 6:*774*;
acaulis 6:*774*, *774*;
jacquini 6:*774*, *774*;
leptocephalus 6:*774*, *774*;
pinnatus 6:*774*, *774*;
platylepis 6:*774*;
radicatus 6:*774*, *774*;
regis-jubae 6:*774*
Sonerila 4:514, *514*
Sonneratia 4:506, 7:*891*
Sonneratiaceae 4:506, 507, 512
Sonoran province 7:*898*
Sophora 3:318, 4:499, 7:*905*, 919
sophora, fourwing 3:318
Sophoreae 4:502
× *Sophrolaeliocattleya* 3:318
Sophronitis 3:318, 5:675
Sorbaria 3:318, 4:491
Sorbus 2:233, 3:318, 4:491, *494*, 494, 7:*903*
Sorby, H. 9:*1263*, **1273**, 1275
Sordaria 3:319
Sorghastrum nutans 7:*863*
Sorghum 3:319, 5:635, 638, 640
sorghum 1:83, *83*, 3:319, 7:*883*, 948;
bicolor 3:319;
caudatum 3:319;
common 3:319;
durra 3:319;
ghally 3:319;
Guinea 3:319;
Indian 3:319;
kafir 3:319;
sweet 1:16, 3:319, 328
sorgo 1:16, 3:319, 328
sorrel 2:146, *147*, 3:301, 4:427, 428;
common 1:112;
creeping lady's 2:257;
French 3:301;
garden 2:174, 3:301;
Indian 2:176;
Jamaica 2:176;
mountain see Oxyria;
sheep 2:174, 3:301;
wood 2:257, 3:314, 7:838
sorrel tree 2:257
sotol 1:117
souari nut 1:77
Souroubea 4:*438*, 439
soursop 1:31, 2:151, *153*, 3:380, 381;
mountain 1:31;
wild 1:31
sourtop 1:60
sourwood 2:257
sou-sou 2:223
South Georgia, aliens of 7:951
South Africa, National Botanic Gardens of 7:*960*
South African region 7:*897*, 897

Southeast Asian region 7:*897*
Southern Andes province 7:*904*
southern beech 6:*801*, 7:*904*, see also Nothofagus
Southern Hemisphere heaths 7:*873-4*
southern leaf blight 7:935
Southern Oceanic region 7:*897*, 904
southernwood 1:42, 3:319
sow thistle 3:318, *318*, 5:613, 618, 6:774, 7:915
soya 2:250, 7:932
Soyauxia 4:453
soybean 2:162, 201, 250, 3:319, *320*, 4:472, 499, 502;
wild 2:162;
see also bean, soya
Soymida 5:552
space groups 8:*1077-8*
spacing 6:716
spaghetti 3:320;
vegetable 2:222
Spaniard 1:9
Spanish bayonet 3:361
Spanish moss 5:644, 646
Spanish-dagger 3:361
Sparattanthelium 3:388
Sparaxis 3:320, 5:662
Sparganiaceae 5:643-4
Sparganium 5:643, 644, 6:747, 826;
erectum 6:*724*;
simplex 7:*885*
Sparmannia 3:320, 4:441
sparse vegetation 6:715
sparteine 2:227
Spartina 3:320, 5:638, 7:890;
alterniflora 6:*777*;
alternifolia 7:*945*;
anglica 6:*777*;
maritima 6:*777*;
× *townsendii* 6:*711*, 777, 7:*889*
Spartium 3:320, 4:*502*;
junceum 6:721
Spartochloa 5:635
Spathiphyllum 3:320
Spathodea 3:321, 5:600
spatial isolation 6:*777*, *778-9*;
and vicariance 7:908
speargrass 1:9
spearmint 2:136, 174, *175*, 227, 230
spearmint oil 2:136
spearwort 3:399;
lesser 7:876, 880, 885
speciation 6:*775-8*, 7:*915-6*
species 6:695;
character 6:729;
and floristic provinces 7:894, 898;
numbers of 6:694;
preferential 6:729;
selective 6:729
sp. nov. 6:699
spectrometry, spectroscopy 8:987;
atomic absorbtion 8:996;
atomic emission 8:995-6;
gamma-ray 8:1073;
X-ray fluorescence 8:996;
see also X-ray spectrometry
speedwell 3:353, 5:595;
common 3:353;
field 3:354;
germander 3:*353*;
gray 3:354;
procumbent 3:354;
rock 3:354;
wall 3:354
Spergula 3:321, 4:419;
arvensis 7:949
Spergularia 4:419, 7:*945*
Sperguleae 4:419
sperylite 8:1110
spessartine 8:1090, 1091
Sphaeradenia 5:654, *655*
Sphaeralcea 4:445
Sphaeranthus 5:615, 617

Sphaeropteris 1:112
Sphaerosepalaceae 4:440, **445**
Sphaerotheca 3:**321**
Sphaerotilus natans 7:944
Sphagnum 3:321, 6:716, 722, 810, 826, 829, 7:866, 873, 876, 877, 879, 884, 885, 903;
  auriculatum 7:*876*;
  cuspidatum 6:716, 7:*876*, 876, 877;
  fuscum 7:876, 877;
  magellanicum 7:876, *910*;
  palustre 7:876;
  papillosum 6:716, 7:*876*, 876;
  pulchrum 7:*876*;
  recurvum 6:716, 7:*876*;
  rubellum 7:876
sphalerite (zinc blende) 8:*1074*, 1078, 1090, **1099**, 1104, 1106
Sphedamnocarpus 5:*581*
sphenacodonts 9:1243
sphene (titanite) 8:*1099*, 1105, 9:1140
Sphenoclea 5:604, 606
Sphenocleaceae 5:604, 606
sphenoid 8:1078-9
sphenopsids *see* horsetails
Sphenopteris elegans 6:*730*
Sphenostylis 2:201, 3:360
spiceberry 1:40
spicebush 1:17, 2:207
spider flower 1:92
spider plant 1:88
spiderwort 5:629, 631, 6:*780*;
  common 3:342
Spigelia 5:572
Spigeliaceae 5:572
Spigelieae 5:572
spikenard 2:238, 5:610;
  American 1:39;
  false 3:317
Spilanthes 5:617
spinach 3:321, *321*, 350, *351*, 4:422, 423;
  amaranth 3:350;
  New Zealand 3:321, 350;
  prickly-seeded 3:350;
  round-seeded 3:350;
  summer 3:350;
  water 3:350;
  winter 3:350
spinach beet 4:422, 423
Spinacia 3:321, 350, 4:423
spindle tree 4:529;
  European 2:137;
  winged 2:137, *138*
spinels 8:973, 975, 1078, *1079*, **1099**, 1103
spinifex grass 6:723, 7:842, 862, 863
Spinifex littoreus 6:826
Spiraea 3:321, 4:491, 494;
  crenata 6:684
spiraea 1:46;
  goatsbeard 1:43;
  Japanese 3:322;
  Reeves 3:322;
  tosa 3:322
Spiraeanthemum 4:487
Spiraeeae 4:491
Spiraeoideae 4:432, 491, 494
Spiranthes 3:322, 5:675
spirit of turpentine 3:346
Spirodela 5:657
Spirogyra 3:322
Spirolobeae 4:423
Splachnum 3:322
spleenwort 1:45;
  mother 1:45
spodumene 8:1097, **1099**, 1102
Spondias 3:322, 5:548, 6:*747*;
  tuberosa 7:848
Spondieae 5:548
sponge:
  dishcloth 2:163;
  vegetable 2:163
sponges 9:1135, 1154, 1164,

1185, 1189, 1191, **1220**, 1221
Spongospora 3:**322**
spoon flower 3:359
spore dispersal 6:816, *818*, 818
spores 9:1149, 1162, 1167, 1185
Sporoboleae 5:638
Sporobolus 5:636, 638, 6:723, 7:860
sporopollenin 6:758
spotted dog 3:284
Sprekelia 3:322, 5:666
spring beauty 1:92
spring bell 3:316
sprouting leaf 2:192
sprouts 1:64
spruce 2:145, 3:322, 324;
  big-cone 1:124;
  black 3:323, *323*, 7:876, 903;
  Colorado 3:323;
  Engelmann 3:323, 341, 7:867, 904;
  hemlock 2:126, *173*, 3:341;
  Norway 1:88, 3:322, 323, 341, 6:791, 7:903, 941;
  red 3:322, 341, 7:904;
  Rocky Mountain 3:323;
  Siberian 7:903;
  Sitka 3:323, 341, 7:938;
  white 3:323, *323*, 341;
  yeddo 3:322, 7:866, 903;
  see also Picea
spurge 3:323, 4:535;
  caper 2:138;
  ipecacuanha 2:138;
  leafy 2:138;
  sea 6:768;
  slipper 2:263;
  wood 6:768
spurge laurel 1:116
spurrey 7:945, 949
squash 1:*111*, 2:222, 3:323, 4:465, 467, 7:925, 931;
  acorn 2:222;
  autumn 2:222;
  banana 2:222;
  bush 2:222;
  butternut 2:222;
  chioggia 2:222;
  cocozelle 2:222;
  Hubbard 2:222;
  Naples 2:222;
  Ohio 2:222;
  pattypan 2:222;
  sea 2:222;
  summer 1:111, 2:222, *223*;
  turban 2:222;
  winter 1:111, 2:222, *223*
squaw carpet 1:79
squaw-bush 3:354
squill 2:227, 3:323, *348*, 5:664;
  autumn 3:311, 323;
  bell-flowered 2:183;
  blue 3:323;
  dwarf 3:311;
  Italian 2:183;
  red 3:348, *348*;
  string 3:311;
  striped 3:285
squirrel corn 1:120
Staavia 4:491
stability:
  of island environments 7:916-7, 919-20;
  of salt marshes 7:889
stabilizing selection 6:769
Stachyoideae 5:589
Stachys 1:42, 3:323, 5:589, *589*
Stachyurus 3:323
Stachyuraceae 4:432
Stackhousia 4:530
Stackhousiaceae 4:529-30
Stackhousioideae 4:530
stacks 8:1056
staff vine 1:80
staggerbush 2:213
staghorn fern 6:*721*
stag's horn plantain 7:*887*

stalactites 8:1044, *1045*
stalagmites 8:1044, *1045*
stands 6:710, *713*
Stangeria 3:323
Stanhopea 3:323, 5:675
Stanleya 4:470
stannite 8:1109
Stapelia 3:323, 4:413, 5:576
Staphylea 5:540, 540
Staphyleaceae 5:540, **540-1**
star anise 2:136, 3:382
star apple 3:324, 4:482, 483
star of Bethlehem 2:227, 256;
  yellow 2:154
star of the Veldt 1:121
starfish plant 1:110, 3:324
star-flower 3:317, 343
starleaf 3:309
starwort 7:944;
  yellow 2:185
statice 2:207, *207*
Stauntonia 3:399, 400
staurolite 8:1099
Stebbins, Ledyard 6:779
steeplebush 3:322
Stegnosperma 4:421, 422
Stegnospermataceae 4:421, 422
Stegnospermatoideae 4:421
Stegolepis 5:629
Stegosaurus 9:1181, 1242
Stelestylis 5:654, 655
Stellaria 1:87, 3:324, 4:417, *419*, 419;
  media 6:724, 751, 7:920, *921*
stem rust of wheat 7:949
stem-herb annuals 6:724
stem-herbs 6:723
stem-succulents, leafy 6:721
Stemona 5:668, 669
Stemonaceae 5:668-9
Stemonurus 4:530, *531*
Stemotria 5:593
Steno, N. 9:1147, 1207, 1258, 1259, **1273-4**, 1275
Stenochilus 5:592, 593
Stenomeris 5:670
Stenomesson 5:664, 666
Stenopetaleae 4:470
Stenopetalum 4:470
Stenosiphon 4:512
Stephanandra 3:324, 4:491
Stephania 3:401
Stephanopodium 4:*533*, 533
Stephanotis 3:324, 5:576
stepladder plant 1:106
stepmother's flower 3:355
steppe 7:*832-3*, 832, *859-60*, *860*
Sterculia 2:249, 4:442, 442;
  tragacantha 6:*771*
Sterculiaceae 4:439, **441-3**, *442*
stereographic projection 8:*1078*
Stereum 3:324
sterile-island successions 6:824-5
Sternbergia 3:324, 5:664, 666
steroidal saponins from *Dioscorea* 7:925
Stevia 5:617
stevia 3:273
Stewartia 3:324, 4:432
stibnite 8:1079, 1098, **1099-100**, *1100*, 1109
Stichoneuron 5:668
stick-tights 1:57
sticky Willie 2:154
Stifftia 5:617
Stigmaphyllon 5:563, 564
Stigmaria 6:743
stilbite 8:1101
Stilbocarpus 7:920;
  polaris 7:*920*
stilt-roots 7:891
stinging nettle 1:122, 3:348, 4:447, 448, 449
stinging tree 4:448
stink tree 3:324
stinkhorn 2:157, 3:284, **324**;
  Australian 3:324;
  common 3:324

stinkwood 1:81, 3:324;
  bastard 3:324;
  black bastard 2:247;
  camdeboo 3:324;
  red 3:324;
  white 3:324
Stipa 2:135, 3:324, 5:*636*, 638, 640, 7:860, 863, 904;
  brachychaeta 6:723;
  capillata 7:860;
  ichu 6:723;
  joannis 7:859;
  pinnata 7:860
Stipeae 5:638
stishovite 8:974
stitchwort 3:324;
  greater 3:324
stock 2:221, 4:472, 8:1030-1, *1032*;
  Brompton 2:221;
  garden 2:221, *221*;
  imperial 2:221;
  night-scented 2:221;
  ten-week 2:221;
  Virginia 3:325;
  winter 3:325
Stokes' aster 3:325, 5:618
Stokesia 3:325, 5:617, 618
stolon of mint 6:*778*
stomach fungi 3:284
stomata:
  and drought avoidance 6:795, *799*, 7:848;
  fossilized 6:*732*
stone, Italian 3:272
stone-cress, Persian 1:12
stonecrop 3:312, 4:495;
  biting 3:312;
  white 3:312;
  see also Sedum
stonewort 3:325
stony meteorites (stones) 8:972, 974, 986, *988*, 989
stony-irons 8:986, 987, *988*, 989
storage laboratories 7:959
storax 2:227, 3:325, 4:407, 483, 484;
  American 2:208;
  Levant 3:325
storesin 2:227
storksbill 2:133, 5:558, 559
stout 1:16
Strabo 9:1219, 1256
Strachey, J. 9:1147
strain meters 8:991
stramonium 5:579
strandflat 8:1051
strandline 7:886
strangler-tree life-form 6:720
Stranvaesia 3:325, 4:494
stratification of vegetation 6:717
stratigraphic correlation 9:1142, 1148
stratigraphy 9:1146-9, 1273;
  of peat 7:882
Stratiolites 6:765
Stratiotes 3:325, 5:621, 6:765;
  aloides 6:725, 7:894
stratovolcanoes 8:1057
strawbell 3:348
strawberry 2:151, *152*, 3:325, 4:491, 494, 6:*778*;
  barren 3:280, 325;
  chiloe 3:325;
  common 3:280;
  hautbois 3:325;
  Indian 3:325;
  Mexican 2:128;
  mock 3:325;
  musk 3:325;
  wild 3:325, *325*;
  yellow 3:282
strawberry bush 2:137
strawberry tomato 3:270
strawberry tree 1:39, 2:151, 7:898, 909;
  hybrid 1:39
strawflower 2:171, *171*

Strelitzia **3:325**, 5:*646*, 647;
  reginae 7:*960*
Strelitziaceae 5:*646*, **647**, 648, 650
strength (rocks) **8:1065**
Streptocarpus 5:596, *596*, 598
Streptochaeta 5:636
Streptochaeteae 5:636
Streptococcus 1:51
Streptogyna 5:636
Streptogyneae 5:636
Streptomyces **3:326**
Streptopetalum 4:454
Streptosolen **3:326**, 5:579
striations, glacial 8:1012, *1049*,
  9:1133
Stricklandia 9:1161-2
Striga **3:326**, 5:593, 595, 7:948
string bean 4:502
string bog 6:*814*, 7:*903*, 903
string of beads 3:313
string-of-beads plant 2:193
Strobilanthes **3:326**
Strobilocarpus 4:474
Stromanthe 5:*650*
stromatolites 6:757, 757; 9:*1152*,
  1165, 1185, 1201-2, 1215
stromatoporoids 9:1163, 1164,
  1165, 1166, 1214, 1220,
  1221
Strombocactus 4:415
Strombosia 4:523
Stronach, David 6:684
strontianite **8:1100**, 1108
strontium 8:979, 988, 997, 1074,
  1087, **1108**
strophanthin 3:326
Strophanthus **3:326**, 5:575
strophanthus 2:227
structural pans **6:805**
structure of vegetation **6:715-7**
Struthiopteris 2:220
Strychnaceae 5:572
Strychneae 5:572
strychnine 1:26, 2:227, **3:326**,
  5:572
strychnine tree 1:26
Strychnos 1:111, **3:326**, 5:572,
  572, 573
Stuartia **3:324**
styfsiekte 1:109
Stylidieae **5:607**
Stylidiaceae **5:606-7**, 618
Stylidioideae 5:607
Stylidium 5:606
Stylites 1:*94*, 95
stylo 2:149
Stylobasiaceae 4:499
Stylobasium 4:499
Styloceras 4:534
Stylocerataceae 4:534
Stylosanthes 2:149
Styphelia 4:478, *478*
Styphelieae 4:478
Styracaceae **4:483-4**
Styrax 3:325, **327**, 4:483, 484
styrax, American 2:208
Suaeda 4:423;
  fruticosa 6:*711*;
  maritima 6:*711*, 750, 7:889,
  945
subalpine zone 7:866, **867-8**, *868*;
  meadows of 7:861, 867, 869
subassociations 6:729
Sub-Atlantic phase **6:751**
Sub-Boreal phase 6:*751*, 751
subclimaxes 6:714
subduction zones 6:741, *see also*
  plate margins (destructive)
subformations 6:718
sub-kingdoms, floristic 7:897
sublittoral zone 6:828
submarine canyons 8:1055, *1060*,
  1061, 1062, 9:1266
submarine mountains **8:**1003, *see
  also* crestal mountains, guyots,
  seamounts
submergence marshes 7:889

submersed water-herbs 6:725
subsequents 8:1037
subsere 6:823
subtropical deserts **7:844**
Subularia 4:470
subungulates 9:1195, **1246-7**
succession 6:823-8, *824-7*, 7:*894*;
  and climax 6:711-2;
  and colonization 6:819;
  on dunes 7:*886-7*, **886-8**;
  and organismal model 6:709;
  and tolerance 6:815
Succisa 5:611
succory 1:89
succulent shrubs 6:721
succulent-leaf trees 6:720
succulent-leaved tuft-trees 6:720
succulents 6:721, *722*, 799
Sudanian–Sindian region 7:897
sudd-plants 6:*724*, **724**
Suess, Edward 6:740, **9:1274-5**
sugar beet 3:327, *327*, 328, *328*,
  4:422, 423, 7:932, 949
sugar berry 1:81;
  Mississippi 1:81
sugar cane 1:58, 2:231, 3:*302*,
  327, *327*, 328, *328*, 5:635,
  638, 640, 7:*926*, 931, 932,
  933
sugar limestone 7:*912*
sugar maple 1:8, 3:328, *328*, **329**,
  7:912
sugar-apple 2:151
sugarbush 3:281
Suina 9:1248
sulfur 8:974, 979, 992, 995, 996,
  1079, 1081, 1083, 1084,
  1096, **1104**, *1112*, 1114,
  1121;
  in plant nutrition 6:806
sulfur bacteria 8:1096
sulfur dioxide 8:997, 1034, 1073;
  in air 7:942, *943*, 944
sulfur flower 2:133
sulla clover 2:171
sultana 3:329, 4:538, 539
sumac 2:126, 3:294, 5:547, 548;
  dwarf 3:294;
  elm-leaved 3:294;
  mountain 3:294;
  poison 3:294;
  scarlet 3:294;
  shining 3:294;
  Sicilian 3:294;
  smooth 3:294;
  staghorn 3:294;
  tanner's 3:294;
  Venetian 3:317;
  wing-rib 3:294
summer annuals 6:*724*;
  and drought evasion 7:850
summerberry 3:354
summer-deciduous forest 7:831,
  838
summer-green shrubs 6:721
summer-green trees 6:719
summer-sweet 1:92
Sun 8:971, 976, 977, 9:1255;
  composition of 8:972, 987, 995;
  radiation from 8:998, 1020
sun plant 3:279, *279*
suncup 2:247, 248
sundew 1:*125*, 125, 4:489, 7:884
sundrop 2:247, 248
sunfern 2:162
sunflower 2:250, *250*, 251, 3:329,
  329, 4:472, 5:613, 615, 618,
  6:*724*, 823, 7:*925*, 932;
  common 3:329;
  cucumber-leaved 3:330;
  darkeye 3:330;
  showy 3:330;
  swamp 3:330
sun-rose 2:171, *171*
superphosphate 8:1104
Superposition, Law of 9:1147-8
Suregada 4:537
Suregadeae 4:537

surface waves *see* seismic waves
Surtsey 8:996, 1033, 1057, 1063
Surtsey colonization 7:920, *921*
surveys, phytosociological 6:727-9,
  see also sampling
survival of the fittest *see* natural
  selection
suspended solids in inland waters
  7:*944*, *945*
Suttonia 4:486
suze 2:160
Swainsona 2:185, 3:330
swamp 7:875;
  mangrove 7:886, *890-1*, **890-1**;
  papyrus 6:*724*
swamp carr 7:883
swamp cypress 6:747
swan flower 1:40, 3:330
sward 7:855
Swartzieae 4:502
swede 1:64, *65*, 3:298, 299, **330**,
  4:472
swede rape 3:330
Swedish turnip *see* swede
sweet alysson 4:472
sweet basil 5:589
sweet bay 2:198, 215
sweet calabash 4:453
sweet chestnut 4:410, 412
sweet corn root 1:70, 5:651
sweet gale 2:237, 6:747-8
sweet gum 2:208, 227, 4:406,
  407, 6:*748*, 749;
  American 3:325;
  Oriental 2:227, 3:325
sweet orange 2:164
sweet pea 4:499, 502
sweet pepper 5:579
sweet pepper bush 4:474
sweet potato 2:186, *186*, 3:298,
  299, *299*, 330, *330*, 5:579,
  580, 7:883, 932, *935*;
  Tennessee 2:222
sweet potato vine 3:330
sweet spire 2:187
sweet sultan 1:81
sweet vernal grass 7:862
sweet William 1:119, *119*, 3:315
sweetbells 2:203
sweetberry 3:354
sweetcup 2:261
sweetleaf 3:330;
  Asiatic 3:330;
  common 3:330
sweetsop 1:31, 2:151, 3:380, *380*,
  381
Swertia 3:330, 5:573, 574
Swida 4:517
Swietenia 2:215, 5:551, 552
Swietenioideae 5:551, 552
Swiss chard 1:54, 3:321, 4:423
Swiss-cheese plant 2:232, *232*
switch-shrub life-form 6:*721*, 721
swizzlestick 3:289
sycamore 1:8, 3:294, 330, 341,
  5:546;
  American 3:274, 4:406;
  Eastern 3:330;
  Egyptian 3:330;
  silver 1:110
syenites 8:1086, 1088, 9:1123,
  1124, **1126**
syenodiorites 9:1124
sylvanite 8:1110
sylvite 8:1100, 1104
Symbegonia 4:463, 464
symmetry (in crystals) **8:1076-8**
sympatric isolation 6:*768*, 776,
  779-80
Symphonia 4:436, *436*
Symphoricarpos **3:330**, 5:610
Symphyandra 5:604, 606
Symphytum **3:330**, 5:586
Sympieza 7:874
Symplocaceae 4:432
Symplocarpon 4:432, *433*
Symplocos **3:330**

sympodial crowns 7:834
synapsids 9:1236, 1243
synecology 6:689, **690-1**, 9:1211
Syngonanthus 5:*631*, 632
synonyms 6:700
synoptic lists and tables 6:727
Synsepalum 2:231
syntaxa 6:729
synusiae 6:709, 729
synzoochory 6:816
syphilis 1:*50*
Syringa 2:206, 5:576, *576*, 577
syringa 3:268;
  rose 3:268
Syringodium 5:627
systematics and taxonomy **6:694-7**
Syzygium 1:93, 2:147, 227, 4:511,
  512
Szent-Gyorgi, Albert 6:759

T

Tabebuia **3:331**, 5:600
Tabellaria 1:51
Tabernaemontana **3:331**, 5:574
tacamahac 3:279
Tacca **3:331**, 5:668
Taccaceae 5:667, **668**
Tacinga 4:413
taenite 8:986
Tageteae 5:617
Tagetes 2:219, **3:331**, 5:617, 618,
  7:949
tagua 3:270
taiga 7:841, 8:1050
tail flowers 1:*37*
t'a-ku-ts'ai 1:64
Talauma 3:377, *377*, 378
talc 8:1082, **1100**
Talinum 4:425
talipot palm 5:651
tall heath 7:872
tall tuft grasses 6:723
tallow, vegetable **3:331**
tallow tree:
  Chinese 2:126, **3:331**;
  Sierra Leone 3:331
tamarack 2:197, *197*, 6:*814*,
  7:876, *902*, 903
Tamaricaceae 4:459, **459-60**, 462,
  468, 525, 7:897
tamarind 2:147, 151, 201, 3:331,
  332, 4:502;
  cow 3:306
Tamarindus 2:147, 151, 201,
  3:331, 4:502
Tamarisceae 4:459, 460
tamarisk 3:332, *332*, 4:459,
  459, 460, 525,
  6:*721*, 7:897;
  Chinese 3:332;
  French 3:332
Tamarix 2:189, 219, **3:332**, 4:*459*,
  459, 460, 525
Tambourissa 3:384, *384*
Tamus 3:332, 5:670
Tanacetum 3:285, **332**, 5:618
tang, black 2:150
tangelo 2:217, **3:332**, 347
tangerine 2:151, 217, 256, 3:332,
  347, 5:552, 554
tanier 3:298, *299*, 328, 359,
  5:659
tannins 2:126
Tansley, Arthur 6:689, 729, 7:967
tansy 2:126, 174, *175*, 3:312,
  332;
  goose 3:280
tapa 2:145
tapa cloth 1:66
Tapeinocheilos 5:648
Taphrina 3:332
Tapinocephalus 9:1176
tapioca 1:*77*, *78*, 2:219, *219*,
  4:537, 7:880

tapirs **9:**1247
Tapiscia **5:***540*, 540
Tapura **4:***533*, 533
Taraktogenos **1:**85, **4:**452
tara-vine **1:**10
Taraxacum **1:**116, **3:**297, **332**,
 5:617, 618, **6:***817*, 817;
 officinale **7:**949
tare **3:**354
taro **3:**298, *299*, 328, 333, **5:**659;
 blue **3:**359;
 giant **1:**24, **3:**328, 333;
 giant swamp **3:**328
tarragon **1:**42, **2:**146, 147, 174,
 175, **3:**333, **5:**618
tarragon vinegar **3:**333
tarsioids **9:**1250
Tartary buckwheat **4:**428
tarweed **2:**214
Tasmannia **1:**125, **3:**378
tassel flower **1:**27, *27*, **2:**130
tatami **2:**190
tau-saghyz **3:**333
tawhiwhi **3:**274, **2:***174*
taxa **6:**696
Taxodiaceae **6:**743
Taxodium **3:**333, **6:**746, 747;
 distichum **7:**837
taxonomy **6:**694-7;
 folk **6:**694;
 scientific **6:**694
Taxus **2:**173, **3:**360, **6:**749
tea **1:**58, 59, **2:**227, **3:**333, *333*,
 4:432, 433, **6:**684, *685*;
 Algerian **2:**260;
 Appalachian **3:**354;
 Arabian **1:**58, **2:**192;
 Assam **3:**333;
 beggar's **3:**302;
 brown **2:**202;
 bush **1:**58;
 Cape **1:**58;
 Caucasian **1:**39;
 China **3:**333;
 Greenland **7:**876;
 Labrador **7:**903;
 Mexican **1:**86;
 New Jersey **1:**80;
 oswego **2:**174, 232;
 Paraguay **1:**26, 58, **2:**178;
 tansy **3:**332
tea bush **1:**50
tea tree **2:**202, 213, **4:**512;
 heath **2:**202
teaberry **2:**155, **3:**354
teak **3:**334, 341, **5:**586, 587,
 6:719, **7:**835;
 African **2:**187, **3:**341;
 bastard **1:**68, **3:**283;
 Bengal **1:**68;
 Cape **3:**327;
 fustic **2:**187
tea-seed oil **3:**334, **4:**432, 433
teasel **1:**122, **5:**611, 612;
 fuller's **1:**122
Tecoma **2:**164, **3:**334
Tecomaria **2:**178, **3:**334, **5:**600
Tecophilaea **5:**669
 cyanocrocus **7:**954
Tecophilaeaceae **5:**669
Tectona **3:**334, **5:**587;
 grandis **7:**835
tectonic dating **9:**1149
Teesdalia **4:**470
teff **2:**132, 149, 230, **5:**640
Tegelen fossil flora **6:**749
tektites **8:***987*, 989-90, *990*
Telanthropus **9:**1252
telegraph plant **1:**119
Telekia **1:**68
teleosts **9:**1184, 1189, *1206*,
 1234-5
Telephium **4:**419
Telesonix **1:**62
Telfairia **2:**245, **4:**465, 467
Teline **2:**160
Tellima **3:**334, **4:**497
tellurides **8:**1110

Telopea **3:**334, **4:**520
telophase in meiosis **6:***763*
 temnospondyls **9:**1235, 1236
temperate regions, cool:
 in Antarctic dominion **7:**904-5;
 bogs of **7:**879-80, *902-3*, 903;
 Boreal vegetation of **7:**902-4;
 cold winter deserts in **7:**845;
 deciduous and Boreal forests of
 7:*832-3*, 838-9;
 dry grasslands of **7:**859-60;
 heathlands of **7:**872-3, *873*;
 humid grasslands of **7:**861-2
temperate regions, warm:
 chaparral scrublands of **7:**843-
 56;
 cool winter and coastal deserts of
 7:845;
 humid grasslands of **7:**860-1;
 sclerophyllous and evergreen
 forests of **7:***832-3*, 836-8
temperate salt marsh **7:***888-9*,
 888-90
temperature:
 and adaptation **6:**770-1;
 and desert plants **7:**848;
 and distribution **6:**785, *789*,
 790;
 and exposure **6:**800-1;
 and flowering **6:***793*;
 and metabolism **6:**787-9, *788*,
 789-92;
 and mountain vegetation **7:**863;
 and tundra vegetation **7:**853
temple tree **3:**275
temporal isolation **6:**781
Tenagocharis **5:**619, 620
tendergreen **1:**87
tennantite **8:**1107
Tephrosia **3:**334
tephra **8:**1034, 1057, 1058
tequila **1:**13, 16
terebinth **3:**273, **334**
Terminal Eocene Event **6:**747
Terminalia **1:**45, **3:**324, **334**,
 4:514, *515*, 515, 516;
 superba **6:**771
Ternstroemia **4:**432
Ternstroemiaceae **4:**432
Ternstroemieae **4:**432
terpenes **6:***822*, 822-3
terra rossa **6:**810, *811*
terrestrial peats **6:**810
terrestrial pollution **7:**945-6
Tertiary **6:***738-9*, 740, 744, 745,
 745-8, *746*, **8:**1001, **9:***1125*,
 1131, **1191-8**, 1216, 1261,
 1271;
 climate **9:**1192, 1193, 1197-8;
 fauna **9:***1192*, 1193-4, 1195,
 1196-7;
 flora **9:***1192*, 1196, 1197;
 geography **9:**1191, *1192*, *1193*,
 1195, *1196*, *1197*;
 formation of coal **8:**1118;
 volcanic activity **8:**1034;
 see also Paleocene, Eocene,
 Oligocene, Miocene, Pliocene
Tessarandra **5:**577
Tethys Ocean **6:**742, 745, **9:**1176,
 1179, 1180, 1181, 1187,
 1188, 1191, 1192, 1193,
 1194, 1237
Tetracentraceae **4:**405
Tetracentron **4:**405
Tetracera **4:***430*, 430, 431
Tetrachondra **5:**590
Tetrachondraceae **5:**590, 591
Tetraclinis **3:**306
tetraethyl lead **8:**1103, 1111
Tetragastris **5:**546, 547
tetragonal system *see* crystal
 systems
Tetragonia **3:**321, 350
Tetragonolobus **2:**211
tetrahedrite **8:**1109
Tetramelaceae **4:**464

Tetrameles **4:**464
Tetrameristicaceae **4:**432
Tetrapanax **5:**568
Tetraphis **3:**334
Tetrapilus **5:**577
Tetraplasandra **5:***568*
Tetrapteris **5:**563
Tetrastigma **4:***539*, 539
Tetratheca **5:**564
Tetroncium **5:**623
tetterbush **2:**213
Teucrium **3:**335, **5:**574, *589*, 589
texture:
 of rocks **9:**1129, 1136, 1138-9;
 of soils **9:**1140
Thalassia **5:**621, 622
Thalassioideae **5:**622
Thalassodendron **5:**627
Thalia **5:**650
Thalictrum **3:**335, **3:**396, *399*,
 399;
 alpinum **6:**750
thallium **8:**1099
thalloid epiphytes **6:**721
thalloid plants, life-forms of **6:**719
 Thamnea **4:**491
Thamnochortus **5:***634*, 634
Thamnosma **5:**554
t-ha-na-sa **2:**226
Thapsia **5:**571
Thassalaria **7:**945
thatch **7:***882*, 883
Thaumatococcus **3:**335
Thea **3:**333, **4:**432
Theaceae **4:**432-3, *433*, 435, 439,
 445, **7:**896
Theales **4:**432-9, 445
thebaine **1:**26
Thecocarpus **5:**571
thecodonts **9:**1181, *1211*, 1236,
 1239, 1241, 1243
theine **1:**26, 58, 69
Theligonaceae **4:**503-4, *504*
Theligonum **4:**504, 504
Thelypodieae **4:**470
Themeda **2:**149, **5:**638;
 australis **7:**940;
 trianda **7:**856, 863
Theobroma **1:**96, **3:**335, **4:***442*,
 442;
 cacao **7:**926
theobromine **1:**26, 58, **2:**227
theol **1:**58
Theophrasta **4:**486
Theophrastaceae **4:**486
Theophrastus **6:**680, 702
therapsids **9:**1243-4
therocephalians **9:**1243
therophytes **6:***725*, 725, 727
Thesieae **4:**521
Thesium **3:**337, **4:***521*, 521
Thevetia **5:**575
thimbleberry **3:**288, 300
Thismia **5:**671
Thismieae **5:**671
thistle **3:**335, **5:**613, 618;
 blessed **1:**93, **3:**335;
 bull **1:**90;
 cabbage **1:**90;
 Canadian **3:**335;
 carline **1:**75, 76;
 common cotton **2:**252;
 creeping **1:**90, *90*;
 globe **2:**128;
 holy **3:**335;
 marsh **1:**90;
 melancholy **1:**90;
 milk **3:**335;
 musk **1:**75, **3:**335;
 nodding **1:**75;
 picknicker's **1:**90;
 Russian **3:**305;
 Scotch **2:**252, 241;
 slender **1:**75;
 spear **1:**90, *90*, **6:***724*;

 stemless **1:**90, **7:**940;
 stemless carline **1:**75;
 torch **1:**82;
 welted **1:**75, **3:**335;
 see also Carduus, Cirsium
Thlaspi **4:***470*, 470
Thoatherium **9:**1205
tholeiitic rock **8:**1092
Thomas, H. H. **6:**733
Thonningia **4:**526
Thoracocarpus **5:**654
thorium **8:**972, 973, 979, 997,
 1007, **1111**, **9:**1126, 1142,
 1143, 1152, 1270
thorn-cushion plants **6:**722
thorn-shrubs **6:**721
thorn-tree life-form **6:**719
thorn:
 babul **1:**7;
 branch **2:**133;
 camel **1:**7;
 cockspur **2:**169;
 Egyptian **1:**7;
 Jerusalem **2:**260;
 kaffir **2:**213;
 kangaroo **1:**7;
 rabbit **2:**213
thorn-apple **1:***117*, **2:**226, 227;
 common **1:**117;
 downy **1:**117, **2:**226
Thottea **3:**391
thousand mothers **3:**337
three faces under a hood **2:**259
thrift **1:**40, *41*, **4:**428, 429;
 prickly **1:**8;
 sea **6:**750
Thrinax **3:**335
throatwood **5:**606
Thuidium **3:**335
Thuja **3:**335, **6:**748;
 plicata **6:**683, **7:**837
Thujopsis **3:**336
Thunberg, Carl Peter **6:**683, 684
Thunbergia **3:**336, **5:**600, 601
Thurmann, Jules **6:**719
Thurnia **5:**641
Thurniaceae **5:**634, **641-2**
Thurnian phase **6:**748
thyme **2:**147, 229, **3:**336, **5:**589;
 cat **3:**335;
 caraway **2:**174;
 common **3:**336;
 cone head **3:**336;
 garden **2:**174, *175*, **3:**336;
 lemon **1:**112, **3:**336;
 wild **3:***336*;
 wild creeping **3:**336
thyme oil **2:**136, **3:**336
Thymelaeaceae **4:**445, **509-11**,
 510, 513, 519, 528
Thymelaeoideae **4:**510
thymol **1:**77, **3:**336
Thymus **3:**336, **5:**589, **7:**836;
 serphyllum **7:**906
Thyrsopteris **3:**342
Tiarella **3:**336, **4:**497
Tibouchina **3:**336, **4:**514
tickseed **1:**57, 104, *105*, **7:**921
tickweed **1:**104
tidal waves *see* tsunamis
tide, red **3:**289
tides in salt marsh **7:**889
Tidestromia **4:**420;
 oblongifolia **6:**792
tidy-tips **2:**199
tiger flower **3:**336;
 Mexican **3:**336;
 Peacock **3:**336
tiger jaw **2:**139
tiger-eye **8:***1085*, 1087, 1098
tigernut **5:**642, 643
Tigridia **3:**336, **5:**662
tile ore **8:**1089
Tilia **3:**336, **6:**750, **7:**838, **4:***441*,
 441;
 americana **7:**896;
 cordata **7:**896
Tiliaceae **4:**439, **440-1**, *441*, 442,
 445, 452

Tiliacora 3:401
till 8:1002, 1019, 1020, 1049, 1050, 1052, 9:1133
Tillandsia 3:336, 5:644, 646
Tillandsioideae 5:644
tillites 8:*1049*, 9:1133, 1162
tilloids 8:*1049*
timber:
   conservation 7:958;
   consumption 7:935, 937-8;
   see also tree plantations
timberline 7:868, *869*, 901
Timothy, Alpine 3:268
tin 8:1084, 1087, 1104, **1109**, *1110*
tinda 4:467
Tingia 6:*740*
Tinomiscium 6:747
Tinospora 3:401, *401*, 6:747
Tinosporeae 3:401
tip layering in blackberry 6:*778*
tips:
   rubbish 7:946;
   colliery 7:946
Tipuana 3:296
tisswood 3:266
titanite *see* sphene
titanium 8:979, 1092, 1098, **1105**
Titanopsis 4:415
titanotheres 9:1195, 1248
Titanotrichum 5:596
Tithonia 3:336, 5:617
Tmesipteris 1:94, *95*
toad plant 3:323:
   giant 3:323;
   hairy 3:324;
   shaggy 3:324
toadflax 2:204, *207*, 3:321, **337**;
   Alpine 2:207;
   bastard 3:337;
   common 3:337;
   ivy-leaved 1:*112*, 3:337;
   pale 2:207;
   purple 2:207;
   striped 2:207
toadshade 3:343;
   painted 3:343
tobacco 1:26, 2:227, 241, 256, 3:**337**, *337*, 5:579, 6:823, 7:926, 927, 932, 943, 946, 948;
   common 2:241;
   Indian 2:209, 227;
   mountain 1:41;
   tree 2:241
Toddalia 2:187, 5:552, 554
Toddalioideae 5:554
toddy 1:16, 41, 2:129, 5:654
Tofieldia 1:45
Toisusu 4:468
Toit, Alexander du 6:741
tola-shrubs 6:721
tolerance 6:*814-5*, **814-6**;
   to air pollution 7:942-3, *943*;
   to drought 7:848;
   to salts 7:890, 891;
   to shade 7:841;
   and zonation 6:828
Tolmiea 3:337, 4:497
tomatillo 2:151, 3:270, 5:579
tomato 3:**337**, *337*, 350, *351*, 5:579, 7:926, 927, 932;
   cherry 7:927;
   currant 3:337;
   Mexican husk 3:270;
   strawberry 3:270;
   tree 1:*113*, 3:337
tombolos 8:1056
tomillares 7:844
tools and early domestication 7:931
toon 1:80, 3:**342**
Toona 5:552
toothbrush tree 4:530
toothwort 2:198, 5:598, *599*, 6:*724*;
   purple 2:198, *199*
topaz 8:1079, 1082, 1087, **1100**, 1109

topee-tambu 1:70, 3:*298*, **342**, 5:651
topoclines 6:706
topogenous moors 7:883
topography:
   and exposure 6:800-1;
   and grassland **7:862**
tor grass 7:940
torbernite 8:1111
torch thistle 1:**82**
Torenia 3:**342**, 5:595
toria 1:64
Toricellia 4:517, *518*
Torilis 5:571
tornillo 3:281
Torresea 1:27
Torreya 3:**342**
torreya:
   Chinese 3:342;
   Japanese 3:342
tors 8:1010, 1043
Tortella 2:234
tortoises 9:1236-7
Tortula 3:**342**, 6:824;
   ruraliformis 6:825
torus herb 1:*123*
tourism and conservation 7:937, 955
tourmaline 8:1009, 1080, 1087, 1089, **1100**, 1102, 1109, 9:*1125*
Tournefort, Joseph Pitton de 6:681
Tournefortia 5:586, 6:826
tournesol 1:88
Tournonia 4:425
Touroulia 4:438
Tovaria 4:469
Tovariaceae 4:469
Tovomita 4:436
Townsendia 3:342
Toxicodendron 3:294
Toxicophloea 1:9
Toxicoscordion 5:362
toxins:
   in atmosphere 7:942;
   in biocides 7:946-7;
   defensive 6:821-3, *822*;
   in farm effluents 7:946;
   see also herbicides, phytotoxins, poisons
trace elements 6:807
trace fossils 9:1154, 1186, 1211, 1224, 1228, **1230**
Trachelium 5:604, 606
Trachelospermum 3:342
Trachycarpus 3:342, 5:651, 654
Trachylobium 2:183
Trachyspermum 1:77
trachytes 8:1093, 9:1126
Tradescant, John 6:682, *683*
Tradescantia 3:342, 5:629, *631*, 631, 6:*683*;
   canaliculata 6:780;
   occidentalis 6:780
Tradescantioideae 5:629
tragacanth 1:46
Tragopogon 3:305, **342**, 5:617, 618
Tragus 5:638
trailing annuals 6:724
trailing herbs 6:*723*, 723
trample burrs 6:817
trampling:
   human 7:888, 937;
   by grazing animals 7:938, 940
tranquillityite 8:979
transects 6:*711*, **714-5**, *715*
transform faults 8:1026, *1060*, *1061*
transition mires 7:876
Transitional rocks 9:1259
translocations in chromosomes 6:777, 7:958
transpiration 7:843, 8:*1069*
transplant gardens 6:*705*, 705-6
Trapa 3:**356**, 4:506;
   natans 6:725, 749, 818
Trapaceae **4:506**
Trapella 5:601

Trautvetteria 3:399
traveller's palm 5:647
traveller's tree 3:289, 5:647
treacleberry 3:317
tree celandine 1:60
Trebouxia 2:204
tree fern 3:**342**, *342*
tree heath 7:872, *see also Erica arborea*
tree of heaven 1:14, 5:549
tree peony 4:432
tree plantations 7:842, 879-80, *936*, 936, 938
tree poppy 1:60
tree senecio 3:313, 7:896
tree toad 3:331
tree tomato 5:579
treeline 7:868, *869*
tree-ring dating 6:734-5, *735*;
   see also dendrochronology
trees, life-forms of 6:719-20
trefoil 3:**343**;
   bird's-foot 2:211, *211*, 3:343;
   hop 3:343;
   shrubby 3:343;
   sweet 3:343;
   yellow 2:149, 3:314, 343
Trema 4:445, 446, *446*
Tremandra 5:564
Tremandraceae **5:564**
trematosaurs 9:1235
Trentepohlia 1:*18*
Treponema 1:*50*
Triadenum 4:435
Triadobatrachus 9:1236
Triassic 6:*738-9*, 740, 741, 9:1173, **1177-81**, *1180*, 1209;
   climate 9:1177, *1179*, 1181;
   fauna 9:1177, *1178*, 1178-9;
   flora 9:1175, 1177-8, *1178*, 1179;
   geography 9:1177, *1178*, 1179-81
Tribonanthes 5:668
Tribulus 5:554;
   terrestris 6:816
Triceratops 9:1189, 1242
Trichilia 5:552
Trichinium 4:420;
   manglesii 6:687
Trichocereus 3:343
Trichocladus 4:407
Trichocladus 4:407
Trichoderma 3:343
Trichodesmium 3:289
Trichomanes 3:343
Trichopus 5:670
Trichosantheae 4:465
Trichosanthes 2:163, 222, 3:350, 4:465, 467, *467*
Trichoscyphella 3:343
Trichosporeae 5:596
Trichosporum 5:596
Trichostigma 4:421, *422*
triclinic system *see* crystal systems
Triclisia 3:401
Triclisieae 3:401
triconodonts 9:1184, 1245
Tricyrtis 3:343
Tridax 5:617, 618
Trientalis 3:**343**, 4:484;
   europaea 7:903
trifoliate orange 5:554
Trifolieae 4:502
Trifolium 1:92, 3:314, 343, 4:499, 502;
   repens 6:706, 7:940
trigger plant 5:606
Triglochin 3:**343**, 5:623
trigonal system *see* crystal systems
Trigonella 3:343
trigonelline 1:26
Trigonia 5:564
Trigoniaceae **5:564**, 565
Trigoniastrum 5:564

Trigonobalanus 4:410, *410*
Trigonocapnos 4:403
Trigonocarpus 6:732
Trillium 3:**343**, 5:662
trillium:
   purple 3:344;
   snow 3:343
trilobites 9:1152-3, 1154, 1155, 1156, 1159, 1160, 1161, 1162, 1165, 1227-8, **1228**
Trimenia 3:384
Trimeniaceae 3:384
Trimerophytales 9:1216
Trinidad devil 3:289
Triodia 7:842, 862, *863*;
   basedowii 6:723
Triosteum 5:610
Tripleurospermum:
   inodorum 7:888;
   maritimum 7:888, *921*
Triplochiton 3:341
Tripsacum 2:149
Tripterococcus 4:530
Trisetum 7:861;
   flavescens 7:862
Tristan da Cunha:
   and aliens 7:921;
   and long-distance dispersal 7:919
Tristellateia 5:563, 564
Triteleia 3:**344**, 5:664
Trithrinax 5:653
Trithuria 5:633
Trithurieae 5:633
Triticale 3:344
triticale 3:344, 7:934
Triticeae 5:638
Triticosecale 3:344, 7:934
Triticum 2:143, 236, 3:344, 5:638, 640;
   aestivum 7:926, *927*;
   dicoccum 7:927;
   durum 7:927;
   monococcum 7:927;
   sativum 7:943;
   timopheevi 7:927
Tritonia 1:109, 3:**344**, 5:662
tritylodonts 9:1244
Triumfetta 4:441, *441*
Triuridaceae **5:627**
Triuridales 5:627
Triuris 5:627
Trochetia melanoxylon 7:921
Trochocarpa 4:478, *478*
Trochodendraceae **4:405**
Trochodendrales 4:405
Trochodendron 4:405, 6:747
Trochomeria 4:465
troilite 8:972, 986, 989, 1097
Trollius 3:**345**, 396, *396*, 399
trona 8:1103
Tropaeolaceae 5:559, *562*, **562-3**
Tropaeolum 2:238, 3:**345**, 396, 5:562, *562*, 563
tropical agriculture 7:842, 880, 935, 935, 952
tropical bogs and peat 7:877-9, *878*, 880
tropical fens and peat 7:883
tropical floristic realms 7:896
tropical forests 7:*832-3*;
   destruction of 7:842, 935, 937, 937-8;
   dry seasonal 7:835, **835-6**;
   wet 6:692, 709, 712, 7:*834*, **834-5**, 890-1
tropical grasslands 7:856-7
tropical mountains 7:*863*, 866
tropical scrub 7:842
tropophytes 6:719
tropophytic crown-trees 6:719
tropophytic shrubs 6:721
truffle 3:**345**;
   false 2:129;
   summer 3:345;
   white Piedmont 3:345
trumpet creeper 1:73
trumpet leaf 3:308

trumpet tree 1:80
trumpet vine 1:73, 5:600
trumpet-flower 1:57;
    Chinese 1:73
tryptophan and maize 7:935
Trystachya 5:636
tsamma 3:357, 4:467
tshwala 3:319
Tsoongiodendron 3:378
Tsuga 2:173, 6:748, 7:841, 896;
    canadensis 6:826;
    heterophylla 6:683, 7:837;
    see also hemlock spruce
tsunamis (tidal waves) 8:1027
tsze-lien 4:407
tuba root 1:119
Tuber 3:345
tuber of potato 6:778
Tuberaria 4:458, 458
tuberose 2:136, 3:277
Tubiflorae 4:506, 5:593, 602
tubocurarine 2:227, 3:327
tu-chung 4:407
tuffs 8:1085, 9:1122
tuft grasses 6:723, 7:855
tuft-trees 6:720, 720
Tulbaghia 5:664
tulip 3:345, 346, 347, 5:662,
    6:680, 723;
    globe 1:72;
    mariposa 1:72;
    large star 1:72;
    small star 1:72
tulip breaking virus 3:346
tulip tree 2:208, 3:321, 346, 377,
    378, 6:748, 749, 749, 7:838;
    Chinese 3:346
tulip wood 3:346
Tulipa 3:345, 5:662, 664;
    michaeliana 6:723
Tulipeae 5:664
tumbleweeds 6:817
tummy wood 4:450
tundra 7:832, 832-3, 850-5, 851-
    5, 8:1019-20, 1050-1, 1050,
    1051;
    alpine 7:850, 851, 854, 868,
        937;
    in Fuegia and New Zealand
        7:905;
    grass- 7:861;
    human influence on 7:936-7,
        937;
    polygons in 6:716, 7:901;
    shrubby 7:902;
    wet meadows in 7:854, 901
tung 3:346
tung oil 2:250, 3:346, 4:535, 537
tung-oil tree 1:15
tungsten 8:1084, 1101, 1110
tunka 2:223
tupelo 2:243, 4:516, 6:747
turbidites 8:1016, 1018, 1060,
    1062
turbidity currents 8:1016, 1055,
    1061, 1062, 1063, 9:1132,
    1157, 1266
Turbina 2:226
Turesson, Göte 6:705, 776, 7:967
turf 7:855
turf fens 7:881
turf-dormant herbs 6:723
Turgenia 5:569
turgor 7:845
Turk's cap 1:9
Turk's cap cactus 4:415
turlough 6:715
turmeric 1:111, 2:126, 146, 147,
    3:346, 5:647, 648
turmeric plant, African 1:73
Turnera 3:346, 4:454, 454
Turneraceae 4:453-4, 454
turnip 1:64, 65, 3:298, 299, 346,
    4:472;
    Dutch 1:64;
    green-top 1:64;
    Indian 1:40, 2:133, 3:283;
    stubble 1:64;

Swedish 1:64, 3:330
turnipwood 2:127
turpentine 3:272, 346, 5:548;
    Cyprus 3:334;
    Swiss 3:323;
    Venice 2:197
turpentine tree 1:68, 3:273
Turpinia 5:540, 540, 541
turquoise 8:1100
Turraea 5:552
Turraeanthus 3:341
turtle head 1:86
turtles 9:1181, 1187, 1189,
    1236-7
tussac 7:862
Tussilago 3:347, 5:617
tussock grass 6:723, 723, 7:855,
    861-2;
    silver 7:861
tussock herbs 6:723
tutsan 2:184
Tuttle, O. 9:1264-5
twayblades 2:208
twin flower 2:207
twinning 8:1076, 1086, 1090,
    1096
twitch-grass 1:13
two-men-in-a-boat 3:293
Tylophoreae 5:576
tylopods 9:1248
type concept 6:699
type specimens 6:699
Typha 1:68, 3:347, 5:643, 6:747,
    810, 826, 7:880, 885, 903;
    latifolia 6:827, 7:903
Typhaceae 5:643, 644
Typhales 5:643-4
typhoid fever 1:51
typhus 1:51
Tyrannosaurus 9:1189, 1241

Uapaca 4:537
ucuhuba 3:347, 3:382
ucuhuba butter 3:347
Uganda tree 3:321
ugli 2:217, 3:347
Ugni 2:237
Ulex 3:347, 4:499, 502, 6:690,
    786;
    europaeus 6:751, 751, 826;
    gallii 7:873
ulexite 8:1102
ulloco (ullucu) 3:299, 347, 350,
    4:425, 426
Ullucus 3:347, 350, 4:425, 426
Ulmaceae 4:445-6, 446, 449
Ulmannia 9:1176
Ulmaria 4:494
Ulmarieae 4:491
Ulmeae 4:445, 446
Ulmus 2:129, 4:445, 446, 446,
    6:749
Ulothrix 1:20, 3:347
ultisols 6:809
ultramarine 8:1093
Ulva 3:311
Umbellales 4:494, 5:567-71
Umbelliferae 5:568, 569-71, 570,
    618
Umbellularia 2:198, 7:843
Umbilicus 3:264, 347, 4:495
umbrella tree 2:224, 3:309;
    Texas 2:224
umzimbeet 3:347;
    giant 3:347
Uncaria 1:112, 2:126, 154, 5:609
Uncarina 5:601
Uncinia 5:643
unconformities 8:1113, 9:1148,
    1152, 1263
underground perennials 6:723-4
unicorn plant 2:220, 5:602, 603

unidimensional ordination 6:730
Uniformitarianism 9:1147, 1148,
    1149, 1261, 1262, 1263,
    1266, 1267, 1270, 1271,
    1273;
    genetic 6:765;
    geological 6:731, 760
unions 6:729
unit cell 8:1075
United Nations Food and
    Agriculture Organization
    7:959
units of vegetation 6:727-9
upas tree 3:347
Uppsala school of plant sociology
    6:729
Ural Mountains 9:1166, 1173
Uralian geosyncline 9:1174, 1176,
    1177
Uralian Sea 9:1176, 1192, 1195
uraninite (pitchblende) 8:1100,
    1111
uranium 8:972, 973, 979, 988,
    997, 1007, 1073, 1083,
    1100, 1104, 1111, 1114,
    9:1142, 1143, 1152, 1270
uranium-lead dating 9:1143, 1146
Uranus 8:971, 972
Urceolina 3:348
Urena 2:144, 4:445
Ureneae 4:445
Urera 4:448
Urginea 3:323, 348, 5:664;
    maritima 6:723
urn plant 1:11
Urogentias 5:573
Ursinia 3:348, 5:617, 618
Ursinieae 5:618
Urtica 2:241, 3:348, 4:447, 448,
    448, 449;
    dioica 7:884
Urticaceae 4:446, 447-9, 448,
    504, 537
Urticales 4:407, 445-9
Urticeae 4:448
urushiol 2:227, 3:276
U-shaped valleys 8:1012, 1019,
    1037, 1039, 1048, 1049
Usnea 3:348, 5:673
usnic acid 2:205
Ussher, J. 9:1275
Ustilago 3:348
utile 3:341, 5:552
Utricularia 3:313, 348, 5:603,
    603, 604, 644, 6:816
Uvaria 3:381
uvarovite 8:1090, 1091
Uvularia 3:348

Vaccinioideae 4:477
Vaccinium 1:59, 60, 108, 3:349,
    4:474, 477, 7:838, 873, 876,
    903;
    macrocarpon 7:880;
    myrtillus 7:873, 875;
    oxycoccus 7:885;
    vitis-idaea 7:873
vadose caves 8:1043
vadose water 8:1069-70, 1070
valence (valency) 8:1101
valerian 1:17, 81, 5:610;
    cat's 3:349;
    common 3:349;
    Greek 3:276;
    red 1:81;
    spur 1:81
Valeriana 1:17, 3:349, 5:610, 611
Valerianaceae 5:610, 611, 618
Valerianella 3:349, 5:610, 611
valid publication 6:699
valley bog 7:876, 880, 883, see
    also fens

valley cooling 6:801, 7:862, 863
valley zonation 6:829
Vallisneria 3:349, 5:621, 621
Vallota 3:309, 349, 5:666
Valonia 3:349
Van Balgooy, M. M. J. 7:895
vanadinite 8:1105
vanadium 8:1105
Vancouveria 3:396
Vanda 3:349, 5:675
Vandeae 5:675
Vanilla 3:349, 5:675
vanilla 2:146, 147, 3:349;
    Pompona 3:349;
    West Indian 3:349
vanillin 5:671, 675
Vantanea 5:556, 556
variability, centers of 7:906-7
variants, phytocoenal 6:729
varnish tree 1:15, 2:194, 195
varves 9:1131, 1267;
    and dating 6:735
vascular plants 9:1163, 1216-7
Vatica 1:122, 4:435
Vaucheria 3:349, 7:944
vauclusian springs 8:1044
Vavilov, N. I. 7:927, 957, 967
vectors of diseases and pests 7:949
vegetable humming bird 3:314
vegetable ivory 5:653, 654
vegetable marrow 4:467
vegetable oyster 3:305, 342
vegetable sheep 3:288, 4:470,
    7:919
vegetable spaghetti 4:467
vegetable tallow 4:535, 537
vegetation:
    azonal 7:872-91;
    classification of 7:831-81;
    cycles of 6:716;
    description of 6:708-30;
    units of 6:727-9;
    zonal 7:831-62
vegetative diversity 6:768
vegetative reproduction 6:777,
    778, 816;
    and early agriculture 7:925,
        928, 931;
    in tundra 7:854
veins 8:1023, 1031, 1084, 1087,
    1090, 1097
Veitch, James Harry 6:685
Veitch, John Gould 6:685, 687
veitchberry 2:151
Veitchia joannis 6:687
veld 7:860, 862, 863
Vella 4:470
Vellozia 5:665, 667
Velloziaceae 5:665, 667, 668
velvet elephant ear 2:192
velvet leaf 1:7, 2:192
velvet plant 2:167;
    trailing 3:301
× *Venidio-arctotis* 3:349
Venidium 3:353, 5:617
Vening Meinesz, F. 8:1005, 9:1269
Ventilago 4:437, 538
Venturia 3:353
Venus 8:971, 981-2, 982;
    greenhouse effect 8:997
Venus' fly trap 1:32, 121, 4:489,
    6:683, 710
Venus hair 1:10
Venus' necklace 2:179
Vepris 5:554
Veratrum 3:353, 5:664
Verbascoideae 5:593
Verbascum 2:233, 5:593, 595, 595
Verbena 3:353, 5:587, 587
verbena 3:353;
    clump 3:341;
    garden 3:353;
    lemon 2:174, 208, 3:353;
    rose 3:353;
    sand 7:849;
    sweet-scented 2:208, 3:353
verbena oil 3:353

Verbenaceae **5:586-7**, *587*, 589, 591
Verbenoideae **5:**587
verdasan **7:**946
Verhuellia **3:**390, *390*
vermiculite **8:**1088, **1100-1**
vermouth **1:**16, 58
vernacular names **6:**697-8
vernal grass, sweet **1:**36
vernalization **6:***793*
Verneuil process **8:**1098
Vernicia **4:**537
Vernonia **3:**353, **5:**617
Vernonieae **5:**617
Veronica **3:**353, **5:**590, 593, 595, *595*;
  repens **6:***723*
Verrucaria maura **6:***829*
Verschaffeltia **5:**651
vertebrates **9:**1176, 1205, **1230-53**
vertical structure **6:**717
vertisol **6:**808, *809*
vervain **2:**174, **3:**353, **5:**587;
  creeping **3:**353;
  rose **3:**353;
  see also verbena
vesuvianite *see* idocrase
Vesuvius **8:**1058, 1092, *1093*
vetch **3:**354, **4:**499, **6:***723*;
  bitter **3:**354;
  common **3:**354;
  crown **1:**105, *105*, **2:**149;
  hairy **2:**149;
  hairy winter **3:**354;
  horseshoe **3:**354, **7:**908;
  kidney **2:**149, **3:**354, **6:**779;
  milk **3:**354, **1:**46;
  purple **3:**354;
  purple milk **1:**46;
  Russian **3:**354;
  spring **2:**149, **3:**354;
vetchling **2:**164, **3:**354;
  meadow **2:**198
vetiver **3:**354
vetiver oil **2:**136, 193
Vetiveria **2:**193, **3:**354, **5:**638
Viburnum **3:**354, **5:***609*, 610
viburnum **3:***354*;
  sweet **3:**354
vicariance **7:***(908)*, **908**
Vicia **3:**354, **4:**499, 502;
  augustifolia **6:***723*
Vicieae **4:**502
Victoria **3:***355*, 357, 394, *394*, 395;
  regia **6:**724
Victoria box **4:**489
Vigna **1:**107, **4:**502
vilea **2:**226
Villarsia **5:**574, 581
vinblastine **2:**227
Vinca **3:**355, **5:**574, *574*, 575
vincristine **2:**227
vine **3:**355, **356**;
  balloon **1:**75;
  bamboo **3:**317;
  black grape **3:**356;
  blue trumpet **3:**336;
  bay star **3:**310;
  clock **3:**336;
  cross **1:**57;
  firecracker **2:**218;
  flame **3:**285, *285*;
  grape **3:**356, *356*;
  Japanese crimson glory **3:**356;
  Japanese hydrangea **3:**310;
  kangaroo **1:**90, *90*;
  kudzu **2:**149;
  link **3:**349;
  matrimony **2:**213;
  moonseed **1:**111;
  Pollyanna **3:**318;
  potato **3:**317;
  quarter **1:**57;
  Russian **3:**277;
  sky **3:**336;
  staff **1:**80;

tara **1:**10;
wire **2:**233;
Wonga-wonga **2:**259;
worm **3:**349
Vine, F. **8:**1004, **9:**1269
vinegar tree **2:**126, **3:**294
Viola **2:**259, **3:**355, **4:***450*, 450, 451;
  canina **7:***887*;
  cunninghamii **6:***687*;
  lactea **7:***896*;
  magellanica **6:***728*;
  rupestris **7:***912*
viola **3:**355, *355*;
  horned **3:**355
Violaceae **4:***450*, **450-1**, 461
Violales **4:**432, 450-67, 468
violet **2:**136, **3:**355, **4:**450, 451;
  African **3:**302, *305*;
  damask **2:**173;
  dame's **2:**173;
  dog **3:**355;
  dog-tooth **2:**135, *135*;
  English **3:**355;
  florist's **3:**355;
  garden **3:**355;
  German **2:**138;
  Labrador **3:**355;
  Northern blue **3:**355;
  Philippine **1:**53;
  sweet **3:**355;
  Teesdale **7:***913*;
  usambar **3:**302;
  water **2:**179;
  white dog-tooth **2:**135;
  wood **3:**355
violet slipper **3:**316
violetta **3:**355
viperids **9:**1238
Virginia bluebell **5:**586
Virginia creeper **2:**260, 261, **4:**538, 539, **6:***772*
Virginia-willow **2:**187
Virola **3:**347, 381, *381*, 382
Viscaceae **4:**524
Visceae **4:**525
Viscoideae **4:**524, 525
Viscum **1:**17, **2:**231, **4:**524, 525, **7:***948*;
  album **7:***898*
Vismia **4:**436, 437
Visnea **4:**432
Vitaceae **4:**441, 537, **538-9**, *539*
Vitex **3:***355*, **5:**587, 587
Viticoideae **5:**587
Vitis **1:**111, **2:***163*, 236, **3:***287*, **329**, 355, 356, **4:**538, 539, 539
vitrite **8:**1118
Viviania **5:**559
Vivianiaceae **5:**559
Vivianoideae **5:**559
Vleisia **5:**625
Voandzeia **2:**201
Vochysia **5:**564, *565*, 565
Vochysiaceae **5:564-5**, *565*
vodka **1:**16, 58
Vogt, William **7:**955
Voladeria **5:***1034*
volcanic bombs **8:***1034*
volcanic rocks *see* igneous rocks
volcanic theory of origin of life **6:***752*, 753-4
volcanoes *see* vulcanicity
Voltzia **9:**1179
Voltziaceae **6:**740
Volvox **3:**356
Vonitra **3:**271
Voyria **5:**573, *573*
Vriesea **3:**356, **5:**644, *644*, 646
vulcanicity (volcanism) **8:**997, 1003, **1032-4**, *1033*, *1034*, 1035, 1037, **1057-8**, *1057*, *1058*, 1063-4, 1071, **9:**1126, 1128, 1149, *1196*, *1201*, 1202-3, *1258*, 1264, 1272-3;
  lunar **8:**977, 980;

Martian **8:**983-5, *985*;
see also plate tectonics
Vulcano **8:**1058

Wachendorfia **5:**668
wadadura wood **4:**450
wadis **8:**1047
Wahlenbergia **3:**356, **5:**604
Wahlenberginae **5:**604
wahoo tree **1:**68
wake-robin **1:**42, **3:**343;
  white **3:**343, *343*
Walchia **9:**1175
Waldsteinia **3:**325
wallaba **3:**341
Wallace, Alfred **6:**745, 760, **7:**967
Wallace's line **6:**745
wallfern **3:**278
wallflower **1:**86, *86*, **3:**356, **4:**469, 472;
  beach **2:**134;
  Canary Islands **1:**86, **3:**356;
  common **3:**356;
  fairy **2:**134;
  Siberian **3:**356;
  Western **2:**134
Wallich, Nathaniel **6:**686
wallpepper **3:**312
wallwort **3:**306
walnut **2:**126, 245, *245*, **3:**356, **5:**555, **6:**749, 765, 823;
  African **3:**356;
  black **2:**126, *245*, **3:**356, 341;
  Chinese **2:**245, **3:**356;
  common **2:**245, *245*, **3:**356;
  East India **1:**14;
  English **2:**245, *245*, **3:**356;
  Japanese **2:**245, **3:**356, 341;
  Persian **2:**245, *245*, **3:**356
Walter, T. **6:**702
Walther, J. **9:**1275
wandering Jew **3:**351, 363, **5:**629, 631
wandering sailor **5:**631
wandflower **1:**120, **3:**320
wapatu **3:**302
waratah **3:**334;
  Tasmanian **3:**334
Warburgia **3:**380
Ward, Nathaniel Bagshaw **6:**681
Wardian case **6:***681*, 684, 686
warm temperate forests **7:**836-8
warm winter deserts **7:**844-5
Warming, Eugene **6:**689, **7:**967
Warming, Johannes **6:**719
Washingtonia **7:**896
wasps and pollination **6:**777
water **6:**785, 795-8, **8:**972, 975, 992, 997, 1021, 1044, 1068, **1069-71**, *1069*, 1074, 1084, 1101, **9:**1122, 1128, 1130, 1131, 1135, 1136;
  absorbed by roots **6:**795;
  in chemical weathering **8:**1009, *1010*;
  and climate **6:**787;
  connate **8:**1069;
  in erosion **8:**1010-1, *1011*, 1013-4, *1014*, 1068, **9:***1139*;
  juvenile **8:**1069;
  meteoric **8:**1069, 1074;
  in physical weathering **8:***1009*;
  polluted **7:**943-5;
  and seed dispersal **6:**817-8;
  in soil **6:**804, 814;
  succession from **6:**826-7, *826*, **7:**894;
  and tundra **7:**855;
  see also groundwater, ice, pore waters, rivers, wetlands
water aloe **3:***325*
water archer **3:**302

water balance **7:**866
water chestnut **3:**356, *356*, 357, **4:**506, **6:**749, 818;
  Chinese **2:**129, **3:**357, **5:**642, 643
water deficit **6:**770, 771, *799*, **7:**845, *see also* drought
water hawthorn **5:**622
water hyacinth **5:**659
water lily **2:**243, *243*, **3:**357, 394;
  Amazon **3:**355;
  Cape blue **2:**243;
  European white **2:***243*, 243;
  fringed **2:**243;
  pygmy **2:**243;
  royal **3:**355;
  Santa Cruz **3:**355;
  yellow **2:**242, 243, **3:**357
water lobelia **5:**606
water melon **2:**222, *223*, **3:**357;
  Chinese **2:**223
water milfoil **4:**504
water net **1:**20
water parting **8:**1037
water plantain **5:**619
water plants, life-forms of **6:**719, *see also* hydrophytes
water poppy **5:**619
water soldier **3:**325, *325*
water table **8:**1066, 1070, 1074, **9:**1132
watercress **1:**64, *65*, **2:**238, **3:**357, **4:**472;
  brown **2:**238;
  fool's **1:**37;
  green **2:**238;
  summer **2:**238;
  winter **2:**238
waterfalls **8:**1039
water-herbs **6:**724-5
waterlogging **7:**875
watermelon **4:**467
water-platter:
  Amazon **3:**355;
  Santa Cruz **3:**355
watershed **8:**1037
waterweed, Canadian **2:**130, **5:**621, 622
Watson, James **6:**761
Watsonia **3:**357
wattle **1:**7, **2:**126, **4:**502;
  black Australia **1:**7;
  Cootamundra **1:**7;
  golden **1:**7;
  silver **1:**7;
  Sydney golden **1:**7
wattle and daub **3:**357
wavellite **8:***1101*
wawa **3:**341
wax **3:**357
wax flower **2:**182;
  clustered **3:**324
wax gourd **4:**467
wax palm **1:**84;
  Andean **3:**357;
  South American **3:**357
wax plant **2:**182, *182*, **5:**575, 576
wax tree, white **3:**281
waxberry **3:**330
waxvine **3:**313
waxwork **1:**80
weather clock **1:**75
weathering **6:**802, **8:1008-10**, 1021, 1040, 1042, 1045-6, 1066, 1073, 1121, **9:***1122*, 1131, 1132, 1133;
  chemical **8:**1009-10, *1010*, 1014, 1015, 1045, 1086, **9:**1130, 1133, 1135, 1136;
  Mars **8:**982;
  meteorites **8:**989;
  physical **8:***1008-9*, 1092, **9:**1136, 1138
Weddellina **4:***503*, 503
weed blackjack **1:**57
weeds **6:**819, 820, **7:**947-52;
  in coastal dunes **7:**888;
  and domestication **7:**925;

in grassland 7:940
weeping willow 4:468
Wegener, Alfred 6:740-1, 8:*1001*, 1001-2, 1003, 9:1263, 1267, **1275**
Weichselian glaciation 6:749-50
Weigela 3:357, 5:*609*, 610;
  rosea 6:684
Weinberg, W. 6:774
Weinmannia 4:487, *487*, 6:744, 7:904
weld 2:126, 229
Wellingtonia 6:747
Wells, William 6:759, 760
Welwitschia 3:357;
  bainesii 6:684
Wendtia 5:559
Wendtioideae 5:559
Werner, A. 9:1259, 1260, 1265, 1271, **1275**
West African region 7:*897*
West Indian arrowroot 5:650
West Indian boxwood 4:451, 452, 5:*600*
West Indian gherkin 4:467
West Indian province 7:*898*;
  explorations in 6:682-3
West Indian silkwood 5:554
wet heaths 7:873
wet tropical grasslands 7:856-7
wetlands 7:875-85
whalebacks 8:1029
whales 9:1195, 1237, **1249**
wheat 1:83, 2:143, 3:328, **344**, *344, 345*, 5:635, 638, 640, 6:*821*, 7:926-7, 932-4, *932*, 943, 958;
  bread 1:83, *83*, 3:344, 7:*927*, 934;
  club 1:83, 3:344;
  common bread 1:83, *83*, 3:344;
  cultivated emmer 1:83;
  dinkel 3:344;
  durum 1:83, *83*, 3:344, 7:*927*;
  dwarf 7:934;
  einkorn 1:83, 3:344, 7:*927*;
  emmer 1:83, 3:344, 7:*927*;
  hard 1:83, *83*, 3:344;
  Inca 2:163;
  Indian 2:139;
  macaroni 7:*927*;
  miracle 2:236;
  mummy 2:236;
  Norin 7:934;
  Persian khorasan 3:344;
  Polish 3:344;
  soft 3:344;
  spelt 1:83, 3:344;
  spring 7:880;
  strand 3:301;
  turgidum 1:83;
  wild emmer 1:83, 3:344;
  winter 3:344, 6:*793*
wheatgrass 1:13;
  crested 1:13, 2:149;
  intermediate 1:13;
  slender 2:149;
  Western 1:13
whin, common 3:347
whisk fern 1:94
whisky 1:16, 58
white alder 4:474
white alkaline soils 6:809
white ash 5:577
white cinnamon 3:379, 380
white currant 4:498
white leaf 2:171
white syringa 5:549
whitebeam 3:318;
  common 3:319;
  Swedish 3:319
white-top 2:133
whitewood 3:336, 341, 346;
  America 3:341;
  Canary 3:346
whitlavia 3:267
whitten tree 3:354
whooping cough 1:51

whorl flower 2:232
whortleberry 1:59, 3:*349*, 7:876;
  bushy 2:182;
  see also Vaccinium
Whyte, R. O. 7:955
widdy 3:280
Widmanstätten pattern 8:986, *988*
widow's frill 3:315
wig tree 5:548
Wigandia 5:585
Wikstroemia 4:510
wild oats 3:358, *358, see also* oats, wild
wild plants:
  related to crops 7:*958*;
  uses of 7:935
wild Spaniard 1:9
wild spice 1:17
Wilkiea 3:384
Willdenovia 5:*634*
Willdenow, Carl 6:689, 7:967
Willis, J. C. 7:906, *967*
willow 2:126, 3:294, 305, *305*, 4:467, 468;
  arctic 6:750;
  basket 3:305, 358;
  bay-leaved 3:305;
  black 3:305;
  crack 3:305;
  creeping 7:*887*;
  cricket-bat 3:305;
  dwarf 3:305, 6:*722*, 749, 750, 7:841, 855;
  florist's 3:358;
  goat 3:305, 358;
  Indian 3:305;
  pussy 3:305, 358;
  reticulate 3:305;
  true 3:305;
  white 3:305;
  woolly 3:305;
  yellow 3:305;
  see also Salix
willow bark 3:358
willow leaf 3:286
willowherb 6:723;
  great hairy 7:885;
  rosebay 1:85, *85*, 2:131
Wilson, Ernest 6:684, 685, 7:967
wilting point 6:804, 7:843
wilwilli 2:134
wind 6:800, *801*;
  and climate 6:*788*, 7:845;
  dispersal by 6:*817*;
  and mountain vegetation 7:866, 868
windflower 1:29;
  grove 1:30
windmill palm 5:654
window plant 2:232
Windsorina 5:629
wine plant 3:293
wineberry 2:151, 3:300, **358**
wing nut 3:**283**, 5:555;
  Caucasian 3:283
winged fruits 6:817
winter aconite 3:396, 399
winter annuals 6:724;
  and drought evasion 7:850
winter biennials 6:724
winter drought 7:853
winter jasmine 5:577
Winteraceae 3:**378**, 379, *379*, 380, 381, 382, 4:405, 5:590, 6:745, 7:919
winterberry 2:177
wintercress 3:295
wintergreen 2:227, 3:285, 343, 4:474, 479, 7:903;
  Arctic 3:285;
  creeping 2:155;
  flowering 3:277;
  spicy 2:155
wintergreen oil 2:155
Winterineae 3:378
winter's bark 1:125, 3:378
wintersweet 1:9, *87*, 3:386
wiregrass 2:129, 3:276

Wisconsin comparative ordination 6:730
Wisconsin glaciation 6:749-50
wishbone flower 3:342
Wisneria 5:620
Wisteria 3:358, 4:499, 502
wisteria 3:358, 6:684;
  Chinese 3:358, *358*;
  Japanese 3:358;
  scarlet 3:314
witch hazel 2:168, 4:406, 407;
  Chinese 2:168, *169*;
  common 2:168;
  Japanese 2:168;
  ozark 2:168
witchweed 5:595, 7:948
Withania 5:579
witherite 8:1101, 1109
witloof 1:87, 89, 2:130, 3:350
Wittsteinia 4:477
Wittsteinioideae 4:477
woad 2:126, 187, 3:358
wolfbane 1:9
wolfberry 3:330;
  Anderson 2:213;
  Arabian 2:213;
  Chinese 2:213
Wolffia 3:359, 5:656, *657*, 657
wolffia, common 3:359
Wolffiella 5:657
Wolffiopsis 5:657
wolframite 8:1087, **1101**, 1110
wollastonite 8:1097, **1101**
Wolstonian glaciation 6:749
wonder tree 3:295
wood consumption 7:937-8
wood crape 3:336
wood mice and land bridges 7:909
wood oil 2:136, 3:288;
  China 2:250, 3:346;
wood sorrel 5:559, 560
woodbine 2:210, 261;
  Italian 2:210;
  perfoliate 2:210;
Woodfordia 4:507
woodland:
  elfin 7:867, 868;
  fen (carr) 7:*884*;
  mire 7:876;
  savanna 7:856
wood-oil tree:
  China 1:15, 3:346;
  Japan 3:346
woodruff 1:44, 5:607, 608;
  dyer's 1:44;
  sweet 1:44, 2:154, 174
woodrush 2:212, 3:301, 7:*909*
Woodsia 3:359
woodsia 3:359;
  fragrant 3:359;
  Northern 3:359;
  Rocky Mountain 3:359;
  rusty 3:359
wood-vamp 1:118
Woodward, J. 9:*1258*, **1275**
Woodwardia 3:359
woody holcus 2:177
woody plants, life-forms of 6:719
woolly sheep 2:254
Wormia 4:430, 431
wormseed, American 1:86
Wormskioldia 4:454, *454*
wormwood 1:58, 2:227, 3:349, 7:843, 940;
  common 1:42
woundwort:
  hedge 3:*322*;
  marsh 3:*323*;
  soldier's 1:9
wrack:
  channeled 1:*19*, 3:264, 6:828;
  knobbed 1:43;
  knotted 6:828;
  lady 2:150;
  serrated 2:154, 6:828;
  spiral 6:828
  yellow 1:43, *43*

wreath:
  purple 3:266;
  Queen's 3:266
Wright, Sewall 6:764, 775
Wrightia 5:574
Wulfenia 3:359, 5:595
wulfenite 8:1108
Würm glaciation 6:749-50
Wyethia 3:359, 5:617

Xanthium 3:359, 5:617, 618, 6:795, 816
Xanthoceras 3:359, 5:544
Xanthophyllaceae 5:566
Xanthophylleae 5:566
Xanthophyllum 5:566, *566*
Xanthorrhiza 3:396
Xanthorrhoea 3:359, 5:666, 667, 6:720, 7:916
Xanthorrhoeaceae 5:633, **666**, 7:916
Xanthosoma 3:359, 5:659
xenoliths 8:973, 975, 9:*1127*, 1129
xenotime 8:1104
Xeranthemum 3:359, 2:185, 5:617
Xerodraba 4:470
xeromorphic coniferous shrubs 6:721
xeromorphic ericoid shrubs 6:721
xeromorphic tuft-trees 6:*720*, 720
Xerophyta 5:667
xerophytes 6:719, *770*, *771*, *799*
xeroseres 6:824-6
Xerosicyos 4:465, 467
Ximenia 4:523, *523*
Xiphidium 5:668
X-ray crystallography 8:1078
X-ray diffraction *see* X-ray spectrometry
X-ray diffraction patterns 8:1078
X-ray fluorescence spectroscopy 8:996
X-ray spectrometry 8:980, 996-7
Xylaria 3:360
Xylocarpus 5:552
Xylonagra 4:512
Xylopia 3:265, 381
xylopod shrubs 6:721
xylopod trees 6:720
Xylosoma 4:452
Xyridaceae 5:627-8, 629, 632
Xyris 5:628

yam 1:83, 2:227, 3:299, 360, *360, 361*, 5:580, 670, 7:931;
  aerial 3:360;
  American 3:298;
  bitter 3:298;
  cush-cush 3:360;
  greater Asiatic 3:298, 328, 360;
  lesser Asiatic 3:298, 360;
  white Guinea 3:298, 328, 360;
  yellow Guinea 3:298, 328, 360
yam bean 2:201, 3:**360**
yampee 3:328
yangtao 1:10
yardangs 8:1012;
  Martian 8:985
yardgrass 2:129
Yarmouth interglacial 6:749
yarrow 1:9;
  fernleaf 1:9, *9*;
  musk 1:9;
  soldier's 3:325;
  woolly 1:9

yaupon 2:178
yautia 3:359, 5:659
year, length of 9:1208
yeast 3:**302**
yellow bark 3:286
yellow cotton tree 4:457
yellow dwarf virus in barley 7:957
yellow oleander 5:575
yellow rattle 5:595
yellow wood 1:45;
    African 3:276
yellow-eyed grass 5:627, 628
yellows in sugar beet 7:949
yerba de maté 1:26, 58, 2:178,
    220, 4:531, 532
yerba linda 3:264
yerba mansa 3:389
yew 2:173, 3:342, **360**, 6:749;
    American 2:173, 3:361;
    Canada 2:173, 3:361;
    Chinese 3:360;
    Chinese plum 1:81;
    common 3:*360*, *361*;
    Irish 3:361;
    Japanese 3:276, 361;
    plum 1:**81**;
    plum-fruited 3:276;
    Prince Albert 3:308;
    stinking 3:342
yield in crops 7:932, **949**
ylang-ylang 2:136, 3:361, 381;
    climbing 3:361
yoco 1:58, 5:544
yohimbine 1:26
yopo 2:226
Yorkshire fog 2:177, 7:940
Young, William 6:683
youngberry 3:300
youth-and-old-age 3:363
youth-on-age 3:337
yttrium 8:1104
Yucca 2:188, 3:361, 5:664, 666,
    6:720, 7:849, 896
yucca 3:**361**
yucca datil, blue 3:361

zacatechichi 2:226
zamang 3:306
Zamia 3:361
Zannichellia 3:361, 5:*625*, 625,
    626
Zannichelliaceae 5:624, *625*, **625-6**, 627
Zanonia 4:*465*, 467
Zanonieae 4:465
Zanonioideae 4:465
zansami 2:258
Zantedeschia 1:**42**, 3:361, 5:659
Zanthoxyleae 5:554
Zanthoxylum 1:31, 3:308, **362**,
    5:554
zapote blanco 3:307
Zauschneria 3:362, 4:512
Zea 2:216, 221, 5:638, 640;
    mays 7:*926*
zebra haworthia 2:169
zebra plant 1:36, 110
zebra wood 1:121, 5:542
zebra-wood tree 6:817
Zebrina 3:362, 5:629, *631*, 631
zedoary 1:111, 2:126, 5:648;
    black 1:111;
    yellow 1:111
Zehneria 4:465
Zelkova 3:362, 4:446
zelkova 3:363, *364*;
    Japanese 3:363;
    saw-leaf 3:363
Zenobia 4:477;
    pulverulenta 6:683
zeolites 8:1083, **1101**
Zephyra 5:669

Zephyranthes 3:**362**, 5:664, 666
Zerna erecta 7:862
Zigadenus 3:**362**
zinc 8:979, 1023, 1075, 1083,
    1090, 1099, **1106**, 1108,
    1121;
    in plant nutrition 6:807
zinc blende *see* sphalerite
Zingiber 2:161, 3:363, 5:*648*, 648
Zingiberaceae 5:644, **647-8**, *648*,
    649, 650
Zingiberales 5:646-51
Zinjanthropus 9:1252
Zinnia 3:363, 5:617, 618
zinnia 3:**363**;
    Mexican 3:363
zinnwaldite 8:1102
zircon 8:1009, 1079, **1101**, 1108
zirconium 8:979, 1101, **1108**,
    1111
Zirkel, F. 9:1265, 1272, 1273,
    1275
zither wood 5:587
Zizania 3:363, 5:636
Ziziphora 5:589
Ziziphus 2:195, 239, 3:363, 4:537,
    538, 538
zoantharia 9:1220
zonal soils 6:*807*, 807, **807-8**
zonal vegetation 7:*832-61*, **832-62**
zonation 6:714-5, **828-9**, *829*;
    in mangrove swamps 7:891;
    and mountain vegetation 7:*863*,
        863-4;
    and temperature 6:785;
    in tropical raised bogs 7:878-9
zooxanthellae 9:1216, 1220
Zostera 3:363, 5:626, 7:885
Zosteraceae 5:625, **626**, 627
Zosterella 5:659
Zosterophyllales 9:1216
Zosterophyllum 6:766
Zoysia 3:363, 5:638;
    japonica 7:862-3
Zoysieae 5:638
zucchini 2:222
Zulu-giant 3:323
Zürich-Montpellier school of plant
    sociology 6:**727-9**, 7:964
Zygogynum 1:125, 3:378
Zygopetalum 3:363, 5:675
Zygophyllaceae 5:552, **554**
Zygophyllum 5:554, 6:*718*
zygopterid ferns in evolution 6:*739*
Zygosepalum 3:363
zygotene in meiosis 6:*763*
zygotes 6:(*762*)

Thematic Index

This index is intended to help you to find material on a particular topic you are interested in. Topics are arranged by subject in 14 numbered sections, given below. Sections 1–5 refer mostly to Volumes 1–5 of the Encyclopedia, while sections 6–14 refer mostly to Volumes 6–9. A few sections are subdivided into more specific areas; these too are given below. Items are arranged alphabetically within each section or subsection.

1. Families of Flowering Plants
2. Families of Conifers
3. Main Groups of Plants
    *Algae—Angiosperms—Bacteria—Blue-green Algae—
    Club Mosses—Ferns—Fungi—Gymnosperms—Horsetails—
    Lichens—Mosses and Liverworts*
4. Crop Plants
    *Brassicas—Cereals—Fiber Plants—Fodder Crops—Fruits—
    Legumes and Pulses—Marrows and Squashes—Nuts—Oil Crops—
    Rootcrops—Starch Crops—Sugar Crops—Timber—Vegetables*
5. Other Plants with Useful Products
    *Alcoholic Beverages—Alkaloids—Beverages, Non-alcoholic—Dyes
    and Tannins—Essential Oils—Flavorings—Herbs—Medicines and
    Narcotics—Resins—Rubber*
6. Scientific Areas of Study
7. Prominent Figures
8. Natural Vegetation Zones
    Azonal Vegetation—Zonal Vegetation
9. Prehistoric Eras and Periods
10. Prehistoric Plants
11. Prehistoric Animals
12. Rocks of the World
13. Chemical Elements
14. Minerals

The conventions are otherwise similar to those followed in the main alphabetical index in this volume. Within each entry, volume numbers are given in **bold** (followed by a colon) before the first page number within each volume; volume numbers are not repeated when successive page numbers belong to the same volume. A **bold** page number indicates a major entry; an *italic* number indicates an illustration.

1. FAMILIES OF FLOWERING PLANTS

Acanthaceae 5:600;
  Acanthus (Bear's Breeches) 1:8;
  Aphelandra (Zebra Plant) 1:36;
  Barleria (Philippine Violet) 1:53;
  Crossandra 1:109;
  Eranthemum 2:132;
  Fittonia 2:143;
  Justicia 2:191;
  Ruellia 3:300;
  Strobilanthes 3:326;
  Thunbergia 3:336
Aceraceae 5:545;
  Acer (Maples and Sycamore) 1:8, 3:328, 329, 330, 338
Achariaceae 4:462
Actinidiaceae:
  Actinidia (Kiwi Fruit) 1:10
Adoxaceae 5:609
Agavaceae 5:666;
  Agave (Istles, Sisal Hemp and Pulque) 1:13, 2:173, 187, 3:316;
  Cordyline (Good Luck Plant and Palm Lily) 1:104;
  Dracaena (Dragon Tree) 1:124;
  Furcraea (Green Aloe) 2:154, 173;
  Phormium (Mountain Flax) 3:269;
  Polianthes (Tuberose) 3:277;
  Sansevieria (Bowstring Hemps) 2:173, 3:306;
  Yucca (Joshua Tree and Palm Lily) 2:188, 3:361
Aizoaceae (Mesembryanthemum Family) 4:415;
  Conophytum 1:99;
  Faucaria (Tiger Jaws) 2:139;
  Lampranthus 2:196;
  Lithops (Living Stones) 2:208;
  Mesembryanthemum (Ice Plants) 2:184, 228;
  Tetragonia (New Zealand Spinach) 3:321, 350
Alangiaceae 4:516
Alismataceae 5:619;
  Alisma (Water Plantains) 1:15;
  Sagittaria (Arrowheads) 3:302
Amaranthaceae 4:420;
  Alternanthera 1:25;
  Amaranthus (Amaranths) 1:25, 2:163, 3:350;
  Celosia (Cockscomb) 1:80;
  Gomphrena (Globe Amaranth) 2:163;
  Iresine (Bloodleaf) 2:186
Amaryllidaceae (Daffodil Family) 5:664;
  Alstroemeria 1:25;
  Amaryllis (Belladonna Lily) 1:27;
  Clivia (Kaffir Lilies) 1:92;
  Crinum (Pyjama Lily) 1:109;
  Cyrtanthus (Fire Lily) 1:114;
  Dorianthes (Spear Lily) 1:123;
  Eucharis (Amazon Lily) 2:137;
  Galanthus (Snowdrops) 3:317;
  Haemanthus (Blood Lily) 2:168;
  Hippeastrum (Amaryllis) 2:177;
  Hymenocallis (Peruvian Daffodil) 2:183;
  Hypoxis (Star Grasses) 2:184;
  Leucojum (Snowflakes) 2:203;
  Narcissus (Daffodils and Narcissi) 1:115, 2:238;
  Nerine (Guernsey Lily) 2:240;
  Pancratium 2:258;
  Sprekelia (Jacobean Lily) 3:322;
  Sternbergia (Winter Daffodil) 3:324;
  Urceolina 3:348;
  Vallota (Scarborough Lily) 3:309;
  Watsonia (Bugle Lily) 3:357;
  Zephyranthes (Atamasco Lily) 3:362

Anacardiaceae 5:547;
  Anacardium (Cashew Nut Tree) 1:8, 28;
  Cotinus (Smoke Trees) 1:106, 3:317;
  Mangifera (Mangos) 2:218;
  Pistacia (Mastics and Pistachio) 2:220, 3:273, 290, 334;
  Rhus (Sumacs and Poison Ivies) 2:195, 3:276, 293;
  Schinopsis (Quebracho) 3:286;
  Schinus (Pepper Trees) 2:220, 3:309;
  Spondias 3:322
Ancistrocladaceae 4:460
Annonaceae 3:380;
  Annona (Sweetsop and Soursop) 1:31;
  Artabotrys (Climbing Ylang-ylang) 3:361;
  Asimina (American Pawpaw) 2:259;
  Cananga (Ylang-ylang) 3:361;
  Duguetia (Lancewood) 1:125;
  Xylopium (Negro Pepper) 3:265
Apocynaceae 5:574;
  Acokanthera 1:9;
  Allamanda 1:15;
  Apocynum (Dogbane) 1:37;
  Aspidosperma (Paddle Wood) 2:258;
  Catharanthus (Rose Periwinkle) 1:79;
  Cryptostegia (Madagascar Rubber) 2:214, 3:297;
  Hancornia (Mangabeira Rubber) 2:169;
  Landolphia (Landolphia Rubber) 1:74, 2:196, 214, 3:297;
  Mandevilla (Chilean Jasmine) 2:217;
  Nerium (Oleanders) 2:240;
  Plumeria (Frangipani) 3:275;
  Rauwolfia 3:289;
  Strophanthus 3:326;
  Tabernaemontana (Tree Toad and Adam's Apple) 3:331;
  Trachelospermum (Star Jasmine) 3:342;
  Vinca (Periwinkles) 3:355
Aponogetonaceae 5:622;
  Aponogeton (Water Hawthorn) 1:37, 2:170
Aquifoliaceae 4:532;
  Ilex (Hollies and Maté) 1:69, 2:127, 177, 220
Araceae (Arum Lily Family) 5:657;
  Acorus (Sweet Flag and Flag Root) 1:9;
  Alocasia (Giant Taro) 1:24, 3:328, 333;
  Amorphophallus 1:27;
  Anthurium 1:36;
  Arisaema 1:40;
  Arum 1:41, 42;
  Caladium 1:70;
  Calla (Bog Arum) 1:70;
  Colocasia (Taro) 3:328, 333;
  Dracunculus 1:124;
  Lysichiton (Skunk Cabbage) 2:213;
  Monstera (Swiss-cheese Plant) 2:232;
  Philodendron 3:268;
  Pistea (River Lettuce) 3:273;
  Sauromatum (Voodoo Lily) 3:308;
  Spathiphyllum (Snowflower) 3:320;
  Xanthosoma 3:328, 359;
  Zantedeschia (Arum Lily) 1:42, 3:361
Araliaceae 5:567;
  Aralia 1:38, 3:308;
  Dizygotheca (False Aralias) 1:122;
  × *Fatshedera* 2:139;
  Fatsia (Paper Plant) 2:139;

  Hedera (Ivies) 2:187;
  Panax (Ginseng) 2:258;
  Schefferia (Umbrella Trees) 3:309
Aristolochiaceae 3:391;
  Aristolochia 1:40
Asclepiadaceae 5:575;
  Asclepias (Milkweeds) 1:43;
  Calotropis (Auricula and Tembega) 1:72;
  Ceropegia 1:82;
  Hoya (Wax Plant) 2:182;
  Marsdenia 2:214, 220, 3:297;
  Stapelia (Toad Plants) 3:323;
  Stephanotis (Madagascar Jasmine) 3:324
Austrobaileyaceae 3:383
Balanopaceae 4:412
Balanophoraceae 4:525
Balsaminaceae 5:561;
  Impatiens (Balsams) 1:49, 2:185
Basellaceae 4:425;
  Ullucus (Ulloco) 3:347, 350
Batidaceae (Saltwort) 4:426
Begoniaceae 4:463;
  Begonia 1:54
Berberidaceae 3:395;
  Berberis (Barberries) 1:52;
  Epimedium 2:131;
  Mahonia (Oregon Grape) 2:215;
  Nandina (Sacred Bamboo) 2:238;
  Podophyllum (May Apples) 3:276
Betulaceae 4:409;
  Alnus (Alders) 1:15;
  Betula (Birches) 1:59, 3:338;
  Carpinus (Hornbeams) 2:127, 179, 187;
  Corylus (Hazels) 2:170;
  Ostrya (Hop Hornbeams) 2:187, 257
Bignoniaceae 5:599;
  Bignonia 1:57;
  Campsis (Trumpet Creeper) 1:73;
  Catalpa 1:78;
  Clytostoma 1:93;
  Crescentia (Calabash Tree) 1:69;
  Eccremocarpus (Chilean Glory Flower) 2:127;
  Incarvillea 2:185;
  Jacaranda 2:127, 188;
  Pandorea 2:259;
  Paulownia (Karri Tree) 2:193, 261;
  Pyrostegia (Flame Vine) 3:285;
  Spathodea (Scarlet Bell) 3:321;
  Tabeluia (Pouis) 3:331;
  Tecoma 2:164, 3:334
Bixaceae 4:455;
  Bixa (Annatto) 1:31
Bombacaceae 4:443;
  Adansonia (Baobab) 1:10;
  Bombax (White Kapok Tree) 1:61;
  Ceiba (Kapok Tree) 1:80, 2:192;
  Durio (Durians) 2:127;
  Ochroma (Balsa Tree) 1:49, 3:338
Boraginaceae 5:585;
  Alkanna (Alkanets) 1:15;
  Anchusa (Bugloss) 1:29;
  Arnebia (Prophet Flower) 1:40;
  Borago (Borage) 1:61;
  Brunnera 1:67;
  Cynoglossum (Hound's Tongue) 1:113;
  Echium 2:128;
  Heliotropium (Heliotropes) 2:172;
  Lithospermum 2:209;
  Mertensia 2:225;
  Myosotis (Forget-me-nots) 2:237;
  Omphalodes (Blue-eyed Mary) 2:249;
  Onosma 2:252;
  Pulmonaria 2:284;
  Symphytum (Comfreys) 3:330
Bromeliaceae (Pineapple Family) 5:644;
  Aechmea 1:10;

  Ananas (Pineapple) 3:272, 7:926;
  Bromelia 1:66;
  Cryptanthus (Earth Stars) 1:110;
  Dyckia 2:127;
  Neoregelia 2:239;
  Nidularium 2:241;
  Pitcairnia 3:273;
  Puya 3:285;
  Tillandsia (Spanish Moss and Wild Pineapple) 3:336;
  Vriesia (Flaming-sword) 3:356
Brunelliaceae 4:490
Bruniaceae 4:490
Brunoniaceae 5:607
Burmanniaceae 5:670
Burseraceae 5:546;
  Bursera (Turpentine Tree) 1:68, 2:129;
  Canarium (Java Almond) 1:24, 2:129;
  Commiphora (Myrrh Trees) 1:99, 2:237;
  Boswellia (Frankincense) 1:61, 2:148;
Butomaceae 5:619;
  Butomus (Flowering Rush) 1:68, 3:301
Buxaceae 4:533;
  Buxus (Boxes) 1:62;
  Pachysandra 2:258;
  Sarcococca (Sweet Boxes) 3:307
Cactaceae (Cactus Family) 1:69, 4:413;
  Cactus 1:69;
  Carnegia (Giant Cactus) 1:76;
  Cereus (Torch Thistles) 1:82;
  Coryphantha 1:106;
  Echinocactus (Barrel Cacti) 2:127;
  Echinocereus 2:128;
  Echinopsis 2:128;
  Epiphyllum 2:132;
  Ferocactus 2:139;
  Gymnocalycium 2:167;
  Lophophora (Peyote) 2:211;
  Mammillaria 2:217;
  Nopalea (Cochineal Cactus) 2:242;
  Notocactus 2:242;
  Opuntia 2:253;
  Pereskia (Rose Cactus) 3:265;
  Rhipsalidopsis (Easter Cactus) 3:290;
  Rhipsalis (Mistletoe and Snowdrop Cacti) 3:290;
  Schlumbergera (Christmas Cacti) 2:132, 3:310;
  Selenicereus (Queen of the Night) 3:312;
  Trichocereus 3:343
Callitrichaceae 5:590
Calycanthaceae 3:385;
  Chimonanthus (Wintersweet) 1:87;
  Calycanthus (Carolina Allspice) 1:17, 76
Calyceraceae 5:612
Campanulaceae (Bellflower Family) 5:604;
  Campanula (Bellflowers) 1:54, 3:287;
  Canarina 1:73;
  Codonopsis 1:97;
  Edraianthus (Grassy-bells) 2:128;
  Jasione (Sheep's-bit Scabious) 2:188;
  Phyteuma (Rampions) 3:270;
  Platycodon (Balloon Flower) 3:275;
  Wahlenbergia 3:356
Canellaceae 3:379;
  Canella (White Cinnamon) 1:73
Cannaceae 5:648;
  Canna (Queensland Arrowroot) 1:41, 73, 3:328
Capparaceae 4:469;

Capparis (Capers) 1:74;
Cleome (Spider Flower) 1:92
Caprifoliaceae (Honeysuckle
Family) 5:609;
Abelia 1:6;
Diervilla 1:120;
Dipelta 1:121;
Kolkwitzia 2:194;
Leycesteria 2:203;
Linnaea (Twin Flower) 2:207;
Lonicera (Honeysuckles) 2:178,
210;
Sambucus (Elders) 1:47, 3:306;
Symphoricarpos 3:330;
Viburnum 3:354;
Weigela 3:357
Caricaceae 4:455;
Carica (Papaya/Pawpaw) 1:75,
2:259
Caryophyllaceae (Carnation
Family) 4:417;
Agrostemma 1:14;
Arenaria (Sandwort) 1:40;
Cerastium (Mouse-ears) 1:82, 87;
Dianthus (Carnations) 1:76, 119;
Gypsophila (Baby's Breath)
2:167;
Herniaria (Rupturewort) 2:173;
Honkenya (Sea Sandwort) 2:178;
Lychnis (Cuckoo Flower and Rose
Campion) 2:213;
Paronychia 2:260;
Saponaria (Soapworts) 3:307;
Silene (Campions, Pinks and
Sweet William) 3:315;
Spergula (Toadflax) 3:321;
Stellaria (Chickweeds and
Stitchworts) 1:87, 3:324
Casuarinaceae 4:412;
Casuarina (She Oak and River
Oak) 1:78, 2:187
Celastraceae 4:528;
Catha (Arabian Tea) 2:192;
Celastrus 1:80;
Euonymus (Spindle Trees) 1:68,
2:137
Centrolepidaceae 5:633
Cephalotaceae 4:496;
Cephalotus (Flycatcher Plant)
1:81, 3:273;
Ceratophyllaceae 3:393;
Ceratophyllum 1:82
Cercidiphyllaceae 4:405;
Cercidiphyllum (Katsura Tree)
1:82
Chenopodiaceae (Beet and Spinach
Family) 4:422;
Atriplex (Orache and Saltbushes)
1:46, 2:168, 254, 3:305;
Beta (Beets, Chards etc) 1:54,
57, 85, 2:218, 3:298, 321,
327, 328, 350;
Chenopodium (Goosefat) 1:86;
Halimione (Sea Purslane) 1:46,
2:168;
Kochia (Summer Cypress and
Saltbush) 1:68, 2:194;
Salicornia (Samphires) 3:302;
Salsoda (Russian Thistle) 3:305;
Spinacia (Spinach) 3:321, 350
Chloranthaceae 3:386
Chrysobalanaceae 4:498;
Chrysobalanus (Coco Plum) 1:89
Cistaceae (Rockroses) 4:458;
Cistus 1:90, 3:290;
Helianthemum 2:171
Clethraceae 4:473;
Clethra (Lily-of-the-valley Tree)
1:92
Cneoraceae (Spurge Olive) 5:552
Cochlospermaceae (Rose Imperial)
4:456
Columelliaceae 5:591
Combretaceae 4:514;
Quisqualis (Rangoon Creeper)
3:286;
Terminalia (Myrobalans) 1:45,
3:324, 334, 338

Commelinaceae 5:629;
Commelina (Day Flower) 1:99;
Rhoeo (Boat Lily) 3:293;
Tradescantia (Spiderwort) 3:342
Compositae (Sunflower Family)
5:613;
Achillea (Yarrows) 1:9;
Ageratum 1:13;
Ambrosia (Ragweeds) 1:27;
Anacyclus 1:28;
Anaphalis (Pearly Everlasting
Flower) 1:29;
Antennaria 1:31;
Anthemis (Yellow Chamomile)
1:36;
Arctotis (African Daisies) 1:40,
3:353;
Arnica (Mountain Tobacco) 1:41;
Artemisia (Tarragon, Wormwood
and Sagebrush) 1:41, 3:319,
333;
Aster (Asters and Michaelmas
Daisies) 1:45, 116, 2:229;
Baccharis (Bush Groundsel) 1:49;
Baileya (Desert Marigold) 2:219;
Balsamita (Costmary) 1:88, 106;
Bellis (Daisies) 1:54, 116;
Berkheya 1:57;
Bidens 1:57, 2:219;
Blumea (Ngai Camphor) 1:60;
Brachycome (Daisies) 1:62, 116;
Buphthalmum (Yellow Oxeyes)
1:68;
Calendula (Marigolds) 1:70,
2:219;
Callistephus (China Aster) 1:45,
71;
Calocephalus (Cushion Bush)
1:71;
Carduus (Thistles) 1:75, 3:335;
Carlina (Carline Thistles) 1:75;
Carthamus (Safflower) 1:77;
Catananche (Cupid's Heart) 1:79;
Celmisia 1:80;
Centaurea (Cornflowers) 1:81,
3:313;
Chamaemelum (Chamomile) 1:85,
2:219;
Chamomilla (Wild Chamomile)
1:85, 2:219, 220;
Chrysanthemum 1:88, 2:219,
3:278, 285;
Cichorium (Chicory and Endive)
1:87, 89, 2:130, 3:350;
Cirsium (Thistles) 1:90, 3:335;
Cnicus (Blessed Thistle) 1:93,
3:335;
Coreopsis (Tickseed) 1:104;
Cosmos 1:106;
Cotula (Brass Buttons) 1:107;
Cynara (Cardoon and Globe
Artichoke) 1:42, 75, 113,
3:350;
Dahlia 1:115, 3:278;
Dimorphotheca (Cape Marigolds)
1:121, 2:219;
Doronicum 1:123;
Echinacea (Purple Cone Flowers)
2:127;
Echinops (Globe Thistle) 2:128;
Erigeron (Fleabane) 2:133;
Eriophyllum 2:133;
Eupatorium (Water Hamp and
Mist Flower) 2:138;
Felicia (Blue Daisy) 2:139;
Galinsoga (Gallant Soldier)
2:154;
Gazania (Treasure Flower) 2:160;
Gerbera (Transvaal Daisy) 2:161;
Gnaphalium (Cudweed) 2:163;
Grindelia (Gumweed) 2:164;
Guizotia (Niger Seed) 2:167;
Gynura (Velvet Plant) 2:167;
Haplopappus 2:169;
Helenium (Bitterweed) 2:171;
Helianthus (Sunflowers and
Jerusalem Artichokes) 1:42,
3:329, 350;

Helichrysum (Strawflower and
Whiteleaf) 2:171, 185;
Heliopsis 2:172;
Helipterum 2:172;
Hieracium (Hawkweeds) 2:177;
Hypochoeris (Cat's Ears) 2:184;
Inula (Elecampine) 2:185;
Jurinea 2:191;
Lactuca (Lettuces) 2:195, 202,
3:350;
Lapsana (Nipplewort) 2:197;
Lasthenia 2:197;
Layia (Tidy-tips) 2:199;
Leontopodium (Edelweiss) 2:128,
202;
Leucanthemum (Marguerite and
Shasta Daisy) 1:89, 116,
2:202;
Liatris (Blazing Star) 2:203;
Lonas 2:210;
Madia 2:214;
Mikania (Climbing Hempweed)
2:229;
Mutisia 2:236;
Olearia (Daisy Bushes) 1:116,
2:248;
Onopordum (Scotch Thistle)
2:252, 3:335;
Osteospermum 2:256;
Parthenium (Guayule) 3:297;
Petasites (Butterburs and Bog
Rhubarb) 3:266;
Picris 3:271;
Piqueria (Stevia) 3:273;
Pyrethrum 1:89, 3:285;
Raoulia (Vegetable Sheep) 3:288;
Rudbeckia 3:300;
Santolina (Cotton Lavenders)
3:307;
Sanvitalia 3:307;
Satureja (Savories) 3:308;
Scorzonera (Black Salsify and Tau-
saghyz) 3:305, 311, 333,
350;
Senecio 1:89, 2:193, 206, 3:312;
Silphium (Rosinweed and Cup
Plant) 3:315;
Silybum (Holy Thistle) 3:335;
Solidago (Golden Rods) 3:318;
Sonchus (Sow Thistles) 3:318,
335;
Stokesia (Stokes' Aster) 3:325;
Tagetes (African and French
Marigolds) 2:219, 3:331;
Tanacetum (Tansy) 1:89, 3:285,
332;
Taraxacum (Dandelions) 1:116,
3:297, 332;
Tithonia 3:336;
Townsendia 3:342;
Tragopogon (Salsify) 3:305, 342,
350;
Tussilago (Coltsfoot) 3:347;
Ursinia 3:348;
× *Venidio-arctotis* 3:349;
Venidium (Cape Daisies) 3:353;
Vernonia (Ironweeds) 3:353;
Wyethia 3:359;
Xanthium (Cocklebur) 3:359;
Xeranthemum 3:359;
Zinnia 3:363
Connaraceae (Zebra Wood) 5:542
Convolvulaceae (Bindweeds)
5:579;
Calystegia 1:59, 2:233;
Convolvulus 1:59, 99, 2:233;
Cuscuta (Dodders) 1:122;
Ipomoea (Morning Glory and
Sweet Potato) 2:186, 188,
233, 3:298, 330, 350
Coriariaceae (Coriarias) 5:550
Cornaceae 4:517;
Aucuba (Spotted Laurel) 1:47,
2:198;
Cornus (Dogwoods) 1:62, 105,
122;
Corokia 1:105;

Curtisia (Cape Lance Tree) 1:45;
Griselina 2:164;
Helwingia 2:172
Corynocarpaceae 4:530
Crassulaceae 4:495;
Aeonium 1:11;
Cotyledon (Pig's Ear) 1:107,
3:347;
Dudleya 1:125;
Echeveria (Hen-and-chickens)
2:127;
Greenovia 2:164;
Kalanchoe 2:191;
Monanthes 2:232;
Rochea 2:295;
Sempervivum (Houseleeks) 2:182;
Sedum (Stonecrops) 3:312;
Umbilicus (Navelwort) 3:347
Crossosomataceae 4:432
Cruciferae (Mustard Family) 4:469;
Aethionema 1:12;
Alyssum 1:25;
Anastatica (Rose of Jericho)
3:290;
Arabis (Rock Cresses) 1:38;
Armoracia (Horseradish) 2:179;
Aubrieta (Aubrietias) 1:47;
Barbarea (Wintercress) 1:108,
3:295;
Brassica (Cabbages, Kales,
Turnips, Mustards, Rapes etc)
1:64, 66, 67, 69, 79, 87, 98,
99, 2:192, 194, 236, 3:288,
298, 301, 308, 330, 346,
350;
Cakile (Sea Rockets) 1:69;
Camelina (False Flax) 1:72;
Capsella (Shepherd's Purse) 1:74;
Cardamine (Bitter Cresses) 1:75;
Cheiranthus (Wallflowers) 1:86,
3:356;
Cochlearia (Scurvy Grasses) 1:96;
Crambe (Sea Kale) 1:108, 3:350;
Draba (Whitlow Grass) 1:124;
Eruca (Garden Rocket) 3:295;
Erysimium (Wallflowers) 2:134,
3:295;
Heliophila 2:171;
Hesperis (Sweet Rocket) 2:173,
3:295;
Iberis (Candytufts) 2:184;
Ionopsidum (Violet Cress) 2:186;
Isatis (Woad) 2:187, 3:358;
Lepidium (True Cress) 1:108,
2:202;
Lunaria (Honesty) 2:212;
Malcolmia (Virginia Stock)
3:325;
Matthiola (Stocks) 2:220, 3:325;
Nasturtium (Watercress) 1:108,
3:357;
Raphanus (Radishes) 3:286, 288,
350;
Rorippa (Yellow Cress) 2:238,
3:296, 357;
Sinapis (Charlock and White
Mustard) 1:85, 3:316;
Cucurbitaceae (Gourd Family)
2:222, 4:465;
Benincasa (Wax Gourd) 2:222;
Bryonia (Briony) 1:67;
Citrullus (Bitter Gourd and Water
Melon) 1:91, 2:222, 224,
357;
Coccinea (Ivy Gourd) 2:222;
Cucumis (Cucumbers, Gherkins
and Melons) 1:110, 2:161,
163, 178, 222, 224, 3:265;
Cucurbita (Marrows, Pumpkins,
and Squashes) 1:107, 111,
2:163, 222, 3:284, 323;
Ecballium (Squirting Cucumber)
2:127, 222;
Lagenaria (Calabash Gourd) 1:69,
2:163, 222;
Luffa (Loofas/Sponge Gourds)
2:163, 212, 222;

Momordica (Balsam Apple and Balsam Pear) 2:232;
Sechium (Chayote) 1:85;
Telfairia (Oyster Nut) 2:244;
Trichosanthes (Snake Gourds) 2:163, 222
Cunoniaceae 4:487;
Ceratopetalum (Scented Satinwood) 3:308
Cyanastraceae 5:669
Cyclanthaceae 5:654;
Carludovica (Panama Hat Plant) 1:75
Cymodoceaceae 5:627
Cynomoriaceae 4:525
Cyperaceae 5:642;
Carex (Sedges) 1:75, 3:312;
Cladium (Fen Sedge) 3:312;
Cyperus (Paper Reeds) 1:113, 3:312;
Eleocharis (Chinese Water Chestnut) 2:129, 3:357;
Eriophorum (Cotton Grass) 2:133;
Leiophyllum (Sand Myrtles) 2:199;
Rhynchospora 3:312;
Scirpus (Club Rush) 1:68, 3:311
Cyrillaceae 4:474;
Cliftonia (Bush Buckwheat) 1:67;
Cyrilla (Leatherwood) 2:187
Datiscaceae (Datiscas) 4:464
Degeneriaceae 3:382
Diapensiaceae 4:480;
Shortia (Oconee-bells and Galax) 3:315
Dichapetalaceae 4:532
Didiereaceae 4:423
Dilleniaceae 4:430;
Hibbertia 2:176
Dioscoreaceae 5:670;
Dioscorea (Yams) 3:298, 328, 360;
Tamus (Black Bryony) 3:332
Dipsacaceae 5:611;
Cephalaria 1:81;
Dipsacus (Teasels) 1:122;
Knautia 2:193;
Morina (Whorl Flower) 2:232;
Scabiosa (Scabious) 3:309
Dipterocarpaceae 4:434;
Balanocarpus (Chengal) 1:116, 3:290;
Dipterocarpus 1:49, 122, 3:338;
Shorea (Almond Dammar) 1:116, 3:290, 315, 338
Droseraceae 4:489;
Dionaea (Venus' Fly Trap) 1:121, 3:313;
Drosera (Sundews) 1:125;
Drosophyllum 1:125
Ebenaceae 4:483;
Diospyrus (Persimmons and Ebonies) 1:121, 2:127, 191, 3:266, 338
Ehretiaceae 5:583;
Cordia 1:104
Elaeagnaceae 4:518;
Elaeagnus (Oleaster and Silverberry) 2:129;
Hippophae (Sea Buckthorn) 2:177;
Shepherdia (Buffalo Berries) 3:314
Elaeocarpaceae (Crinodendrons and Aristotelias) 4:439
Elatinaceae 4:437
Empetraceae 4:478;
Empetrum (Crowberries) 2:130
Epacridaceae 4:477
Ericaceae (Heath Family) 4:474;
Andromeda (Bog Rosemary) 1:29;
Arbutus (Madrona and Strawberry Tree) 1:39;
Arctostaphylos (Bearberry and Manzanitas) 1:39;
Calluna (Heather) 1:71, 2:170;

Cassiope (White Heather) 1:78, 2:170;
Daboecia (Irish Heath) 1:115;
Daphniphillum 1:116;
Enkianthus 2:131;
Erica (Heaths) 1:63, 2:133, 170;
Gaultheria 2:155;
Gaylussacia (Huckleberries) 2:182;
Kalmia 2:192, 198;
Leucothoe (Sweetbells) 2:203;
Lyonia (Tetterbush and Staggerbush) 2:213;
Menziesia (Minniebush) 2:225;
Monotropa (Indian Pipe and Yellow Bird's Nest) 2:232;
Oxydendrum (Sourwood) 2:257;
Pernettya (Chaura) 3:266;
Phyllodoce (Red Heather) 3:269;
Pieris 3:271;
Rhododendron (Rhododendrons and Azaleas) 1:48, 3:290;
Vaccinium (Blueberries and Cranberries) 1:59, 60, 108, 2:182, 3:349
Eriocaulaceae 5:631
Erythroxylaceae 5:560;
Erythroxylum (Coca/Cocaine) 1:93, 2:135
Eucommiaceae 4:407
Eucryphiaceae 4:490;
Eucryphia 2:137
Euphorbiaceae (Spurge Family) 4:535;
Acalypha 1:8;
Aetoxicon (Palo Muerto) 1:12;
Aleurites (Tung Oil Trees) 1:15, 3:346;
Bischofia 1:60;
Chrozophora 1:88;
Cnidoscolus (Spurge Laurel) 3:323;
Codiaeum 1:97;
Croton 1:110;
Euphorbia (Poinsettia and Spurges) 2:138, 3:276, 323;
Hevea (Para Rubber Tree) 1:74, 2:176, 198, 214, 3:297, 7:926;
Jatropha (Physic Nuts) 2:188;
Manihot (Cassava and Ceara Rubber) 1:41, 74, 77, 2:219, 3:297, 298, 328, 7:926;
Mercurialis (Mercury) 2:225;
Pedilanthus 2:263;
Phyllanthus (Emblic and Indian Gooseberry) 3:269;
Ricinus (Castor Oil Plant) 1:78, 3:295;
Sapium (Chinese Tallow Tree) 3:331
Eupomatiaceae 3:383
Fagaceae 4:410;
Castanea (Chestnuts) 1:86, 2:130;
Fagus (Beeches) 1:54, 3:338;
Quercus (Oaks) 1:105, 2:246, 3:338;
Nothofagus (Southern Beeches) 2:242
Flacourtiaceae 4:451;
Azara 1:48;
Caesaria (West Indian Boxwood) 1:62;
Hydnocarpus (Chaulmoogra Oil) 1:85;
Idesia (Ilgiri Tree) 2:184
Flagellariaceae 5:632
Fouquieriaceae 4:455;
Fouquieria (Ocotillo) 2:148
Frankeniaceae 4:461
Fumariaceae 4:403;
Corydalis (Yellow Fumitory) 1:106;
Dicentra (Bleeding Heart) 1:120;
Fumaria (Common Fumitory) 2:154

Garryaceae 4:516;
Garrya (Silk-tassel Bush) 2:155
Geissolomataceae 4:528
Gentianaceae 5:573;
Exacum (German Violet) 2:138;
Gentiana (Gentians) 2:160;
Gentianella 2:160;
Swertia 3:330
Geraniaceae 5:558;
Erodium (Storksbill) 2:133;
Geranium (Cranesbills) 2:160;
Pelargonium (Geraniums) 2:263
Gesneriaceae 5:596;
Achimenes 1:9;
Aeschynanthus (Basket Plant) 1:11;
Columnea 1:98;
Episcia 2:132;
Gloxinia 2:162;
Kohleria (Tree Gloxinias) 2:194;
Ramonda 2:287;
Saintpaulia (African Violets) 3:302;
Sinningia (Gloxinias) 2:162, 3:316;
Smithiantha (Naegelias) 3:317
Globulariaceae 5:595;
Globularia (Globe Daisies) 2:162
Gomortegaceae 3:383
Goodeniaceae (Leschenaultias and Scaevolas) 5:607
Gramineae (Grass Family) 5:635;
Aegiltops 1:11;
Agropyron (Couch-grasses) 1:13;
Agrostis (Bent-grasses and Red Tops) 1:14;
Alopecurus (Foxtails) 1:24;
Ammophila (Beachgrass and Marram Grass) 1:27, 2:220;
Andropogon (Bluestem) 1:29;
Anthoxanthum 1:36;
Arundinaria (Bamboos) 1:43, 49;
Arundo (Giant Reed) 1:43, 3:289;
Avena (Oats) 1:47, 83, 2:143, 246, 3:358;
Axonopus (Savanna Grass) 1:48;
Bambusa (Bamboos) 1:49, 52, 3:350;
Bouteloua (Grama Grass) 1:62;
Briza (Quaking Grass) 1:63;
Bromus (Bromes) 1:66;
Calamagrostis (Small-reeds) 3:290;
Chloris (Rhodes Grass) 1:88;
Coix (Job's Tears) 1:97;
Cortaderia (Pampas Grass) 1:105;
Cymbopogon (Oil and Lemon Grass) 1:112;
Cynodon (Couch Grass) 1:113;
Cynosurus (Crested Dog's Tail) 1:113;
Dactylis (Cock's Foot) 1:115;
Dendrocalamus (Giant Bamboos) 1:49, 118;
Deschampsia 1:119;
Digitaria (Fundi) 1:83, 2:230;
Echinochloa (Japanese Barnyard Millet) 1:83, 2:230;
Eleusine (African Millet) 1:83, 2:129, 230;
Elymus 2:130;
Eragrostis (Love Grasses) 1:83, 2:132, 230;
Erianthus (Plume Grass) 2:132;
Euchlaena (Teosinte) 2:216, 3:334;
Festuca (Fescue) 2:139;
Glyceria (Manna Grass) 2:162, 3:290;
Helioctrichon (Oat Grass) 2:171;
Holcus (Velvet Grass) 2:177;
Hordeum (Barleys) 1:53, 83, 2:143, 262, 3:328;
Lagurus (Hare's Tail) 2:196;
Lolium (Ryegrasses) 3:301;
Lygeum (False Alfa) 2:135, 213;

Melica 2:224;
Milium (Golden Millet) 2:229;
Miscanthus 2:231;
Molinia (Moor Grass) 2:232;
Oryza (Rice) 1:41, 83, 105, 2:143, 256, 3:294, 328;
Panicum (Common Millet) 1:83, 2:230, 259;
Paspalum (Kodo Millet) 1:83, 2:230, 261;
Pennisetum (Pearl Millet) 1:83, 2:230, 3:264;
Phalaris 3:267, 290;
Phleum (Timothy Grasses) 3:268;
Phragmites (Reeds) 3:269, 289;
Phyllostachys (Bamboos) 1:49, 3:270, 350;
Poa (Bluegrasses) 3:275;
Saccharum (Sugar Cane) 1:49, 2:231, 3:302, 327, 328, 7:926;
Sasa (Bamboo Grass) 1:49, 3:308;
Secale (Ryes) 1:83, 2:143, 3:301, 311, 344;
Setaria (Italian Millet) 1:83, 2:230, 3:314;
Sorghum 3:319, 328;
Spartina (Cord Grasses) 3:320;
Stipa (Needle Grasses) 2:135, 3:324;
Triticale 3:344;
Triticum (Wheats) 1:83, 2:143, 236, 3:320, 344, 7:926;
Vetiveria (Khus Khus) 2:193, 3:354;
Zea (Maize/Corn) 1:83, 105, 2:143, 216, 221, 3:270, 7:926;
Zizania (Wild Rice) 3:363;
Zoysia (Manila Grass) 3:363
Grubbiaceae 4:474
Guttiferae 4:435;
Calophyllum (Alexandrian Laurel) 1:72, 2:198;
Garcinia (Gamboges and Mangosteen) 2:155, 218;
Hypericum (St John's Worts) 2:183;
Mammea (Mammee Apple) 2:217;
Mesua 2:228;
Pentadesma (Sierra Leone Tallow Tree) 3:331
Haemodoraceae 5:667;
Anigozanthus (Kangaroo Paw) 1:31
Haloragaceae 4:504;
Gunnera (Gunneras and Chile Rhubarb) 2:167;
Myriophyllum (Water Milfoils) 2:237
Hamamelidaceae 4:406;
Altingia (Rasamala) 3:288;
Corylopsis (Buttercup Winter Hazel) 1:106;
Fothergilla 2:148;
Hamamelis (Witch Hazels) 2:168;
Liquidambar (Sweet Gums) 2:208, 3:325;
Parrotia (Persian Ironwood) 2:260
Hernandiaceae 3:388
Himantandraceae 3:378
Hippocastanaceae 5:544;
Aesculus (Horse Chestnuts and Buckeyes) 1:12
Hippuridaceae 4:505;
Hippuris (Mare's Tail) 2:177
Houmiriaceae (Bastard Bullet Tree) 5:556
Hydnoraceae 4:528
Hydrocharitaceae 5:621;
Elodea (Canadian Waterweed) 2:130;
Enhalus 2:130;
Hydrocharis (Frog's Bit) 2:183;

Stratiotes (Water Aloe) 3:325;
Vallisneria (Water Celery and Eel Grass) 3:349
Hydrophyllaceae 5:584;
   Nemophila (Fivespot and Baby-blue-eyes) 2:239;
   Phacelia (California Bluebell) 3:267
Hydrostachydaceae 5:601
Icacinaceae 4:530
Illiciaceae 3:382;
   Illicium (Anise Trees) 1:31, 2:185
Iridaceae (Iris Family) 5:661;
   Acidanthera 1:9;
   Crocosmia 1:109;
   Crocus (Crocuses and Saffron) 1:109;
   Cypella 1:113;
   Dierama (Angel's Fishing Rod) 1:120;
   Freesia 2:150;
   Gladiolus (Gladioli) 2:161;
   Iris 2:186, 256;
   Ixia 2:188;
   Lapeirousia 2:197;
   Libertia 2:203;
   Moraea (Peacock Iris) 2:232;
   Romulea 3:296;
   Schizostylis (Crimson Flag) 3:310;
   Sisyrinchium (Eyed Grasses) 3:316;
   Sparaxis (Wandflowers) 3:320;
   Tigridia 3:336;
   Tritonia 3:344
Juglandaceae 5:555;
   Carya (Hickories and Pecan Nut) 1:77, 2:262, 3:338;
   Juglans (Walnuts) 3:338, 356;
   Pterocarya (Wing Nuts) 3:283
Julianiaceae 5:544
Juncaceae 3:301, 5:640;
   Juncus (Bog Rushes) 2:189, 3:301;
   Luzula (Woodrushes) 2:212, 3:301;
   Prionum (Palmiet) 3:281;
   Triglochin (Shore Podgrass) 3:343
Juncaginaceae 5:623
Krameriaceae 5:566
Labiatae (Mint Family) 5:589;
   Ajuga (Bugle) 1:14;
   Ballota (Black Horehound) 1:49;
   Calamintha (Calamint) 1:70;
   Coleus (Sudan Potato) 1:98, 3:350;
   Dracocephalum (Dragon Head) 1:124;
   Galeopsis (Hemp Nettles) 2:154;
   Glechoma (Ground Ivy) 2:162;
   Horminum (Dragon Mouth) 2:178;
   Hyssopus (Hyssops) 2:184;
   Lamium (Dead Nettles) 2:196, 241;
   Lavandula (Lavenders) 2:198, 199;
   Marrubium (Horehound) 2:220;
   Melissa (Lemon Balm) 2:224;
   Melittis (Bastard Balm) 2:224;
   Mentha (Mints) 2:230, 3:265;
   Micromeria 2:229;
   Moluccella (Molucca Balm) 2:232;
   Monarda (Bergamot) 1:57, 2:232;
   Monardella 2:232;
   Nepeta (Catmint) 2:240;
   Ocimum (Basils) 1:53, 2:247;
   Oreganum (Marjoram) 2:220, 256;
   Perilla 3:265;
   Perovskia 3:266;
   Phlomis (Jerusalem Sage) 3:268;
   Physostegia (Obedient Plant) 3:270;

Plectranthus (Kaffir Potato) 3:275, 350;
   Pogostemon (Patchouli) 3:276;
   Prostanthera (Mintbushes) 3:281;
   Rosmarinus (Rosemary) 3:297;
   Salvia (Sages) 1:91, 3:302, 305;
   Scutellaria (Skullcap Flowers) 3:311;
   Stachys (Wood Betony and Chinese Artichoke) 1:42, 3:323, 350;
   Teuchrium (Germanders) 3:335;
   Thymus (Thymes) 3:336
Lacistemataceae 4:452
Lactoridaceae 3:383
Lardizabalaceae 3:399;
   Akebia 1:14
Lauraceae 3:387;
   Cinnamomum (Cinnamon, Cassia and Camphor) 1:73, 89;
   Cryptocarya 1:110, 3:324;
   Laurus (Bay Laurel and Canary Island Laurel) 2:198;
   Lindera (Spicebush and Jove's Foot) 2:207;
   Ocotea (Greenheart and Stinkwood) 2:164, 247, 3:338;
   Persea (Avocado and Red Bay) 1:47, 3:266, 350;
   Sassafras 3:308;
   Umbellularia (California Laurel) 2:198
Lecythidaceae 4:449;
   Bertholletia (Brazil Nut) 1:63;
   Couroupita (Cannonball Tree) 1:107;
   Foetidia (Stinkwood) 3:324;
   Lecythis (Sapucaia) 3:307
Leguminosae (Pea and Bean Family) 1:53, 2:200, 4:499;
   Abrus (Rosary Pea) 1:6, 2:203, 262;
   Acacia 1:7, 78, 112, 2:187, 3:357;
   Adenocarpus 1:10;
   Aeschynomene 1:11;
   Afrormosia 1:12, 3:338;
   Afzelia 1:12, 2:187;
   Albizia 1:14;
   Amburana 1:27;
   Amherstia 1:27;
   Arachis (Peanut/Ground Nut) 1:38, 2:200;
   Astragalus 1:46, 2:203;
   Baptisia 1:52, 2:185;
   Bauhinia 1:53, 2:127;
   Butea 1:68, 2:193, 195;
   Caesalpina 1:69, 122, 2:127;
   Cajanus (Pigeon Pea) 2:200, 262, 3:271;
   Calliandra 1:71;
   Canavalia 1:73, 2:200;
   Caragana (Pea Shrubs) 1:74;
   Carmichaelia 1:76;
   Cassia (Senna) 1:78, 3:313;
   Ceratonia (Carob Tree) 1:15, 76, 2:200, 209;
   Cercis (Judas Tree) 1:82;
   Chorizema (Flame Pea) 1:88, 2:262;
   Cicer (Chick Pea) 1:87, 89, 2:200, 262;
   Clianthus (Glory Pea) 1:92;
   Clitoria (Butterfly Pea) 1:92, 2:262;
   Colutea (Bladder Senna) 1:98;
   Copaifera (Copals) 1:49, 99, 3:290;
   Coronilla 1:105;
   Crotolaria 1:109, 2:173;
   Cyamopsis (Cluster Bean) 2:200;
   Cylicodiscus (African Greenheart) 2:164;
   Cytisus (Brooms) 1:66, 114, 2:195;
   Dalbergia (Rosewoods) 1:116, 3:296, 338, 346;

Delonix (Poincianas) 1:118;
   Derris (Tuba Root) 1:119;
   Desmodium (Telegraph Plant) 1:119;
   Dillwynia 1:121;
   Dipteryx (Tonka Bean) 3:342;
   Dolichos 1:44, 123, 2:195, 200;
   Erinacea (Hedgehog Broom) 2:133;
   Erythrina (Coral Trees) 2:134, 185;
   Galega (Goat's Rue) 2:154;
   Genista (Brooms) 1:66, 2:160;
   Gleditsia (Honey Locust) 2:162, 209;
   Glycine (Soybean) 2:143, 162, 200, 3:319;
   Glycyrrhiza (Licorice) 2:163, 203;
   Gymnocladus (Kentucky Coffee and Soap Trees) 2:167;
   Haematoxylon (Logwood) 2:168, 210;
   Hardenbergia 2:169, 3:308;
   Hedysarum (Licorice Root) 2:171, 203;
   Hymenaea (Locust Tree and Copals) 1:104, 2:183, 209, 3:290;
   Indigofera (Indigos) 2:185;
   + *Laburnocytisus* 2:195;
   Laburnum 2:195;
   Lathyrus (Grass Pea and Sweet Pea) 2:164, 198, 262, 3:273;
   Lens (Lentils) 2:199, 200;
   Lespedeza (Bush Clovers) 2:202;
   Lonchocarpus 2:185, 210;
   Lotus (Bird's Foot Trefoils) 2:211, 3:343;
   Lupinus (Lupins) 2:200, 212;
   Medicago (Alfalfa/Lucerne) 1:92, 2:211, 221, 3:270, 314, 343;
   Melilotus (Melilots) 2:224;
   Milettia (Umzimbeets) 3:347;
   Mimosa 2:230, 3:313;
   Mucuna 2:233;
   Myroxylon 1:49, 2:237;
   Onobrychis (Sainfoin) 2:252;
   Ononis (Spiny Restharrow) 2:252;
   Oxytropis 2:257;
   Pachyrhizus (Yam Bean) 2:200, 3:350, 360;
   Parkia (Locust Beans) 2:200, 209, 260;
   Parkonsonia 2:260;
   Phaseolus (Beans) 2:143, 169, 200, 207, 236, 3:267;
   Piptanthus (Nepal Laburnum) 3:273;
   Pisum (Peas) 2:143, 200, 261, 3:273;
   Pithecellobium 3:273;
   Prosopis (Algarroba) 1:15, 3:281;
   Psophocarpus (Asparagus Pea) 1:44, 2:200, 262, 3:283;
   Psoralea 3:283;
   Pterocarpus (Kino Trees) 2:193, 3:283, 289, 306;
   Robinia (False Acacia) 2:209, 3:295;
   Samanea (Rain Tree) 3:274, 306;
   Schotia (Hottentot Beans) 2:179;
   Sesbania 3:314;
   Sophora 3:318;
   Spartium (Spanish Broom) 1:66, 3:320;
   Swainsonia 2:185, 3:330;
   Tamarindus (Tamarinds) 2:200, 3:331;
   Tephrosia (Hoary Pea) 3:334;
   Thermopsis 3:335;
   Trifolium (Clovers) 1:92, 3:314, 343;
   Trigonella 3:343;
   Ulex (Gorse) 3:347;

Vicia (Vetches and Broad Bean) 2:200, 3:273, 354;
   Vigna (Cowpea) 1:44, 107, 2:200, 262, 3:267;
   Wisteria 3:358
Leitneriaceae (Florida Corkwood) 4:407
Lemnaceae 5:656;
   Lemna (Duckweeds) 1:125;
   Wolffia 3:359
Lennoaceae 5:582
Lentibulariaceae 5:603;
   Pinguicula (Butterworts) 3:272;
   Utricularia (Bladderworts) 3:313, 348
Lilaeaceae 5:623;
   Lilaea 2:206
Liliaceae (Lily Family) 5:662;
   Agapanthus (African Lilies) 1:12;
   Allium (Onions, Leeks, Chives and Garlic) 1:17, 87, 2:155, 199, 249, 3:314, 350;
   Aloe 1:24;
   Anthericum 1:36;
   Asparagus 1:43, 3:350;
   Asphodelus (Asphodel) 1:44;
   Aspidistra 1:45;
   Brodliaea 1:66;
   Bulbocodium 1:67;
   Calochortus (Globe and Star Tulips) 1:72;
   Camassia (Quamash) 1:72;
   Chionodoxa (Glory-of-the-snow) 1:87;
   Chlorophytum (Spider Plant) 1:88;
   Clintonia 1:92;
   Colchicum (Autumn Crocus) 1:98;
   Convallaria (Lily of the Valley) 2:206;
   Dasylirion (Sotol) 1:117;
   Eremurus (Fox-tail Lily) 2:132;
   Erythronium 2:134;
   Fritillaria 2:150;
   Gagea (Yellow Star of Bethlehem) 2:154;
   Galtonia (Spire Lily) 2:154;
   Gasteria 2:155;
   Gloriosa (Glory Lily) 2:162;
   Haworthia 2:169;
   Hemerocallis (Daylilies) 2:172;
   Hosta (Plantain Lilies) 2:179;
   Hyacinthoides (Bluebells and Harebells) 2:182;
   Hyacinthus (Hyacinths) 2:183;
   Ipheion 2:186;
   Kniphofia (Torch Lily) 2:194;
   Lachenalia 2:195;
   Lapageria (Copihue) 2:197;
   Lilium (True Lilies) 2:206;
   Liriope 2:208;
   Maianthemum (May Lily) 2:215;
   Merendera 2:225;
   Muscari (Grape Hyacinth) 2:236;
   Nomocharis 2:242;
   Ophiopogon (Lilyturf) 2:252;
   Ornithogalum (Star of Bethlehem) 2:256;
   Paradisea (Paradise Lily) 2:260;
   Paris 2:260;
   Puschkinia (Striped Squill) 3:284;
   Ruscus (Box Holly) 3:301;
   Scilla (Squills) 3:311, 323;
   Smilacina (Star-flower) 3:317;
   Tricyrtis (Toad Lily) 3:343;
   Trillium 3:343;
   Triteleia 3:344;
   Tulipa (Tulips) 3:345;
   Urginea (Sea Onion/Red Squill) 3:348;
   Uvularia (Strawbell and Wild Oats) 3:348;
   Veratrum (White Hellebores and Corn Lily) 3:353;
   Zigadenus (Camas) 3:362
Limnanthaceae 5:560;

Limnanthes (Poached Egg Flower) 2:207
Limnocharitaceae (Water Poppy) 5:619
Linaceae 5:557;
  Linus (Flax and Linseed) 2:143, 207, 208, 221
Loasaceae 4:464;
  Mentzelia (Blazing Star) 2:225
Lobeliaceae 5:606;
  Lobelia 2:209
Loganiaceae 5:572;
  Buddleia 1:67;
  Desfontainea 1:119;
  Strychnos (Strychnine and Curare Poison Nut) 1:111, 3:326
Loranthaceae (Mistletoes) 4:524;
  Arceuthobium (Dwarf Mistletoe) 2:231;
  Loranthus 2:211, 231;
  Phoradendron 2:231;
  Psittacanthus (Red Mistletoe) 2:231;
  Viscum 2:231
Lythraceae 4:506;
  Cuphea (Cigar Flower) 1:111;
  Lagerstroemia (Crape Myrtles) 2:196;
  Lawsonia (Henna) 2:173;
  Lythrum (Purple Loosestrife) 2:213
Magnoliaceae 3:377;
  Liriodendron (Tulip Trees) 3:338, 346;
  Magnolia 2:198, 214;
  Michelia 2:229
Malesherbiaceae 4:454
Malpighiaceae 5:563;
  Malpighia 2:217
Malvaceae 4:444;
  Abutilon (China Jute) 1:7, 87, 2:216;
  Alcea (Hollyhocks) 2:178;
  Althaea (Marsh Mallow) 1:25, 2:216;
  Gossypium (Cottons) 1:107, 2:163;
  Hibiscus (Okras) 2:173, 176, 248, 3:350;
  Hoheria (Lace Bark) 2:177, 195;
  Lavatera (Tree Mallow) 2:198, 216;
  Malope 2:217;
  Malva (Mallows) 2:216, 217, 236;
  Pavonia 2:261;
  Sida (Virginia Mallow and Queensland Hemp) 3:315;
  Sidalcea (Checker Bloom) 3:315;
  Urena (Aramina) 1:39
Marantaceae (Arrowroots) 5:650;
  Calathea 1:70, 3:298, 342;
  Maranta 1:41, 2:219, 3:328;
  Thaumatococcus (Miraculous Fruit) 3:335
Marcgraviaceae 4:438
Martyniaceae 5:602;
  Martynia (Unicorn Plant) 2:220
Mayacaceae 5:629
Medusandraceae 4:522
Melastomataceae 4:513;
  Melastoma 2:224;
  Miconia 2:229;
  Tibouchina (Glory Bush) 3:336
Meliaceae (Mahoganies) 5:551;
  Aglaia 1:13;
  Cedrela (Toons) 1:80, 2:215, 3:342;
  Chloroxylon (East Indian Satinwood) 1:88, 3:308, 338;
  Dysoxylum 2:127, 215;
  Entandrophragma (Sapeles) 3:307, 338;
  Guarea 1:8, 2:167, 215, 3:289;
  Khaya 2:193, 215, 3:338;
  Lovoa (African Walnut) 3:356;
  Melia (Umbrella Trees) 2:215, 224;

Ptaeroxylon (Cape Mahogany) 2:215, 3:283;
  Swietenia 2:215, 3:338
Melianthaceae 5:541;
  Greyia 2:164
Menispermaceae 3:400;
  Chondrodendron (Moonseed Vine) 1:111
Menyanthaceae 5:581;
  Menyanthes (Bogbean) 2:225;
  Nymphoides (Floating Hearts) 2:243
Misodendraceae 4:525
Monimiaceae 3:384;
  Laurelia (Peruvian Nutmeg) 2:198
Moraceae 4:446;
  Antiaris 3:347;
  Artocarpus (Breadfruit) 1:42, 3:350, 7:926;
  Brosimum 1:66;
  Broussonetia (Paper Mulberry) 1:66;
  Cannabis (Indian Hemp) 1:73, 2:256;
  Castilla (Caucho/Panama Rubber) 1:74, 78, 3:297;
  Cecropia (Trumpet Tree) 1:80;
  Chlorophora (Iroko) 2:187;
  Dorstenia (Torus Herb) 1:123;
  Ficus (Figs and India Rubber) 1:52, 2:142, 195, 3:297, 330;
  Humulus (Hops) 1:178, 182;
  Maclura (Osage Orange) 3:256;
  Morus (Mulberries) 2:233
Moringaceae 4:472;
  Moringa (Horse-radish Tree) 2:232
Musaceae 5:646;
  Ensete (Abyssinian Banana) 2:131;
  Musa (Bananas and Manila Hemp) 1:6, 52, 2:173, 236, 7:926
Myoporaceae (Emu Bushes) 5:592
Myricaceae 4:408;
  Myrica (Bayberries and Sweet Gale) 2:237
Myristicaceae 3:381;
  Myristica (Nutmeg and Mace) 2:214, 237, 243
Myrsinaceae 4:484;
  Ardisia 1:40
Myrtaceae 4:511;
  Callistemon (Bottlebrushes) 1:71;
  Correa (Botany Bay Tea) 1:105;
  Eucalyptus 1:43, 62, 2:135, 187, 193, 233, 3:265, 338, 7:926;
  Eugenia 2:137, 187;
  Feijoa (Pineapple Guava) 2:139;
  Leptospermum (Tea Trees) 2:202;
  Melaleuca 2:221;
  Metrosideros 2:228;
  Myrtus (Myrtles) 2:237;
  Pimenta (Allspice and Evergreen Bayberry) 1:17, 3:265, 272;
  Psidium (Guavas) 3:282;
  Syzygium (Clove Tree) 1:93;
  Virola (Ucuhuba) 3:347
Najadaceae 5:624;
  Najas 2:238
Nepenthaceae (Pitcher Plants) 3:392;
  Nepenthes 2:240, 3:273
Nolanaceae 5:577;
  Nolana 2:242
Nyctaginaceae 4:419;
  Bougainvillea 1:62;
  Mirabilis 2:230;
  Pisonia 2:273
Nymphaeaceae (Water-lilies) 3:394;
  Nelumbo (Lotuses) 2:239, 3:350;
  Nophar (Yellow Water-lilies) 2:243;
  Nymphaea 2:243;
  Victoria 3:355

Nyssaceae 4:516;
  Davidia (Pocket Handkerchief Tree) 1:118;
  Nyssa (Tupelo Trees) 2:243
Ochnaceae 4:433;
  Lophira (African Oak) 2:187, 211;
  Ochna 2:247
Olacaceae 4:523;
  Coula (African Walnut) 3:356
Oleaceae 5:576;
  Fontanesia 2:148;
  Forestiera (Swamp Privet) 2:148;
  Forsythia 2:148;
  Fraxinus (Ashes) 1:43, 2:219, 3:328, 338;
  Jasminum (Jasmines) 2:188;
  Ligustrum (Privet) 3:281;
  Olea (Olives) 2:248;
  Osmanthus 2:256;
  Phillyrea (Jasmine Box) 3:268;
  Syringa (Lilacs) 2:206
Oliniaceae 4:512
Onagraceae 4:512;
  Chamaenerion (Rosebay Willowherb) 1:85;
  Circaea (Enchanter's Nightshade) 1:90, 2:241;
  Clarkia 1:91, 2:163;
  Epilobium 2:131;
  Fuchsia 2:150;
  Lopezia 2:210;
  Ludwigia 2:212;
  Oenothera (Evening Primroses) 2:247;
  Zauschneria (Californian Fuchsia) 3:362
Orchidaceae (Orchid Family) 2:255, 5:671;
  Anacamptis 1:28;
  Angraecum 1:31;
  Anoectochilus (Jewel Orchids) 1:31;
  Brassia 1:63, 2:247;
  Bulbophyllum 1:68;
  Calanthe 1:70;
  Catasetum 1:79;
  Cattleya 1:79, 2:196, 3:318;
  Cephalanthera (Helleborines) 1:81, 2:172;
  Coeloglossum (Frog Orchid) 1:97;
  Coelogyne 1:97;
  Cymbidium 1:112;
  Cypripedium (Lady's-slipper Orchids) 1:114, 2:259;
  Dactylorhiza 1:115;
  Dendrobium 1:118;
  Disa 1:122;
  Epidendrum 2:131;
  Epipactis (Helleborines) 2:131, 172;
  Eria 2:132;
  Eulophia 2:137;
  Goodyera (Jewel Orchids) 2:163;
  Gymnadenia 2:167;
  Habenaria 2:168;
  Himantoglossum (Lizard Orchid) 2:177;
  Laelia 2:195, 196, 3:318;
  × *Laeliocattleya* 2:196;
  Listera 2:208;
  Lycaste (Nun Orchid) 2:212;
  Masdevallia 2:220;
  Maxillaria 2:221;
  Miltonia 2:230, 247;
  Neottia (Bird's-nest Orchid) 2:239;
  Odontoglossum (Lily-of-the-valley Orchid) 2:247;
  Oncidium (Butterfly Orchids) 2:247, 249;
  Ophrys (Bee and Fly Orchids) 2:252;
  Orchis 2:255;
  Paphiopedilum 2:259;
  Phalaenopsis (Moth Orchids) 3:267;
  Pleione (Indian Crocuses) 3:275;

Polystachya 3:278;
  × *Sophrolaeliocattleya* 3:318;
  Sophronitis 3:318;
  Spiranthes (Lady's Tresses) 3:322;
  Stanhopea 3:323;
  Vanda 3:349;
  Vanilla 3:349;
  Zygopetalum 3:363
Orobanchaceae 5:598;
  Lathraea (Toothworts) 2:198;
  Orobanche (Broomrapes) 2:256
Oxalidaceae 5:559;
  Oxalis (Wood Sorrel and Bermuda Buttercup) 1:68, 2:257, 3:314, 350
Paeoniaceae 4:431;
  Paeonia (Peonies) 2:258
Palmae (Palm Family) 3:328, 5:651;
  Areca (Betel Nut) 1:57;
  Arenga (Sugar Palm) 1:40, 3:302;
  Attalea (Bahia Piassaba) 1:49, 3:271;
  Borassus (Palmyra Palm) 1:61;
  Brahea (Blue Fan Palm) 1:63;
  Calamus (Rattan Palms) 1:70, 2:216, 3:289;
  Caryota (Fishtail Palm) 1:77, 3:302;
  Ceroxylon (Andean Wax Palm) 1:84, 3:357;
  Chamaedoria (Parlor Palm) 1:85;
  Chamaerops 1:85;
  Chrysalidocarpus (Butterfly Palm) 1:88;
  Cocos (Coconut Palm) 1:41, 96, 97;
  Copernicia (Carnauba Wax Palm) 1:76, 104, 3:357;
  Corypha (Gebang Palm) 1:106;
  Daemonorops (Malayan Dragon's Blood) 1:115, 124, 3:289;
  Dictyosperma (Princess Palm) 1:120, 3:271;
  Elaeis (Oil Palms) 2:129;
  Euterpe (Assai Palms) 2:138;
  Geonoma 2:160;
  Howea 2:182;
  Jubaea (Chilean Wine Palm) 2:189;
  Latania 2:197;
  Leopoldinia 3:271;
  Livistona 2:209;
  Lodoicea (Double Coconut) 1:123;
  Metroxylon (Ivory Nut and Sago Palms) 2:228, 3:302;
  Nypa 2:243;
  Orbignya (Babassú and Cohune Palms) 2:255;
  Palmetto 2:258;
  Phoenix (Date Palms) 1:117, 3:268;
  Raphia (Raffia Palms) 3:271, 286, 288;
  Roystonea (Royal Palms) 3:297;
  Thrinax 3:335;
  Trachycarpus (Chinese Windmill Palm) 3:342
Pandaceae 4:535
Pandanaceae 5:655;
  Pandanus (Screw Pines) 2:258
Papaveraceae (Poppies) 3:279, 4:402;
  Argemone 1:40, 3:279;
  Bocconia (Tree Poppies) 1:60;
  Dendromecon (Bush Poppy) 1:119;
  Eschscholzia (Californian Poppy) 2:135, 3:279;
  Glaucium (Horned Poppies) 2:162, 3:279;
  Hunnemannia 3:279;
  Macleaya (Plume Poppy) 2:214, 3:279;
  Meconopsis (Welsh and Himalayan Poppies) 2:221, 3:279;

Papaver (Opium Poppy etc)
2:198, 252, 259, 3:279;
Romneya (California Tree Poppy)
3:279, 296;
Sanguinaria (Bloodroot) 3:306
Passifloraceae 4:452;
Passiflora (Passion Flowers and
Granadillas) 2:261
Pedaliaceae 5:601;
Sesamum (Sesame) 3:314
Penaeaceae 4:508
Peperomiaceae (Pepper Elders)
3:390
Philydraceae 5:661
Phrymaceae 5:591
Phytolaccaceae 4:421;
Phytolacca (Pokeweeds) 3:270;
Rivina (Bloodberry) 1:60, 3:295
Piperaceae 3:388;
Peperomia 3:264;
Piper (Pepper and Kava) 3:265,
272
Pittosporaceae 4:488;
Billbergia (Appleberry) 1:59;
Pittosporum 3:274
Plantaginaceae 5:591;
Littorella (Shoreweeds) 2:209;
Plantago (Plantains) 3:274
Platanaceae 4:405;
Platanus (Plane and Buttonwood
Trees) 3:274, 330
Plumbaginaceae 4:428;
Acantholimon (Prickly Thrift) 1:8;
Armeria (Thrift) 1:40;
Ceratostigma 1:82;
Limonium (Sea Lavender) 2:207;
Plumbago 3:275
Podostemaceae 4:502
Polemoniaceae 5:583;
Cobaea (Cathedral Bell) 1:93;
Phlox 3:268;
Polemonium (Jacob's Ladder)
3:276
Polygalaceae 5:565;
Polygala 3:277
Polygonaceae 4:427;
Coccoloba (Sea Grape and Pigeon
Plum) 1:96, 2:193;
Eriogonum (Wild Buckwheat)
1:67, 2:133;
Fagopyrum (Buckwheats) 1:67,
2:139;
Muehlenbeckia (Wire Vine)
2:233;
Polygonum (Smartweeds and
Fleece Flowers) 1:59, 3:277;
Rheum (Rhubarbs) 3:290, 293,
350;
Rumex (Docks and Sorrels)
3:301
Pontederiaceae 5:659;
Eichhornia (Water Hyacinth)
2:129;
Pontederia (Pickerel Weed) 3:279
Portulacaceae 4:424;
Calandrinia 1:70;
Lewisia (Bitter Root) 2:203;
Portulaca 3:279
Posidoniaceae 5:626;
Posidonia 3:279
Potamogetonaceae 5:624;
Potamogeton (Pondweeds) 3:279
Primulaceae (Primrose Family)
4:484;
Anagallis (Pimpernels) 1:28;
Androsace 1:29;
Cortusa 1:106;
Cyclamen 1:112;
Dionysia 1:121;
Dodecatheon 1:122;
Glaux (Sea Milkwort) 2:162;
Hottonia (Water Violet) 2:179;
Lysimachia 2:213;
Polyanthus (Common Primrose
and Cowslip) 3:277;
Primula (Primroses) 1:47, 3:280;
Soldanella 3:318;

Trientalis (Chickweed
Wintergreen) 3:343
Proteaceae 4:519;
Banksia 1:52;
Embothrium (Chilean Fire Tree)
2:130;
Grevillea (Silk Oak) 2:164;
Hakea 2:168;
Macadamia (Australia Nuts)
2:214;
Protea 3:281;
Telopea (Waratahs) 3:334
Punicaceae 4:512;
Punica (Pomegranate) 3:278,
284
Pyrolaceae 4:479;
Pyrola (Wintergreens) 3:285
Quiinaceae 4:438
Rafflesiaceae 4:527;
Rafflesia 3:286
Ranunculaceae (Buttercup Family)
3:396;
Aconitum (Monkswood and
Wolfbane) 1:9;
Actaea 1:10;
Adonis (Pheasant's Eye) 1:10;
Anemone 1:29;
Aquilegia (Columbines) 1:38;
Caltha (Marsh Marigold) 1:72,
2:220;
Cimicifuga (Bugbane and Black
Cohosh) 1:89;
Clematis 1:92;
Coptis 1:104;
Delphinium (Delphiniums and
Larkspurs) 1:118;
Eranthis (Winter Aconite) 2:132;
Helleborus (Hellebores and
Christmas Rose) 1:88, 2:172;
Hepatica (Liverleaf) 2:173;
Nigella (Love-in-a-mist and Black
Cumin) 2:241;
Pulsatilla 3:284;
Ranunculus (Buttercups) 1:68,
3:287;
Thalictrum (Meadow Rue) 3:335;
Trollius (Globe Flower) 3:345
Rapateaceae 5:628
Resedaceae 4:472;
Reseda (Mignonettes) 2:229,
3:295
Restionaceae 5:633
Rhamnaceae 4:537;
Ceanothus 1:80;
Colletia 1:98;
Frangula (Alder Buckthorn)
2:148;
Paliurus (Jerusalem Tree) 2:258;
Pomaderris 3:278;
Rhamnus (Buckthorns) 1:67, 77;
Sageretia 3:302;
Ziziphus (Jujubes) 2:195, 239,
3:363
Rhizophoraceae 4:507;
Rhizophora (Mangroves) 2:218,
3:290
Rosaceae (Rose Family) 4:491;
Acaena (New Zealand Bur) 1:7;
Agrimonia (Agrimony) 1:13;
Alchemilla (Lady's Mantles) 1:15;
Amelanchier 1:27;
Aruncus 1:42, 3:321;
Chaenomeles (Flowering Quinces)
1:84, 3:286;
Cotoneaster 1:106;
Crataegus (Hawthorn) 2:169,
219;
Cydonia (Quince) 1:112, 3:286;
Dryas 3:321;
Eriobotrya (Loquat) 2:133;
Exochorda (Pearl Bush) 2:138;
Filipendula (Meadowsweet)
2:142, 3:321;
Fragaria (Strawberries) 3:325;
Geum (Wood and Water Avens)
2:161;
Gillenia 2:161;

Holodiscus (Creambush) 2:178,
3:321;
Kerria (Jew's Mallow) 2:192;
Malus (Apples) 1:37, 89, 108,
2:217;
Mespilus (Medlar) 2:221;
Photinia (Chinese Hawthorn)
2:170, 3:269;
Potentilla 3:280, 325;
Prunus 3:282, 324;
Amygdalus (Almond and
Peach) 1:17, 2:239, 262;
Armeniaca (Apricot) 1:38;
Cerasus (Cherries) 1:86,
2:219, 3:282;
Laurocerasus (Cherry Laurels)
2:198, 3:282;
Padus (Bird Cherries) 3:282;
Prunophora (Plums and Sloe)
1:60, 116, 2:164, 3:275,
282, 316;
Pyracantha (Firethorn) 3:285;
Pyrus (Pears) 2:262, 3:285;
Quillaja (Soap-bark Tree) 3:286;
Rhaphiolepis (Indian and Yedda
Hawthorns) 3:290;
Rhodotypos 3:293;
Rosa (Roses) 1:46, 3:296;
Rubus (Blackberries, Raspberries
and Loganberry) 1:60, 63,
2:210, 3:288, 300, 358;
Sanguisorba (Burnets) 3:306;
Sorbaria 3:318, 321;
Sorbus (Rowans, Whitebeams
and Service Trees) 2:233,
3:318;
Spiraea 3:321;
Stephanandra (Lace Shrub)
3:324;
Stranvaesia 3:325
Rubiaceae 5:607;
Asperula (Woodruff) 1:44;
Bouvardia 1:62;
Cephaelis (Ipecac) 2:186;
Cinchona (Quinine) 3:286;
Coffea (Coffee) 1:69, 97, 7:926;
Galium 2:154;
Gardenia (Cape Jasmine) 2:155;
Hamelia (Scarlet Bush) 2:168;
Hoffmannia 2:177;
Houstonia (Bluets) 2:182;
Ixora 2:188;
Manettia 2:218;
Morinda (Indian Mulberry)
2:232;
Psychotria (False Ipecac) 2:186;
Randia 3:287;
Rondeletia 3:296;
Rubia (Madders) 2:214, 3:300;
Uncaria (Bengal Gambier) 2:154
Ruppiaceae 5:626;
Ruppia (Ditch Grasses) 3:301
Rutaceae (Citrus Fruit Family)
5:552;
Aegle 1:11;
Boronia 1:61;
Choisya (Mexican Orange) 1:88;
Citrus (Oranges, Lemons, Limes,
Grapefruit etc) 1:91, 92,
2:163, 194, 199, 207, 217,
254, 256, 3:278, 308, 314,
332, 347, 7:926;
Cusparia (Angostura) 1:30, 112;
Dictamnus (Burning Bush/
Dittany) 1:68, 120;
Euodia 2:137;
Fortunella (Kumquats) 2:194;
Murraya (Orange Jasmine)
3:308;
Phellodendron (Cork Tree) 3:267;
Pilocarpus 3:271;
Poncirus (Trifoliate Orange)
2:194, 3:279;
Ptelea (Hop Tree) 3:283, 343;
Ruta (Rue) 3:300, 301;
Skimmia 3:316;
Zanthoxylum (Szechwan Pepper

and Prickly Ashes) 1:31, 43,
3:308, 338, 362
Sabiaceae 5:544
Salicaceae 4:467;
Populus (Aspens and Poplars)
1:43, 44;
Salix (Willows, Sallows and
Osiers) 3:305, 358
Salvadoraceae 4:530
Salviniaceae:
Salvinia (Kariba Weed) 2:192,
3:305
Santalaceae 4:520;
Acanthosyris 1:8;
Santalum (Sandalwood) 3:306,
307;
Thesium (Bastard Toadflax)
3:337
Sapindaceae 5:543;
Blighia (Akee/Sapida) 1:14;
Cardiospermum (Balloon Vine)
1:75;
Harpullia (Tulip Tree) 3:346;
Koelreuteria (Flamegold and
Varnish Tree) 2:194;
Litchi (Lychee) 2:208;
Melicoccus (Spanish Lime) 2:224;
Nephelium (Rambutan) 3:287;
Paullinia (Guarana) 1:56, 69;
Scleicheria (Lac Tree) 2:195, 214;
Xanthoceras 3:359
Sapotaceae 4:482;
Chrysophyllum (Star Apple)
3:324;
Manilkara (Balata, Chicle and
Sapodilla) 1:49, 87, 2:219,
230, 3:300;
Mimusops (Balata) 2:230;
Palaquium (Gutta-percha) 2:167,
3:300;
Pouteria (Sapote/Egg Fruit)
2:128;
Synepsalum (Miraculous Berry)
2:231
Sarcolaenaceae 4:445
Sarraceniaceae (Pitcher Plants)
4:404;
Darlingtonia (Cobra Plant) 1:117,
3:273;
Heliamphora 2:171, 3:273;
Sarracenia 3:273
Saururaceae 3:388;
Houttuynia 2:182
Saxifragaceae 4:496;
Astilbe (False Goatsbeard) 1:45;
Bergenia (Winter Begonia) 1:57;
Boykinia 1:62;
Decumaria 1:118;
Deutzia 1:119;
Escallonia 2:135;
Francoa (Bridal Wreath) 2:148;
Heuchera (Alum Roots) 2:173;
Hydrangea 2:183;
Itea (Sweet Spire) 2:187;
Kirengeshoma 2:193;
Mitella (Mitterwort) 2:231;
Parnassia (White Buttercup)
1:68, 2:260;
Philadelpus (Mock Orange)
2:267;
Ribes (Currants and
Gooseberries) 1:112, 2:163,
3:294;
Rodgersia 3:296;
Saxifraga (Saxifrages) 2:210,
3:308;
Schizophragma 3:310;
Tellima (Fringe Cups) 3:334;
Tiarella (False Mitterwort) 3:336;
Tolmiea (Pickaback Plant) 3:337
Scheuchzeriaceae (Arrowgrass)
5:623
Schisandraceae 3:382;
Schisandra (Wild Sarsaparilla)
3:308, 310
Scrophulariaceae (Foxglove
Family) 5:593;

Alonsoa (Maskflower) 1:24;
Antirrhinum (Snapdragon) 1:36;
Bacopa (Water Hyssop) 1:49;
Calceolaria (Slipperworts) 1:70;
Celsia 1:80;
Chelone (Turtle Head) 1:86;
Collinsia 1:98;
Cymbalaria 1:112, 2:264, 3:337;
Digitalis (Foxgloves) 2:148;
Erinus 2:133;
Euphrasia (Eyebrights) 2:138;
Hebe 2:170;
Linaria (Toadflax) 2:207, 3:337;
Mimulus (Monkey-flowers)
  2:230, 236;
Nemesia 2:239;
Ourisia 2:257;
Pedicularis (Louseworts) 2:263;
Penstemon (Beard-tongues)
  3:264;
Phygelius (Cape Fuchsia) 3:269;
Rhinanthus 3:290;
Striga 3:326;
Torenia (Blue-wings) 3:342;
Verbascum (Mulleins) 2:233;
Veronica (Speedwells) 3:353;
Wulfenia 3:359
Scytopetalaceae 4:439
Simaroubaceae 5:549;
Ailanthus (Tree of Heaven) 1:14;
Quassia (Bitter Wood) 3:286;
Simarouba (Paradise Tree) 3:315
Smilacaceae 5:670;
Smilax (Sarsaparillas) 3:308,
  317
Solanaceae (Potato and Tomato
  Family) 5:579;
Atropa (Deadly Nightshade) 1:46,
  2:241;
Browallia 1:66;
Brunfelsia (Lady of the Night)
  1:67;
Capsicum (Chili and Sweet
  Peppers) 1:74, 79, 87, 2:164,
  260, 3:265, 272, 289, 330,
  350;
Cestrum (Bastard Jasmines) 1:84;
Cyphomandra (Tree Tomato)
  1:113, 3:337;
Datura (Thorn-apples) 1:117;
Hyoscyamus (Henbanes) 2:183;
Iochroma 2:185;
Lycium 2:213;
Lycopersicon (Tomatoes) 3:337,
  350, 7:926;
Mandragora (Mandrakes) 2:218;
Nicandra (Apple of Peru) 2:241;
Nicotiana (Tobaccos) 2:241, 256,
  3:337, 7:926;
Petunia 3:266;
Physalis 3:270;
Salpiglossis (Painted-tongue)
  3:305;
Schizanthus (Butterfly-flower)
  3:310;
Solanum (Aubergine, Potatoes,
  Nightshades etc) 1:46, 2:128,
  143, 238, 241, 3:265, 279,
  317, 328, 350, 7:926;
Streptosolen (Fire Bush) 3:326
Sonneratiaceae 4:506
Sparganiaceae (Bur-reeds) 5:643
Sphaerosepalaceae 4:445
Stackhousiaceae 4:529
Staphyleaceae (Bladder Nuts)
  5:540
Stemonaceae 5:668
Sterculiaceae 4:441;
Abroma (Devil's Cotton) 1:6;
Cola (Kola) 1:69, 98, 2:194;
Dombeya 1:123;
Freemontodendron 2:150;
Theobroma (Cocoa/Cacao) 1:69,
  96, 3:335, 7:926
Strelitziaceae 5:647;
Heliconia 2:171;
Ravenala (Traveller's Tree) 3:289;

Strelitzia (Bird of Paradise
  Flower) 3:325
Stylidiaceae (Trigger Plant) 5:606
Styracaceae 4:483;
Halesia (Snowdrop Trees) 2:168;
Styrax (Snowbell and Mock
  Orange Trees) 3:325, 327
Taccaceae 5:668;
Tacca (East Indian and Hawaiian
  Arrowroot) 1:41, 3:328, 331
Tamaricaceae 4:459;
Tamarix (Tamarisks) 2:189, 219,
  3:332
Tetrachondraceae 5:590
Theaceae 4:432;
Camellia (Teas and Camellias)
  1:69, 72, 3:333;
Caryocar (Butter Nut) 1:77;
Franklinia 2:150;
Stachyurus 3:323;
Stewartia 3:324;
Symplocos (Sweetleafs) 3:330
Theligonaceae 4:503
Thurniaceae 5:641
Thymelaeaceae 4:509;
Daphne 1:116, 2:198, 3:323;
Lagetta (Lace Bark) 2:195;
Pimelia (Riceflowers) 3:271
Tiliaceae 4:440;
Corchorus (Jutes) 1:104, 2:191,
  3:350;
Sparmannia (African Hemp)
  3:320;
Tilia (Limes/Lindens and
  Basswoods) 3:336, 338
Tovariaceae 4:469
Trapaceae 4:506;
Trapa (Water Chestnuts) 3:356
Tremandraceae 5:564
Trigoniaceae 5:564
Triuridaceae 5:627
Trochodendraceae 4:405
Tropaeolaceae 5:562;
Tropaeolum (Nasturtiums and
  Canary Creeper) 2:238, 3:345,
  350
Turneraceae 4:453;
Turnera (Damiana and West
  Indian Holly) 3:346
Typhaceae 5:643;
Typha (Bulrushes) 1:68, 3:301,
  347
Ulmaceae 4:445;
Celtis (Hackberries) 1:81, 3:324;
Ulmus (Elms) 2:129, 1:338;
Zelkova 3:362
Umbelliferae (Carrot Family)
  5:569;
Aciphylla 1:9;
Aegopodium 1:11;
Anethum (Dill) 1:121;
Angelica 1:30;
Anthriscus (Cow Parsley and
  Chervil) 1:36;
Apium (Celery and Celeriac)
  1:37, 80, 3:350;
Archangelica 1:39;
Arracacia (Arracacha) 1:41,
  3:350;
Astrantia (Masterworts) 1:46;
Azorella (Balsam-bog) 1:46;
Bupleurum (Hare's Ears) 1:68;
Carum (Caraway) 1:77;
Chaerophyllum (Chervils) 1:84,
  3:350;
Cicuta (Cowbane and Musquash
  Root) 1:89;
Conium (Hemlock) 1:99, 2:172;
Conopodium (Pignut) 1:99;
Coriandrum (Coriander) 1:104;
Crithmum (Samphire) 1:109;
Cuminum (Cumin) 1:111;
Daucus (Carrot) 1:77, 117,
  3:350;
Dorema 1:123;
Eryngium (Sea Holly and
  Snakeroot) 2:134;

Ferula (Giant Fennel) 2:139,
  3:290;
Foeniculum (Fennel) 2:139, 143,
  3:350;
Hacquetia 2:168;
Heracleum (Hogweeds) 2:173;
Hydrocotyle (Pennyworts) 3:264;
Levisticum (Lovage) 2:211;
Ligusticum (Scotch Lovage)
  2:206;
Myrrhis (Myrrh/Sweet Cicely)
  2:237;
Pastinaca (Parsnip) 2:261,
  3:350;
Petroselinum (Parsley) 2:260,
  3:350;
Pimpinella (Anise) 1:31;
Sanicula (Sanicles) 3:306;
Smyrnium (Black Pot Herb)
  3:317
Urticaceae 4:447;
Boehmeria (Ramie and False
  Nettles) 1:60, 2:241;
Laportea (Wood Nettle) 2:241;
Pilea 3:271;
Soleirola (Baby's-tears) 3:318;
Urtica (Stinging Nettles) 2:241,
  3:348
Valerianaceae 5:610;
Centranthus 1:81;
Nardostachys (Spikenard) 2:238;
Valeriana (Valerians) 3:349;
Valerianella (Corn Salads) 3:349
Velloziaceae 5:667
Verbenaceae 5:586;
Callicarpa 1:71;
Caryopteris 1:77;
Clerodendrum 1:92;
Lantana (Yellow Sage) 2:197;
Lippia (Lemon Verbena) 2:208;
Petrea (Purple Wreath) 3:266;
Tectona (Teaks) 3:334, 338;
Verbena (Vervains) 3:353;
Vitex (Chaste Trees) 3:355
Violaceae 4:450;
Viola (Violets and Pansies)
  2:259, 3:355
Vitaceae 4:538;
Ampelopsis 1:28;
Cissus (Kangaroo Vine) 1:90;
Parthenocissus (Virginia Creeper)
  2:261;
Rhoicissus (Cape Grape) 3:293;
Vitis (Grapevines) 1:111, 2:163,
  236, 3:287, 329, 355, 356
Vochysiaceae 5:564
Winteraceae 3:378;
Drimys (Winter's Bark) 1:125
Xanthorrhoeaceae (Grass Trees)
  5:666;
Xanthorrhoea 3:359
Xyridaceae (Yellow-eyed Grasses)
  5:627
Zannichelliaceae 5:625;
Zannichellia (Horned Pondweed)
  3:361
Zingiberaceae 5:647;
Amomum 1:75;
Aframomum (Melegueta Pepper)
  1:75, 3:265;
Costus 1:106;
Curcuma (Turmeric and
  Zedoaries) 1:41, 111, 3:328,
  346;
Elattaria (Cardamom) 1:75;
Hedychium (Butterfly Ginger)
  2:170;
Kaempferia (Galanga) 2:191;
Roscoea 3:296;
Zingiber (Ginger) 3:363
Zosteraceae 5:626;
Zostera (Eel Grasses) 3:363
Zygophyllaceae 5:554;
Guaiacum (Lignum Vitae) 2:167,
  206;
Larrea (Creosote Bush) 2:197;
Peganum (Harmal) 2:263

2. FAMILIES OF CONIFERS

Araucariaceae:
  Agathis (Kauri Pines) 1:104,
    2:192, 3:290;
  Araucaria (Monkey Puzzles) 1:39,
    103, 2:242
Cephalotaxaceae:
  Cephalotaxus (Plum Yews) 1:81
Cupressaceae:
  Callitris (Cypress Pines) 1:71,
    3:272, 306;
  Chamaecyparis (False Cypresses)
    1:85, 113;
  × *Cupressocyparis* (Hybrid
    Cypresses) 1:100, 111;
  Cupressus (True Cypresses)
    1:113;
  Fitzroya (Patagonian Cypress)
    2:143;
  Juniperus (Junipers and Red
    Cedars) 1:103, 2:190, 3:338;
  Libocedrus (Incense Cedars)
    2:203;
  Tetraclinis (Alerce) 3:306;
  Thuja (Arbor-vitae) 3:335, 338;
  Thujopsis (False Arbor-vitae)
    3:336
Ginkgoaceae:
  Ginkgo (Maidenhair Tree) 1:100,
    103, 2:216
Pinaceae:
  Abies (Firs) 1:6, 49, 3:346;
  Cedrus (True Cedars) 1:80, 100;
  Larix (Larches) 2:197, 3:346;
  Picea (Spruces) 3:322;
  Pinus (Pines) 1:100, 2:195,
    3:272, 290, 296, 346;
  Pseudolarix (Golden Larch)
    3:282;
  Pseudotsuga (Douglas Fir) 1:123;
  Tsuga (Hemlock Spruces) 2:173
Podocarpaceae (Southern Pines):
  Dacrydium (Red, Huon and
    Mountain Pines) 1:115,
    3:272;
  Podocarpus 3:276;
  Saxegothaea (Prince Albert Yew)
    3:308
Taxaceae:
  Taxus (Yews) 2:173, 3:360;
  Torreya (Nutmeg Trees) 3:342
Taxodiaceae:
  Cryptomeria (Japanese Red
    Cedar) 1:110;
  Cunninghamia (Chinese Fir)
    1:111;
  Metasequoia (Dawn Redwood)
    2:228, 3:289;
  Sciadopitys (Parasol Pine) 3:310;
  Sequoia (Coast Redwood) 3:289,
    313, 338;
  Sequoiadendron (Sierra Redwood)
    3:289, 313;
  Taxodium (Swamp Cypresses)
    3:333

3. MAIN GROUPS OF PLANTS

Algae 1:18, 9:1214
Bacillariophyceae (Diatoms) 1:20,
  45, 120, 9:1215;
  Asterionella 1:22, 45;
  Navicula 2:238;
  Melosira 1:22;
  Tabellaria 1:51
Charophyceae (Stoneworts) 1:20,
  3:325;
  Chara 1:23;
  Nitella 2:241

Chlorophyceae (Green Algae) 1:20, 2:164, 9:1215;
Acetabularia (Mermaid's Wine Glass) 1:9, 22;
Chlamydomonas (Red Snow) 1:20, 22, 88, 3:289;
Chlorococcum 1:20, 88;
Cladophora 1:23, 91;
Closterium 1:20;
Codium 1:21, 22, 97;
Cosmarium 1:23;
Draparnaldia 1:124;
Enteromorpha 1:21, 2:131;
Eudorina 1:20;
Halimeda 2:168;
Monostroma 1:19, 2:232;
Oedogonium 1:21, 23, 2:247;
Pediastrum 1:20, 22, 2:263;
Spirogyra 1:21, 3:322;
Tetraspora 1:22;
Trentepohlia 1:18;
Ulothrix 1:22, 3:347;
Ulva (Sea Lettuce) 2:19, 20, 22, 3:311;
Valonia 1:20, 21, 22, 3:349;
Volvox 1:20, 21, 3:356;
Zygnema 1:23
Chrysophyceae (Golden-Brown Algae) 1:20, 9:1215;
Chrysoamoeba 1:22;
Dinobryon 1:22;
Ochromonas 1:22
Cryptophyceae 1:20;
Cryptomonas 1:22
Dinophyceae (Dinoflagellates) 1:20, 9:1215;
Ceratium 1:22;
Gonyaulax (Red Tide) 2:163, 3:289;
Gymnodium (Red Tide) 2:167, 3:289;
Peridinium 3:265
Euglenophyceae 1:20;
Colacium 1:23;
Euglena 1:23, 2:137
Haptophyceae 1:20;
Coccolithus 1:23
Phaeophyceae (Brown Algae) 1:20, 66;
Ascophyllum (Yellow Wrack) 1:18, 43;
Bifurcata 1:23;
Cutleria 1:22, 112;
Dictyota 1:21, 22, 120;
Fucus 1:18, 21, 2:150, 3:264;
Himantha 1:18;
Hormoseira 2:178;
Laminaria (Oarweeds) 1:18, 21, 23, 2:192, 196;
Macrocystis (Giant Kelps) 1:18, 22, 67, 2:192, 214;
Nereocystis (Bull Kelps) 1:18, 22, 67, 2:192, 240;
Pelvetia (Channelled Wrack) 1:18, 3:264;
Sargassum 1:18, 3:307;
Turbinaria 1:23
Prasinophyceae 1:20;
Halosphaera 2:168;
Prasinocladus 1:23;
Pyramimonas 1:23
Rhodophyceae (Red Algae) 1:20, 9:1215;
Batrachospermum (Frog-spawn Alga) 1:53;
Ceramium 1:22, 82;
Chrondrus (Carragheen/Irish Moss) 1:23, 77, 88;
Corallina 1:104;
Gelidium 2:160;
Gigartina 1:18, 2:161;
Polysiphonia 1:22, 3:272, 278;
Porphyra (Laver Bread) 1:19, 21, 23, 2:199, 3:279;
Rhodymenia 1:19
Xanthophyceae (Yellow-green Algae) 1:20;

Centribactus 1:23;
Heterococcus 1:23;
Vaucheria 1:21, 23, 3:349

Angiosperms 1:32, 9:1218, see FAMILIES OF FLOWERING PLANTS

Bacteria 1:50
Azotobacter 1:48, 51
Bacillus 1:49
Bordetella (Whooping Cough) 1:51
Clostridium (Botulism) 1:51
Corynebacterium (Diphtheria) 1:51
Diplococcus (Pneumonia) 1:51
Escherichia 1:51
Lactobacillus 3:308
Mycobacterium (Tuberculosis) 1:51
Neisseria (Gonorrhea) 1:50
Nitrobacter 1:51, 2:242
Nitrosomonas 1:51, 2:242
Pseudomonas 3:282
Rhizobium 3:290
Rickettsia (Typhus) 1:51
Salmonella (Typhoid) 1:51
Shigella (Dysentery) 1:51
Treponema (Syphilis) 1:50

Blue-green Algae 1:50, 9:1215
Anabaena 1:28, 48, 51
Microcystis 1:50
Nostoc 1:36, 51, 2:219, 242
Oscillatoria 2:256
Rivularia 1:51
Scytonema 1:51

Club Mosses 1:94, 9:1216
Isoetes 1:95
Lycopodium 1:94, 2:213
Phylloglossum 1:94
Psilotum (Whisk Ferns) 1:95
Selaginella 1:94, 3:290
Stylites 1:95
Tsemipteris 1:95

Ferns 2:140, 9:1217
Acrostichum 1:10
Adiantum (Maidenhair Fern) 1:10, 2:141
Alsophila 3:342
Anemia 1:29
Asplenium (Spleenworts) 1:45
Athyrium (Lady Fern) 1:46, 2:141
Azolla (Mosquito Ferns) 1:48, 2:140
Blechnum (Hard Fern) 1:60, 2:141
Botrychium (Moonwort and Grape Fern) 1:62, 2:141
Chaelanthes 1:86
Christensenia 1:88
Cibotium 3:342
Cryptogramma 1:110
Cyathea 2:112, 140, 141, 3:342
Cyrtomium (Holly Fern) 1:114
Cystopteris (Bladder Ferns) 1:114
Davallia (Ball Fern) 1:117
Dicksonia 1:120, 2:140, 141, 3:342
Didymoglossum 2:141
Diplazium 2:140
Dryopteris (Buckler Ferns) 1:125, 2:140, 141
Gleichenia (Sun Ferns) 2:140, 162
Gymnocarpum 2:141
Lygodium (Climbing Fern) 2:140, 213
Marattia (King Fern) 2:219
Marsilea (Water Clovers) 2:140, 220
Matteuccia (Ostrich Fern) 2:140, 221
Nephrolepis (Sword Ferns) 2:140, 240
Notholaena (Cloak Ferns) 2:242
Onoclea (Sensitive Fern) 2:252
Ophioglossum 2:141, 252
Osmunda (Royal and Cinnamon Ferns) 2:256

Phyllitis (Hart's Tongue Fern) 2:141, 3:269
Pilularia (Pillwort) 3:271
Platycerium (Staghorn Ferns) 2:140, 141, 240, 3:274
Polypodium (Polypody) 2:140, 3:277
Polystichum (Shield Ferns) 3:278
Pteridium (Bracken) 1:62, 2:140, 141, 3:283
Pteris (Brakes) 2:141, 3:283
Schizaea (Comb Ferns) 3:310
Thyrsopteris 3:342
Trichomanes 3:343
Woodsia 3:359
Woodwardia (Chain Ferns) 3:359

Fungi 2:156 (*see also* Lichens)
Agaricus (Mushrooms) 1:13
Allomyces 1:43
Amanita (Death Cap and Fly Agaric) 1:25, 2:159
Armillaria (Honey Fungus) 1:40, 2:156
Ascolobus 1:43
Aseroe (Australian Stinkhorn) 3:324
Aspergillus 1:44
Auricularia (Jew's Ear Fungi) 2:188
Boletus (Boletes) 1:61
Chaetomium 1:84
Cladosporium 1:91
Clathrus 3:324
Clavaria (Fairy Clubs) 1:91
Claviceps (Ergot) 2:132
Clitocybe 1:92
Coleosporium 1:98
Colletotrichum 1:98
Coprinus (Ink Caps) 1:104, 2:157
Cordyceps 1:104
Cortinarius 1:105
Crucibulum (Bird's Nest Fungi) 1:60, 3:284
Cyathus (Bird's Nest Fungi) 1:60, 3:284
Dictyostelium 1:120
Elaphomyces (False Truffles) 2:129, 3:345
Endothia 2:130
Entomophthora 2:131
Erysiphe 2:134
Fomes 2:143
Fusarium 2:154
Ganoderma 2:155
Geastrum (Earth Stars) 2:127, 3:284
Gyromitra (False Morels) 2:232
Helvella (Saddle Fungi) 2:172
Hemileia 2:172
Hypocrea 2:184, 3:343
Lactarius 2:195
Langermannia (Puffballs) 2:156, 3:284
Lycoperdon (Puffballs) 2:157, 3:284, 324
Melampsora (Flax Rust) 2:221
Merulius 2:228
Morchella (Morels) 2:232
Mucor 2:233
Nectria 2:239
Neurospora (Bakery Mold) 2:241
Olpidium 2:249
Penicillium (Penicillins) 3:264
Peronospora 3:266
Peziza 2:156, 3:266
Phallus (Common Stinkhorn) 3:324
Phragmidium 3:269
Physoderma 3:270
Phytophthora 3:270, 285
Pilobolus 3:271
Plasmodiophora 3:274
Polyporus (Dryad's Saddle) 2:156, 3:278
Psilocybe (Sacred Mushroom) 3:282
Puccinia 3:283
Pythium 3:285

Rhizopus 3:290
Rhytisma 3:294
Saccharomyces (Yeasts) 3:302
Saprolegnia 3:307
Scleroderma (Earth Balls) 2:127, 3:284
Sclerotinia 3:311
Septoria 3:313
Serpula (Dry Rot) 3:314
Sordaria 3:319
Sphaerotheca 3:321
Spongospora 3:322
Stereum 3:324
Streptomyces 3:326
Taphrina 3:332
Trichoderma 3:343
Trichoscyphella 3:343
Tuber (Truffles) 3:345
Ustilago 3:348
Venturia 3:353
Xylaria (Dead Men's Fingers) 3:360

Gymnosperms 1:100
Coniferinae (Conifers and Ginkgo) 9:1218, see FAMILIES OF CONIFERS
Cycadinae (Cycads) 1:100, 112, 9:1217;
Cycas (Sago Palm) 1:112, 3:302, 328;
Dioon 1:121;
Encephalartos (Bread Tree) 2:130, 3:328;
Lepidozamia 2:214;
Macrozamia 2:214;
Stangeria (Hottentot's Head) 3:323;
Zamia (Sago Cycas) 3:361
Gnetinae 1:100;
Ephedra 2:131;
Gnetum 2:163;
Welwitschia 3:357

Horsetails 2:180, 9:1217
Equisetum 2:180

Lichens 2:204
Cetraria 1:84
Cladonia 1:91
Lecanora 2:219
Parmelia 2:205, 260
Peltigera 2:263
Ramelina 2:205
Rhozocarpon 2:205
Usnea (Old Man's Beard) 2:204, 3:348

Mosses and Liverworts 2:234
Andreaea 1:29, 2:234
Anthoceros 1:36
Atrichum 1:46
Aulacomnium 1:47
Brachythecium 1:62
Bryum 1:67
Buxbaumia 1:68
Camptothecium 1:73, 2:234
Ceratodon 1:82
Conocephalum 1:99
Cratoneuron 1:108
Dawsonia 1:118
Dicranum 1:120
Diplophyllum 1:121
Drepanocladus 1:124, 2:234
Eurynchium 2:138
Fissidens 2:143
Fontinalis 2:148
Frullania 2:150
Funaria 2:154
Grimmia 2:164, 234
Hypnum 2:184
Leucobryum 2:203, 3:290
Lophocolea 2:211
Lunularia 2:212
Marchantia 2:219
Merceya 2:234
Metzgeria 2:228
Mnium 2:231

Neckera 2:234, 238
Pellia 2:235, 263
Philonotis 3:268
Plagiothecium 3:274
Polytrichum 1:46, 2:234, 3:278
Rhacomitrium 2:234, 3:290
Riccia 3:294
Scapania 2:234, 3:309
Sphagnum (Bog Mosses) 2:234, 3:321
Splachnum 3:322
Tetraphis 3:334
Thuidium 3:335
Tortella 2:234
Tortula 3:342

4. CROP PLANTS (*see also* OTHER PLANTS WITH USEFUL PRODUCTS)

Brassicas 1:64, 3:350, 4:470, 472
Broccoli 1:66, 69
Brussels Sprouts 1:67
Cabbage 1:69, 3:308
Calabrese 1:69
Cauliflower 1:79
Chinese Cabbage 1:87
Collards 1:98
Colza Oil 1:99, 2:250
Curly Kale 2:192
Kale 2:149, 192
Kohlrabi 2:194
Mustard 2:227, 236, 250
Rape 2:149, 236, 250, 3:288, 330
Swede 3:298, 301, 330
Turnip 3:298, 346

Cereals 1:83, 2:143, 3:328, 5:635
Barley 1:53, 2:262
Buckwheat 1:67, 2:139, 163
Corn/Maize 1:105, 2:216, 221, 3:270, 7:926
Millets 2:129, 132, 230, 259, 261, 3:264, 314
Oats 1:47, 2:246
Rice 1:41, 105, 2:256, 3:294
Rye 3:301, 311, 344
Sorghum 3:319
Sugar Cane 1:49, 2:231, 3:302, 327, 7:926
Wheat 2:236, 3:320, 344, 7:926

Fiber Plants 144 (*see also* Timber)
Abaca 1:6, 2:173, 236
Abyssinian Banana 2:131
African Jute 3:320
Aramina 1:39
Bahia Piassava 1:49, 3:271
Balsa 1:49
Bamboo 1:43, 49, 52, 3:270, 308
Bow-string Hemp 2:173, 3:307
Cannabis 1:73
Cantala 1:13, 3:316
China Grass 1:60
China Jute 1:7, 87, 2:216
Chinese Windmill Palm 3:342
Coconut Palm 1:96, 97
Coir 1:96, 97
Congo Jute 1:39
Cotton 1:107, 2:163
Deccan Hemp 2:173, 176
Devil's Cotton 1:6
Dogbane 1:37
Esparto 2:135, 3:324
Flax 2:143, 207, 208, 3:269
Hemps 1:6, 37, 73, 109, 2:154, 173, 176, 236, 3:307, 314, 315, 316
Henequin 3:316
Indian Hemp 1:37, 73, 2:176
Indian Mallow 1:7, 87, 2:216
Istli 2:187

Jutes 1:7, 39, 87, 104, 2:191, 216, 3:320
Kapa 1:66
Kapok 1:61, 80, 2:192
Kenaf 2:173, 176
Linen 2:143, 207, 208
Maguey 1:13, 3:316
Malacca Cane 1:70, 115, 2:216, 3:289
Manila Hemp 1:6, 2:173, 236
Mauritius Hemp 2:154, 173
Milkweeds 1:43
New Zealand Flax 3:269
Nypa Palm 2:243
Palms 1:40, 49, 61, 70, 75, 97, 115, 2:216, 228, 243, 3:271, 286, 288, 289, 302, 342
Palmyra Palm 1:61
Panama Hat Palm 1:75
Para Piassava 3:271
Pavonia 2:261
Piassava 1:49, 3:271
Pineapple 3:272, 7:926
Pita 1:10
Queensland Hemp 3:315
Raffia 3:286, 288
Ramie 1:60
Rattan Cane 1:70, 115, 2:216, 3:289
Roselle 2:176
Sago Palm 2:228, 3:302
Silk Cotton 1:61, 80, 2:192
Sisal Hemp 2:173, 3:316
Snake Plant 3:307
Spanish Moss 3:336
Sugar Palm 1:40
Sunn Hemp 1:109, 2:173, 3:314
Tapa 1:66

Fodder Crops 2:149
Alfalfa 2:211
Bahia Grass 2:261
Beggarweed 1:119
Bent-grass 1:14
Bluegrass 3:275
Bluestem 1:29
Broad Bean 2:200
Brome 1:66
Carpet Grass 1:48
Clover 1:92
Cock's Foot 1:115
Corn 1:105, 2:216, 221, 3:270, 7:926
Couch Grass 1:113
Elephant Grass 3:264
Fescue 2:139
Grama 1:62
Guinea Grass 2:259
Kale 2:149, 192
Love Grass 2:132
Lucerne 2:211
Maize 1:105, 2:216, 221, 3:270, 7:926
Millets 2:230
Orchard Grass 1:115
Rape 1:64, 2:149, 236, 250, 3:288, 330
Reed Grass 3:267, 290
Rhodes Grass 1:88
Rye 3:301, 311, 344
Ryegrass 2:130, 3:301
Sainfoin 2:252
Sedge 1:75, 3:312
Teff 2:132, 230
Timothy Grass 3:268
Velvet Bean 2:233
Vetch 3:354
Wheatgrass 1:13, 2:130

Fruits 2:151
Apple 1:37, 2:217
Apricot 1:38
Avocado 1:47, 3:350
Bananas 1:52, 2:236, 7:926
Bilberry 1:59
Blackberries 1:60, 63, 3:300
Blackcurrant 1:112, 3:294

Blueberries 1:59, 60
Breadfruit 1:42, 7:926
Cashew Apple 1:28
Cherimoya 1:31
Cherries 1:86, 2:219, 3:282
Citron 1:91
Coconut 1:96, 2:244, 250, 3:328
Conch Apple 2:261
Cranberries 1:108
Currants 1:111, 112, 3:294
Custard Apple 1:31
Damsons 1:116
Dates 1:117, 3:268
Durian 2:127
Figs 2:142
Gooseberry 2:163, 3:294
Granadillas 2:261
Grapefruit 1:91, 2:163, 3:347
Grapes 2:163, 236, 3:356
Greengage 2:164
Guavas 3:282
Huckleberries 2:182
Jackfruit 1:42
Kiwi Fruit 1:10
Kumquat 1:91, 2:194
Lemon 1:91, 2:199
Limes 1:91, 2:207
Loganberry 2:210
Loquat 1:133
Lychee 2:208
Mammee Apple 2:217
Mandarin 1:91, 92, 2:217, 256, 3:308, 332
Mango 2:218
Mangosteen 2:155, 218
Medlars 2:133, 221
Mulberries 2:233
Nectarine 2:239
Olive 2:248
Oranges 1:91, 2:254, 256, 7:926
Passion Fruit 2:261
Pawpaw 1:75, 2:259
Peach 2:262
Pear 2:262, 3:285
Persimmons 1:121, 2:191, 3:266
Pineapple 3:272, 7:926
Plums/Prune 3:275, 282
Pomegranate 3:278, 284
Quince 1:112
Raisin 3:287
Raspberries 3:288, 300, 358
Red Currant 1:112, 3:294
Sapodilla 2:219
Sapote 2:128
Shaddock 1:91, 3:278, 314
Soursop 1:31
Strawberry 3:325
Strawberry Tree 1:39
Sultana 3:329
Sweetsop 1:31
Tamarind 3:331
Tangerine 3:332, 347

Legumes and Pulses 2:200, 4:499
Asparagus Bean 1:107
Asparagus Pea 1:44, 3:283
Broad Bean 2:200
Butter Bean 2:207, 3:267
Carob Bean 1:15, 76, 2:209
Chick Pea 1:87, 89
Cowpea 1:107
French Bean 2:169, 3:267
Ground Nut 1:38, 2:244, 250
Haricot Bean 2:169, 3:267
Horse Gram 1:123, 2:195
Hyacinth Bean 1:123, 2:195
Jack Bean 1:73
Kidney Bean 2:169, 2:267
Lablab 1:123, 2:195
Lentil 2:199
Lima Bean 2:207, 3:267
Locust Beans 2:209, 260
Lupins 2:212
Mung Bean 2:236
Peanut 1:38, 2:244, 250
Peas 2:143, 261, 3:273
Pigeon Pea 3:271

Runner Bean 2:169
Soybean 2:143, 162, 250, 3:319
Sword Bean 1:73
Tamarind 3:331
Tepary Bean 3:267
Yam Bean 3:360
Yard-long Bean 1:107

Marrows and Squashes 2:222, 3:350, 4:465
Bitter Gourd 1:91, 2:163
Calabash Gourd 1:69, 2:163
Chayote 1:85
Courgette 1:107, 111
Cucumber 1:110, 3:265
Gherkin 2:161
Gourds 1:111, 2:163
Loofa 2:163, 212
Marrow 1:111, 2:163, 3:320, 323
Melons 2:178, 224
Pumpkins 1:111, 3:284, 323
Snake Gourd 2:163
Sponge Gourd 2:163, 212
Squirting Cucumber 2:127
Summer Squash 1:111
Water Melon 1:91, 2:224, 3:357
Winter Squashes 1:111

Nuts 2:244
Almond 1:17, 3:282
Australia Nut 2:214
Betel Nut 1:57
Brazil Nut 1:63, 2:250
Butternut 3:356
Cashew Nut 1:28, 2:250
Chestnuts 1:86
Cobnut 2:170
Coconut 1:96, 2:151, 250, 3:328
Filbert 2:170
Ground Nut 1:38, 2:200, 250
Hazels 2:170
Hickories 1:77
Java Almond 1:24
Kola Nuts 2:194
Macadamia Nuts 2:214
Peanut 1:38, 2:200, 250
Pecan Nut 2:262
Pine Kernels 3:272
Pistachio 2:250, 3:273
Sapucaia 3:307
Walnuts 2:250, 3:356
Water Chestnuts 1:129, 3:356

Oil Crops 2:227, 250
Babassú 2:255
Brazil Nut 1:63, 2:244
Candlenut 1:15
Cashew Nut 1:28, 2:244
Castor Oil Plant 1:73, 3:295
Chaulmoogra 1:85
Cocoa 1:96, 7:926
Coconut 1:96, 2:151, 244, 3:328
Cohune 2:255
Colza 1:64, 99
Cotton Seed 1:107
Croton Oil Plant 1:110
Eng Tree 1:122
Ground Nut 1:38, 2:200, 244
Gurjun 1:49
Hempseed 1:74
Horseradish Tree 2:232
Illipe Nut 3:315
Kapok Seed 1:80, 2:192
Lac Tree 2:214
Linseed 2:207
Maw Seed 2:252
Mustard 1:64, 2:236
Niger Seed 2:167
Oil Palms 2:129
Olive 2:248
Peach 2:262
Peanut 1:38, 2:200, 244
Perilla 3:265
Pistachio 2:244, 3:273
Rape Seed 1:64, 2:236, 3:288, 330
Sesame Seed 3:314
Soybean 2:143, 162, 200, 3:319

Sunflower 3:329
Tung-oil Tree 1:15, 3:346
Walnut 2:244, 3:356
Wood-oil Tree 1:15, 3:346

Rootcrops 3:298, 350
Anu 3:345
Beetroot 1:54, 57
Black Salsify 3:305, 311
Carrot 1:77, 117
Cassava 1:77, 2:219, 3:328, 7:926
Celeriac 1:80
Chervil 1:84
Chinese Artichoke 1:42, 3:323
Garlic 1:17, 2:155
Jerusalem Artichoke 1:42, 3:329
Leek 1:17, 2:199
Lotus 2:239
Mangelwurzel 1:57, 2:218
Manioc 1:77, 2:219, 3:328, 7:926
Oca 2:257
Onions 1:17, 2:243
Parsnip 2:261
Potato 2:143, 3:279, 328, 7:926
Radishes 3:286
Salsify 3:305, 311, 342
Shallot 1:17, 3:314
Sugar Beet 3:327, 328
Swede 1:64, 3:301, 330
Sweet Potato 2:186, 3:330
Topee-tambu 1:70, 3:342
Turnip 1:64, 3:346
Ulluco 3:347
Yams 3:328, 360

Starch Crops 3:328
Arrowroots 1:41, 73, 111, 2:219, 3:331
Bread Tree 2:130
Cocoyam 3:359
Corn/Maize 1:83, 105, 2:216, 221, 3:270, 7:926
Potato 2:143, 3:279, 298, 7:926
Rice 1:41, 83, 105, 2:256, 3:295
Tanier 3:359
Taro 1:24, 3:333, 359
Sago Palms 1:40, 77, 112, 2:228, 3:302, 361
Wheat 1:83, 2:236, 3:320, 344, 7:926
Yams 3:298, 360

Sugar Crops 3:328
Barley 1:53, 83, 2:262
Coconut Palm 1:96, 2:151, 244, 250
Date Palm 3:268
Honey Palm 2:189
Manna Ash 1:119
Maples 1:8, 3:329
Nypa Palm 3:243
Palms 1:40, 77, 96, 2:151, 189, 243, 244, 250, 3:268, 302
Sago Palm 1:77, 3:302
Sorghum 1:83, 3:319
Sugar Beet 3:298, 327, 328
Sugar Cane 1:49, 83, 2:231, 3:302, 327, 7:926
Sugar Palm 1:40, 3:302
Sugar Maple 1:8, 3:329

Timber 3:338
Afara 3:334
Afrormosia 1:12
Arbor-vitae 3:335
Ashes 1:43
Balsa 1:49
Beeches 1:54
Birches 1:59
Cedars 1:80, 2:190, 3:335
Douglas Fir 1:123
Ebonies 1:121, 2:127, 3:266
Eucalyptus 2:135, 187, 7:926
Elms 2:129
Firs 1:6
Greenheart 2:164, 247
Gurjun 1:122

Hemlocks 2:173
Hickories 1:77
Ironbarks 2:187
Junipers 2:190
Kauri Pines 2:192
Keruing 1:122
Larches 2:197
Lignum Vitae 2:167, 206
Limes 3:336
Mahoganies 1:88, 2:193, 215, 3:307, 308
Maples 1:8
Monkey Puzzles 1:29
Oaks 1:105, 2:246
Pines 1:29, 2:192, 3:272
Redwoods 3:289, 313
Rosewoods 3:296, 346
Sapeles 3:307
Satinwoods 1:88, 3:308
Seraya 3:315
Spruces 2:173
Teaks 1:12, 3:334
Tulip/Whitewood 3:346

Vegetables 3:350 (see also Brassicas, Legumes, Marrows, Rootcrops)
Anu 3:345
Artichokes 1:42, 113, 3:323, 329
Asparagus 1:43
Aubergine 1:46, 2:128, 3:317
Avocado 1:47, 2:151
Bamboo Shoots 1:49, 52, 3:270
Beetroot 1:54, 57, 3:298
Black Salsify 3:305, 311
Breadfruit 1:42, 7:926
Cardoon 1:75, 113
Carrot 1:77, 117
Cayenne Pepper 1:74, 79
Celeriac 1:80
Celery 1:80
Chards 1:54, 85
Chervil 1:84
Chicory 1:87, 89
Chili Pepper 1:74, 87
Chinese Artichoke 1:42, 3:323
Chives 1:17, 87
Endive 1:89, 2:130
Fennel 2:139, 143
Garlic 1:17, 2:155
Globe Artichoke 1:42, 113
Green Pepper 2:164, 3:272
Jackfruit 1:42
Jerusalem Artichoke 1:42, 3:329
Jute 1:104
Leek 1:17, 2:199
Lettuce 2:195, 202
Lotus 2:239
Oca 2:257
Onions 1:17, 2:243
Orache 1:46, 2:254
Paprika Pepper 1:74, 2:260
Parsley 2:260
Parsnip 2:261
Peppers 1:74, 79, 87, 2:164, 260, 3:265, 272, 289, 330
Potato 2:143, 3:279, 298, 328, 7:926
Radishes 3:286
Rhubarbs 3:290, 293
Salsify 3:305, 311, 342
Seakale 1:108
Seakale Beet 1:54
Shallot 1:17, 3:314
Spinach 1:27, 3:321
Spinach Beet 1:54, 3:321
Red Pepper 3:272, 289
Sweet Pepper 1:74, 2:164, 3:272, 289, 330
Tomato 3:337, 7:926
Ulluco 3:347

5. OTHER PLANTS WITH USEFUL PRODUCTS
(see also CROP PLANTS)

Alcoholic Beverages 1:16, 58
Agaves (pulque, tequila) 1:13
Apples (cider, wine, spirits) 1:37, 108
Barley (beer, whisky) 1:53
Cherries (wine, spirits) 1:86, 2:219
Corn (gin, whisky) 2:216
Cowslip (wine) 3:280
Elders (wine) 3:306
Ginger (ginger beer) 3:363
Grapevine (wines, brandy, liqueurs) 2:163, 263, 3:356
Hops (beer) 2:178, 182
Juniper (gin) 2:190
Kava Pepper (beer) 3:273
Maize (gin, whisky) 2:216
Millet (beer) 2:230
Palms (toddy, arrack) 1:61, 77, 2:189, 243, 3:268
Pear (perry) 2:262
Potato (spirits) 3:279
Quinoa (beer) 1:86
Rice (saki, arrack) 1:41, 3:294
Rye (beer, spirits) 3:301
Sloe (gin) 1:60
Sorghum (beer) 3:319
Sugar Cane (spirits, liqueurs) 2:231, 3:329
Wheat (spirits) 3:344
Wormwood (wines, liqueurs) 1:42

Alkaloids 1:26, 2:226
Autumn Crocus (colchicine) 1:98
Barberries (berberine) 1:52
Belladonna (atropine and scopolamine) 1:46, 2:241
Betel Nut Palm (arecoline) 1:57
Broom (sparteine) 1:114
Calisaya (quinine) 3:286
Castor Oil Plant (ricinine) 1:78, 3:295
Cheromoya (caffeine) 1:31
Coca (cocaine and hygrine) 1:93
Cocoa (caffeine and theobromine) 1:69, 96, 3:335, 7:926
Coffee (caffeine) 1:69, 97, 7:926
Curare Poison Nut (curarine) 1:111, 3:326
Deadly Nightshade (atropine and scopolamine) 1:46, 2:241
Ephedra (ephedrine) 2:131
Ergot (ergotamine) 2:132
Fenugreek (trigonelline) 3:343
Guarana (caffeine) 1:56, 69
Heliotrope (heliotrine and lasiocarpine) 2:172
Hemlock (coniine) 2:172
Henbane (hyoscamine) 2:183
Huanaco (quinine) 3:286
Indian Snakeroot (reserpine) 3:289
Indian Tobacco (lobeline) 2:209
Ipecac (emetine) 2:186
Kola (caffeine) 1:69, 2:194
Laburnum (cytisine) 2:195
Mandrake (scolopamine) 2:218
Maté (caffeine) 1:69, 2:178, 220
Monkswood (aconitine) 1:9
Moonseed Vine (tubocurarine) 1:111
Opium Poppy (opium: narcotine, morphine, codeine etc) 2:252
Pepper (piperine and piperidine) 3:265, 273
Pilocarpus (pilocarpine) 3:271
Quinine (quinine) 3:286
Rose Periwinkle (vinblastine and vincristine) 1:79
Strychnine Tree (brucine and strychnine) 3:326

Tea (caffeine) 1:69, 3:333
Thorn-apple (hyoscine) 1:117
Tobacco (nicotine) 2:241, 3:337, 7:926
Yellow Lupin (lupinine) 2:212

Beverages, Non-alcoholic 1:58 (see also Alcoholic Beverages)
Apple 1:37, 2:217
Barley 1:53
Blackcurrant 1:112, 3:294
Cassina Holly/Carolina Tea 1:69, 2:178
Chicory 1:87
Cocoa/Cacao 1:69, 96, 3:335, 7:926
Coconut 1:96
Coffee 1:69, 97, 7:926
Dandelion 1:116, 3:332
Fig 2:142
Granadilla 2:261
Grapefruit 1:91, 2:163
Guarana 1:56, 69
Khat/Arabian Tea 1:69, 2:192
Kola 1:69, 2:194
Lemon 1:91, 2:199
Limes 1:91, 2:207
Lime/Linden 3:336
Maté/Paraguay Tea 1:69, 2:178, 220
Pineapple 3:272
Tea (China and Assam Teas) 1:69, 3:333

Dyes and Tannins 2:126
Alder (brown, gray, black, yellow) 1:15
Alkanet (red) 1:15
Annatio (red, yellow) 1:31
Ash (brown, green) 1:43
Birch (gray; tannin) 1:59
Blackberry (gray) 1:60, 3:300
Blackthorn (reddish brown) 1:60
Bloodroot (red) 3:306
Bracken (gray, yellow-green) 1:62, 2:140
Brazil Wood (red, purple) 1:69
Broom (green) 1:66, 114
Butternut (tan) 3:356
Chervil (yellow-green) 1:36
Chestnut (tannin) 1:86
Chinese Tallow Tree (black) 3:331
Coconut (green) 1:96
Coreopsis (orange, yellow) 1:104
Crottle (brownish red) 2:260
Cutch (brown) 1:7, 112
Divi-divi (tannin) 1:69, 122
Dyer's Broom (yellow) 2:160
Dyer's Knotweed (blue) 3:277
Dyer's Rocket (yellow, gold) 2:229, 3:295
Eucalyptus (tannin) 2:135
Fustic (yellow) 2:187
Gambier (black) 1:112, 2:154
Gamboge (yellow) 2:155
Golden Rod (yellow) 3:318
Guava (black) 3:282
Hemlock Spruce (tannin) 2:173
Henna (orange) 2:173
Indigo (blue) 2:185
Jackfruit tree (yellow) 1:42
Juniper (brown) 2:190
Kava (black) 3:273
Lady's Bedstraw (yellow, red) 2:154
Logwood (black, brown, gray) 2:168, 210
Madder (red) 2:214, 3:300
Mangrove (tannin) 2:218, 3:290
Myrobalan (green) 3:334
Oak (tannins) 2:246
Onion (orange) 1:17, 2:249
Orseille (red) 2:205
Osage Orange (yellowish tan, gold) 2:256
Persimmon (black) 1:121, 2:191, 3:266

Pineapple (green) 3:272
Quebracho (tannin) 3:286
Red Stone-lichen (brown) 2:260
Reindeer Moss (yellow, brown) 1:84, 91
Saffron (yellow) 1:109
Safflower (yellow, red) 1:77
Sappan (red) 1:69
Sumac (yellow-tan, gray, brown; tannin) 3:294
Tansy (yellow-green) 3:332
Turmeric (yellow) 1:111, 3:346
Walnut (black, dark brown) 3:356
Wattle (tannin) 1:7, 3:357
Weld (yellow, gold) 2:229, 3:295
Willow (brown) 3:305
Woad (blue) 2:187, 3:358
Yellow-barked Oak (yellow) 2:246
Yellow Chamomile (yellow) 1:36
Zedoary (yellow, green) 1:111

Essential Oils 2:136, 226
Anise 1:31, 2:185
Bergamot 1:57, 3:314
Boronia 1:61
Cajuput 2:221
Camphor 1:73, 89
Caraway 1:77
Cedar Wood see Juniper
Celery 1:37, 80
Citronella 1:113
Cloves 1:93
Eucalyptus 2:135
Gardenia 2:155
Geranium 2:263
Ginger 3:363
Jasmine 2:188
Juniper (Cade and Cedar Wood) 1:80, 2:190
Khus-khus 2:193, 3:354
Lavender 2:198, 199
Lemon 2:199
Lemon Grass 1:113
Lime 2:207
Mustard 2:236
Nutmeg 2:237, 243
Orange 2:254
Patchouli 3:276
Peppermint 2:230, 3:265
Pine 3:272
Roses (Attar of Roses) 1:46, 3:296
Sandalwood 3:306, 307
Sassafras 3:308
Spearmint 2:230
Star Anise 1:31, 2:185
Thyme 3:336
Tuberose 3:277
Wintergreen 2:155
Ylang-ylang 3:361

Flavorings 1:136, 146
Allspice 1:17, 3:265, 272
Angelica 1:30, 39
Angostura 1:30, 112
Anise 1:31, 2:185
Balm 1:57, 99, 2:224, 232
Basil 1:53, 2:247
Bay Laurel 2:198
Bergamot 1:57, 2:232
Capers 1:74
Caraway 1:77
Cardamom 1:75
Celery 1:80
Chilli 1:74, 87
Chives 1:17, 87
Cinnamon 1:89
Cloves 1:93
Coriander 1:104
Cumin 1:111
Fenugreek 3:343
Garlic 1:17, 2:155
Ginger 3:363
Hops 2:178, 182
Horseradish 2:179
Jasmine 2:188
Juniper 2:190
Lemon 2:199

Lemon Balm 2:224
Licorice 2:163, 203
Lime 2:207
Mace 2:214, 237, 243
Marjoram 2:220, 256
Mustard 2:236
Nutmeg 2:214, 237, 243
Orange 2:254
Parsley 2:260
Pepper 3:265
Peppermint 2:230, 3:265
Poppies 1:40, 2:162, 252, 259, 3:279
Roselle 2:176
Rue 3:300, 301
Saffron 1:109
Sarsaparilla 3:308, 317
Sassafras 3:308
Sesame 3:314
Spearmint 2:230
Star Anise 1:31, 2:185
Tamarind 2:200, 3:331
Tarragon 1:42, 3:333
Thyme 3:336
Turmeric 1:111, 3:346
Vanilla 3:349
Wintergreen 2:155
Ylang-ylang 3:361

Herbs 2:174
Alexanders 3:317
Angelica 1:30, 39
Anise 1:31, 2:185
Balm 1:57, 99, 2:224, 232
Basil 1:53, 2:247
Bay Laurel 2:198
Bergamot 1:57, 2:232
Betony 3:323
Borage 1:61
Burnet 3:306
Calamint 1:70
Caraway 1:77
Catmint 2:240
Celery 1:80
Chamomile 1:85, 2:219
Chervil 1:36
Chives 1:17, 87
Coriander 1:104
Costmary 1:106
Dill 1:121
Fennel 2:139
Hyssop 2:184
Lemon Balm 2:224
Lemon Grass 1:113
Lemon Verbena 2:208
Lovage 2:211
Marigold 1:70, 2:219
Marjoram 2:220, 256
Melilot 2:224
Mint 2:230
Myrrh 2:237
Parsley 2:260
Peppermint 2:230, 3:265
Rocket 3:295
Rosemary 3:297
Rue 3:300, 301
Sage 1:91, 3:302
Savory 3:308
Sorrel 3:301
Spearmint 2:230
Sweet Cicely 2:237
Sweet Woodruff 1:44, 2:154
Tansy 3:332
Tarragon 1:42, 3:333
Thyme 3:336
Turmeric 1:111, 3:346
Vanilla 3:349
Vervain 3:353

Medicines and Narcotics 2:226
Alder Buckthorn (anthraquinone) 2:148
Aloe (anthraquinone) 1:24
Angel's Trumpet 1:117
Aniseed 1:31
Asafoetida 2:139
Belladonna (atropine and scopolamine) 1:46, 2:241

Betel Nut Palm (arecoline) 1:57
Boletus 1:61
Broom (sparteine) 1:114
Buckthorn (anthraquinone) 1:67, 77, 2:148
Cajuput (cineole) 2:221
Calisaya (quinine) 3:286
Camphor 1:73, 89
Cannabis 1:73
Caraway 1:77
Cascara (anthraquinone) 1:67, 77
Christmas Rose (cardiac glycoside) 1:88, 2:172
Cloves (eugenol) 1:93
Coca (cocaine and hygrine) 1:93
Cocoa (caffeine and theobromine) 1:69, 96, 3:335, 7:926
Coffee (caffeine) 1:69, 97, 7:926
Deadly Nightshade (atropine and scopolamine) 1:46, 2:241
Ephedra (ephedrine) 2:131
Ergot (ergotamine) 2:132
Eucalyptus (cineole) 2:135
Flag Root 1:9
Fly Agaric 1:25, 2:159
Foxglove (cardiac glycoside) 2:148
Ginger 3:363
Ginseng (saponin) 2:258
Guarana (caffeine) 2:69
Heliotrope (heliotrine and lasiocarpine) 2:172
Hemlock (coniine) 2:172
Henbane (hyoscamine) 2:183
Horn-a-plenty 1:117
Huanaco (quinine) 3:286
Indian Poke 3:270
Indian Snakeroot (reserpine) 3:289
Indian Tobacco (lobeline) 2:209
Ipecac (emetine) 2:186
Kola (caffeine) 1:69, 2:194
Laburnum (cytisine) 2:195
Licorice (saponin) 2:163, 203
Lily of the Valley (cardiac glycoside) 2:206
Lupins (lupinine) 2:212
Mace 2:214, 237, 243
Mandrake (scolopamine) 2:218
Marijuana 1:73
Mescal Button (mescaline) 2:211
Mezerion (coumarin) 1:116
Monkswood (aconitine) 1:9
Moonseed Vine (tubocurarine) 1:111
Morning Glory 2:186, 233
Mustard 2:236
Nutmeg 2:214, 237, 243
Oleander (cardiac glycoside) 2:240
Opium Poppy (opium: narcotine, morphine, codeine etc) 2:252
Pepper (piperine and piperidine) 3:265, 273
Peppermint (carvone) 2:230, 3:265
Pepper Tree (urushiol) 2:220, 3:309
Peru Balsam (cinnamein) 1:49, 2:237
Peyote (mescaline) 2:211
Pheasant's Eye (cardiac glycoside) 1:10
Queen of the Night (cardiac glycoside) 3:312
Quinine (quinine) 3:286
Rhubarb (anthraquinone) 3:290, 293
Rose Periwinkle (vinblastine and vincristine) 1:79
Sacred Mushroom 3:282
Sassafras (safrole) 3:308
Senna (anthraquinone) 1:78
Spearmint (carvone) 2:230
Squill (cardiac glycoside) 3:323, 348
Star of Bethlehem (cardiac glycoside) 2:256
Storax (benzoin) 3:325, 327
Strophanthus (cardiac glycoside) 3:326

Strychnine Tree (brucine and strychnine) 3:326
Sweet Flag 1:9
Sweet Gums (storesin) 2:208, 3:325
Tea (caffeine) 1:69, 3:333
Thorn-apple (hyoscine) 1:117
Tobacco (nicotine) 2:241, 3:337, 7:926
Wintergreen 2:155
Wormwood (coumarin) 1:42
Yam (saponin) 3:360

Resins 2:226, 3:290
Almond Dammar 1:116, 3:315
Asafoetida 2:139
Balsams 1:49, 122, 2:237, 3:346
Bengal Teak 1:68, 2:193
Chengal 1:116
Copals 1:49, 99, 104, 2:183
Cypress Pines 1:71, 3:306
Dammar Trees 1:116, 3:315
Dragon's Blood Trees 1:115, 124
Elemi Trees 1:24, 68, 2:129
Firs 1:8, 49, 3:346
Eucalyptus 2:135, 193
Guaiacum 2:167, 206
Gurjun Balsam 1:49, 122
Kauri Pines 1:104, 2:192
Kino Trees 2:193, 3:283
Larch 2:197, 3:346
Lignum Vitae 2:167, 206
Mastic Trees 2:220, 3:273, 309
Myrrh Tree 1:99
Pepper Tree 2:220, 3:309
Peru Balsam 1:49, 2:237
Pines 2:195, 3:272, 296, 346
Rock-roses 1:90
Sea Grape 2:193
Storax 3:325, 327
Sweet Gums 2:208, 3:325
Tolu Balsam 1:49, 2:237
Turpentine Trees 1:68, 2:129, 3:273
Varnish Tree 2:195

Rubber 2:197, 3:297, 300
Balata 1:49, 2:219
Caucho 1:74, 78
Ceara Rubber 1:74, 2:219
Gutta-percha 2:167
India Rubber 2:142
Jequie Rubber 2:219
Madagascar Rubber 2:196, 214, 220
Panama Rubber 1:78
Para Rubber 1:74, 2:176, 198, 7:926
Russian Dandelion 3:333

6. SCIENTIFIC AREAS OF STUDY

Agriculture 7:879, 923
Animal Evolution 9:1219
Animal Geology 9:1152, 1219
Archaeology of Crop Plants 7:928
Astronomy 8:971
Biology of Plants 6:708, 717
Botany:
    History of 6:679;
    Paleobotany 6:730, 765, 9:1214
Chorology 6:707, 7:893
Classification of Plants 6:694
Climate 6:787, 8:998
Conservation 7:952, 963
Crystallography 8:1075
Ecology:
    Paleoecology 9:1211;
    of Plants 6:689, 708, 715, 783, 7:935, 941
Engineering Geology 8:1065
Evolution 9:1201;
    of Animals 9:1219;
    of Plants 6:737, 751, 9:1214

Forestry 7:841, 879, 937
Fossils *see* Paleontology
Gardening *see* Horticulture
Genecology 6:704
Genetics 6:704, 760, 7:956
Geochemistry 8:995, 1101
Geography:
 Paleogeography 9:1149;
 of Plants 6:688, 707, 7:831
Geology:
 of Animals 9:1152, 1219;
 Engineering 8:1065;
 History of 9:1254;
 Mining 8:1071, 1115;
 of Plants 6:739, 9:1152, 1214
Geomorphology 8:1008, 1035
Geophysics 8:990, 1001
History:
 of Botany 6:679;
 of Geology 9:1254
Horticulture 7:959
Hydrology 8:1069
Mineralogy 8:1081, 1111, 9:1122
Mining Geology 8:1071, 1115
Oceanography 8:1059
Paleobotany 6:730, 765, 9:1214
Paleoecology 9:1211
Paleogeography 9:1149
Paleontology 9:1149, 1206
Paleozoology 9:1219
Phytosociology 6:709, 727
Plant Biology 6:708, 717
Plant Ecology 6:689, 708, 715,
 783, 7:935, 941
Plant Evolution 6:737, 751,
 9:1214
Plant Geography 6:688, 707,
 7:831
Plant Geology 6:739, 9:1152,
 1214
Plant Sociology 6:709, 727
Plant Taxonomy 6:694
Seismology 8:990, 1024
Sociology of Plants 6:709, 727
Stratigraphy 9:1146
Taxonomy of Plants 6:694
Vulcanology 8:1032, 1057

7. PROMINENT FIGURES

Agassiz, Jean Louis Rodolphe
 9:1263
Albertus Magnus 9:1257, **1263**
Argand, Émile 9:1263
Aristotle 6:680, 9:1255, 1263,
 1264
Arrhenius, Svante August 9:1264
Bailey, Sir Edward Battersby
 9:1264
Barrell, Joseph 9:1264
Barrois, Charles Eugène 9:1264
Beaumont, Élie de *see* Élie de
 Beaumont
Beche, de la *see* De la Beche
Bowen, Norman Levi 9:1264
Braun-Blanqet, Josias 6:689, 729,
 7:964
Brongniart, Alexandre 6:731,
 7:964, 9:1260
Brown, Lancelot ('Capability')
 7:960, 964
Brown, Robert 7:964
Buch, Christian Leopold von
 9:1260, **1265**
Buckland, William 9:1261, 1262,
 1265, 1271
Buffon, Georges Louis Le Clerc,
 Comte de 9:1258, **1265**
Candolle, De *see* De Candolle
Chamberlin, Thomas Chrowder
 9:1265
Clark, Sir W. E. Le Gros *see* Le Gros
 Clark
Clements, Frederic Edward 7:964
Cloos, Hans 9:1263, **1266**

Cope, Edward Drinker 9:1262,
 1266, 1272
Cuvier, Georges 9:1207, 1260,
 1261, 1262, 1263, **1266**
Daly, Reginald Aldworth 9:1266
Dana, James Dwight 9:1260,
 1263, **1266**, 1269
Dart, Raymond Arthus 9:1266,
 1271
Darwin, Charles Robert 6:679,
 688, 691, 731, **759**, 761,
 766, 7:964, 8:1064, 9:1126,
 1152, 1203, 1260, 1262,
 1266, 1270, 1271, 1273
Darwin, George Howard 9:1267
Davis, William Morris 9:1263,
 1267
De Candolle, Anphonse Louis Pierre
 Pyramus 6:689, 821, 7:964
De Candolle, Augustin Pyramus
 7:964, 965
De Geer, Gerard Jacob, Baron
 9:1267
De la Beche, Henry Thomas
 9:1260, 1262, 1267, 1271
Douglas, David 6:683, 7:965
Drude, Carl Georg Oskar 6:689,
 719, **7:965**
Du Toit, Alexander Logie 8:1002,
 9:1267
Élie de Beaumont, Léonce 9:1260,
 1262, **1267**
Engler, Heinrich Gustav Adolf
 7:914, 965
Eskola, Pentti Eelis 9:1268
Farrer, Reginald 6:686, 7:965
Forbes, Edward A. 7:965
Forrest, George 6:685, 7:965
Fortune, Robert 6:684, 7:965
Geer, Baron de *see* De Geer
Geikie, Archibald 9:1260, **1268**,
 1272
Gesner, Conrad 9:1257, **1268**
Gilbert, Grove Karl 8:1053,
 9:1260, **1268**
Goldschmidt, Victor Moritz 9:1268
Grabau, Amadeus William 9:1263,
 1268
Gray, Asa 6:760, 7:965
Grisebach, August Heinrich
 Rudolph 6:708, 717, 719,
 7:965
Guettard, Jean-Étienne 9:1268
Gutenberg, Beno 9:1268
Hall, James 9:1260, **1268**
Hall, Sir James 9:1260, 1261,
 1268
Haug, Gustave Émile 9:1263,
 1269
Haüy, René-Just 8:**1075**, 1078,
 1086, 9:1269
Hess, Harry Hammond 8:1004,
 1005, 9:1269
Holmes, Arthur 8:1002, 9:1269
Hooke, Robert 9:1207, 1258,
 1259, **1269**
Hooker, Sir Joseph Dalton 6:679,
 682, 687, 702, 760, 7:905,
 966
Hooker, Sir William Jackson 7:966
Horne, John 9:1263, 1269, 1272
Humboldt, Friedrich Alexander,
 Baron von 6:679, 682, 689,
 708, 718, 719, **7:966**,
 9:1260, 1269
Hutton, James 9:1148, 1258,
 1259, 1260, 1261, 1262,
 1264, 1268, **1269**
Huxley, Thomas Henry 9:1260,
 1262, **1270**, 1271, 1272
Kelvin, William Thomson, Lord
 9:1262, 1263, 1265, 1267,
 1269, **1270**
Kingdon-Ward, Frank 6:685,
 7:966
Lamarck, Jean Baptiste Pierre
 Antoine de Monet, Chevalier
 de 6:731, 759, 764, **7:966**,
 9:1203, 1258, 1266, **1270**,
 1271

Lapworth, Charles 9:1152, 1156,
 1160, 1260, 1263, **1270**
Leakey, Louis Seymour Bazett
 9:1250, **1271**
Le Gros Clark, Sir Wilfrid Edward
 9:1271
Lehmann, Johann Gottlob 9:1259,
 1260, 1271
Leonardo da Vinci 9:1257, **1271**
Linnaeus, Carolus/Linné, Carl von
 6:683, 688, 698, 699, 702,
 759, **7:966**, 9:1203
Logan, Sir William Edmond 9:1271
Lyell, Sir Charles 6:688, 731, 760,
 9:1147, 1191, 1193, 1195,
 1197, 1260, 1261, 1262,
 1264, 1266, **1271**, 1272
Marsh, Othniel Charles 9:1262,
 1271
Meyen, Franz Julius Ferdinand
 7:966
Murchison, Roderick Impey
 9:1152, 1156, 1159, 1161,
 1163, 1173, 1260, 1261,
 1262, 1270, **1271**, 1272,
 1273
Murray, John 9:1263, **1271**
Mutis, José Celestino 6:682, 7:966
Orbigny, Alcide Charles Victor des
 Sallines d' 9:**1272**
Osborn, Henry Fairfield 9:1262,
 1272
Owen, Sir Richard 9:**1272**
Peach, Benjamin Neeve 9:1263,
 1269, **1272**
Penck, Albrecht 9:1263, **1272**
Playfair, John 9:1260, 1261, **1272**
Powell, John Wesley 9:1260,
 1268, **1272**
Raunkiaer, Christen 7:966
Rosenbusch, Karl Harry Ferdinand
 9:1265, **1272**, 1273, 1275
Rübel, Eduard 7:966
Schimper, Andreas Franz Wilhelm
 7:967
Scrope, George Julius Poullett
 9:1260, 1262, **1272**
Sedgwick, Adam 9:1152, 1156,
 1159, 1163, 1261, 1262,
 1266, 1270, 1271, 1272,
 1273
Sernander, J. Rutger 7:967
Skottsberg, Carl Johan Fredrik
 7:967
Smith, William 9:1147, 1207,
 1260, **1273**
Sorby, Henry Clifton 9:1263,
 1273, 1275
Steno, Nicolaus 9:1147, 1207,
 1260, 1261, **1273**, 1275
Suess, Edward 6:740, 9:**1274**
Tansley, Sir Arthur George 7:967
Thomson, William *see* Kelvin, Lord
Toit, Du *see* Du Toit
Turesson, Göte Wilhelm 6:705,
 776, **7:967**
Ussher, James 9:1275
Vavilov, Nikolai Ivanovich 7:927,
 957, 967
Vinci, Leonardo da *see* Leonardo da
 Vinci
Wallace, Alfred Russel 6:760,
 7:967
Walther, Johannes 9:1275
Warming, Johannes Eugen Bülow
 6:689, 719, 7:967
Wegener, Alfred 6:740, 8:1001,
 1002, 1003, 9:1263, 1267,
 1275
Werner, Abraham Gottlob 9:1259,
 1260, 1265, 1271, **1275**
Willdenow, Carl Ludwig von
 6:689, 7:967
Willis, John Christopher 7:906,
 967
Wilson, Ernest Henry 6:685, 7:967
Woodward, John 9:1275
Zirkel, Ferdinand 9:1265, 1272,
 1273, **1275**

8. NATURAL VEGETATION ZONES

Azonal Vegetation 7:872
Coastal 6:828, 7:885, 8:1051,
 1055,
 Dunes 6:825, 7:886;
 Mangrove Swamp 7:890;
 Salt Marsh 6:826, 7:888
Heaths 7:872
Wetlands 7:875;
 Bog 6:810, 7:875, 903;
 Carr 7:884;
 Fen 6:810, 7:880;
 Marsh 7:884

Zonal Vegetation 7:832
Deserts 6:808, 7:844, 8:1045
Forests 7:833, 937, 938;
 Antarctic 7:904;
 Boreal 7:838, 902;
 Mediterranean 7:836;
 Monsoon and Thorn 7:835;
 Mountain 7:866, 867, 868;
 Temperate Deciduous 6:808,
 7:838;
 Tropical Rain 7:834;
 Warm Temperate 7:837
Grasslands 7:855, 938;
 Meadow 7:860, 868;
 Prairies 7:860, 940;
 Savanna 6:808, 7:856;
 Steppe 7:859
Mountains 7:856, 861, **863**, 912,
 8:1035;
 Alpine 7:851, 868;
 Montane 7:866;
 Subalpine 7:867
Scrub 7:842;
 Chaparral 6:822, 7:843;
 Continental Semidesert 7:842
Tundra 7:850, 868, 936, 8:1050

9. PREHISTORIC ERAS AND PERIODS 6:738, 9:1144

Archaean 6:756, 757, 9:1150,
 1152
Cambrian 6:739, 742, 743,
 9:1149, **1152**, 1156, 1158,
 1159, 1177, 1213, 1219,
 1220, 1261, 1271, 1273
Carboniferous 6:739, 740, 741,
 743, 766, 8:1002, 1117,
 9:1152, 1163, **1166**, 1179,
 1206, 1209, 1216, 1217,
 1223, 1229, 1235, 1236,
 1261
Cenozoic 6:739, 740, **745**, 9:1191,
 1209
Cretaceous 6:740, 742, 743, 744,
 765, 8:992, 1052, 9:1134,
 1173, 1181, **1187**, 1209,
 1214, 1215, 1216, 1219,
 1226, 1242, 1244, 1261
Devonian 6:739, 743, 766,
 9:1152, **1163**, 1170, 1172,
 1175, 1209, 1214, 1229,
 1231, 1232, 1234, 1261,
 1271, 1273
Eocene 6:740, 742, 746, 9:1191,
 1192, 1193, **1193**, 1216, 1245
Holocene 6:750, 9:1200
Jurassic 6:740, 742, 8:1001,
 1105, 1118, 9:1148, 1175,
 1181, 1188, 1209, 1224,
 1232, 1261
Mesozoic 6:739, **740**, 9:**1177**,
 1209, 1214, 1216, 1236
Miocene 6:740, 742, 747, 9:1191,
 1193, **1195**, 1198, 1250

Mississippian **6:**739, **9:**1171, *see also* Carboniferous
Oligocene **6:**740, 742, 747, **8:**1083, **9:**1191, 1192, **1195**, 1229, 1250
Ordovician **6:**739, **8:**1034, **9:**1152, 1154, **1156**, 1160, 1162, 1228, 1260, 1270
Paleocene **6:**740, 745, **9:1191**
Paleozoic **6:**739, **9:**1152, 1209, 1210, 1213, 1235
Pennsylvanian **6:**739, **9:**1171, *see also* Carboniferous
Permian **6:**740, 741, 743, **9:**1152, 1154, **1173**, 1178, 1205, , 1209, 1236
Phanerozoic **6:**739, 757
Pleistocene **6:**740, 742, 749, **9:**1191, 1197, **1200**
Pliocene **6:**740, 742, 748, **9:**1191, **1197**, 1216
Precambrian **6:**756, **8:**1020, 1087, 1092, 1105, **9:**1134, 1142, 1146, **1149**, 1153, 1954, 1955, 1157, 1158, 1198, 1201, 1220, 1224, 1230
Proterozoic **6:**756, 757, **9:**1150, 1151
Quaternary **6:**740, 742, **748**, **9:**1149, 1191, **1198**
Silurian **6:**739, 743, 766, **9:**1152, 1154, **1159**, 1164, 1231, 1260, 1261, 1271, 1272
Tertiary **6:**740, 744, **745**, **8:**1001, 1034, 1118, **9:**1191, 1216, 1261, 1271
Triassic **6:**740, 741, **9:**1173, **1177**, 1209

10. PREHISTORIC PLANTS 6:730, 9:1214

Algae 1:18, **6:**739, **8:**997, 1044, 1117, **9:**1134, 1152, 1153, 1154, 1162, 1163, 1165, 1170, 1185, 1189, 1209, **1214**, 1226;
  Blue-green *see* Blue-green Algae;
  Brown 1:20, **9:**1214;
  Golden-brown 1:20, **9:1215**, 1216;
  Green 1:20, **9:**1213, **1215**;
  Red 1:20, **9:**1215
Angiosperms 1:32, **6:**739, 766, **9:**1185, 1188, 1209, 1216, **1218**, 1229, 1242
Blue-green Algae 1:50, **9:**1151, 1185, 1201, 1202, 1208, **1215**
Brown Algae *see* Algae, Brown
Chlorophyta *see* Algae, Green
Chrysophyta *see* Algae, Golden-brown
Club Mosses 1:94, **6:**739, **9:**1209, **1216**
Coccolithophores 1:20, **8:**1015, 1087, **9:**1134, 1163, 1185, 1186, 1189, 1190, 1191, 1215, **1216**
Coniferopytes **9:1218**
Conifers 1:100, **6:**739, **9:**1176, 1179, 1185, 1188, 1189, 1218
Cyanophyta *see* Blue-green Algae
Cycadophytes **9:1217**, 1218
Cycads 1:100, **9:**1176, 1179, 1185, 1188, 1189, 1217
Diatoms 1:20, **9:**1163, 1191, **1215**
Dinoflagellates 1:20, **9:**1185, 1189, 1190, **1215**, 1220
Ferns 2:140, **9:**1163, 1176, 1179,

1185, 1209, 1216, **1217**, 1218
Flowering Plants *see* Angiosperms
Ginkgos 1:100, **6:**740, **9:**1176, 1179, 1185, 1218
Golden-Brown Algae *see* Algae, Golden-brown
Green Algae *see* Algae, Green
Gymnosperms 1:100, **6:**739, **9:**1185, 1189, **1217**
Horsetails 2:180, **6:**739, **9:**1175, 1176, 1179, 1185, 1209, 1216, **1217**
Lycopsids *see* Club Mosses
Phaeophyta *see* Algae, Brown
Psilopsids **6:**739, **9:**1163, **1216**
Pterophytes *see* Ferns
Rhodophyta *see* Algae, Red
Sphenopsids *see* Horsetails

11. PREHISTORIC ANIMALS 9:1219

Acanthodians *see* Spiny Sharks
Actinopterygians **9:**1232, **1234**
Agnatha *see* Jawless Fishes
Ammonites **9:**1176ff (*passim*), 1213, 1223, 1224, 1225, 1261
Ammonoids **9:**1163, 1164, 1177, 1178, 1189, 1223, **1224**
Amphibians **9:**1170, 1173, 1176, 1178, 1206, 1232, 1234, **1235**
Anthozoans *see* Corals
Apes **9:**1249, 1250
Archaeocyathids **9:**1152, 1154, 1155, **1221**
Arthropods **9:**1189, 1209, 1224, **1227**, 1228, 1229
Artiodactyls **9:**1195, 1197, 1247, **1248**
Bats **9:**1239, **1246**
Belemnoids **9:**1189, **1226**
Birds **9:**1181, 1187, 1189, 1191, 1209, 1210, 1236, 1239, **1244**
Bivalves **8:**1015, **9:**1154, 1156, 1165, 1178, 1185, 1188, 1189, 1221, 1224, **1227**
Blastoids **9:1223**
Bony Fishes **9:**1164, **1232**
Brachiopods **9:**1153ff (*passim*), 1176, 1177, 1185, 1189, **1221**, 1227
Bryozoans **9:**1154, 1156, 1160, **1221**, 1227
Carnivores **9:**1195, **1246**, 1249
Cartilaginous Fishes **9:**1189, **1232**, 1234
Caviomorphs **9:**1249
Chelicerates **9:**1227, 1228, **1229**
Chelonians *see* Turtles
Condylarths **9:**1192, 1195, 1246, 1249
Conodonts **9:**1154, 1159, 1162, 1163, 1166, 1167, **1229**
Corals **8:**1015, 1096, **9:**1134, 1154ff (*passim*), 1178, 1185, 1188, **1220**, 1221
Cotylosaurs **9:**1176, **1236**, 1238
Creodonts **9:**1192, 1195, 1246
Crinoids **9:**1154, 1156, 1160, 1170, 1185, 1189, **1223**
Crocodiles **9:**1181, 1187, 1206, 1209, 1236, 1239, **1243**
Crossopterygians **9:**1232, **1234**, 1235
Crustaceans **9:**1156, 1168, 1189, **1228**
Cystoids **9:1223**
Dinosaurs **9:**1205, 1209, 1236, 1239, **1241**, 1243, 1249
Dipnoans *see* Lungfish

Echinoderms **9:**1154, 1185, 1189, **1223**, 1224, 1227
Echinoids **8:**1015, **9:**1156, 1185, 1189, 1223, **1224**
Edentates **9:**1195, **1248**
Elephants **9:**1197, 1198, 1246, 1247
Fishes **9:**1154ff (*passim*), 1170, 1184, 1189, 1197, 1206, 1209, **1230**
Fissipeds **9:**1246
Foraminifera **8:**1007, 1087, **9:**1167, 1176, 1185ff (*passim*), 1198, 1208, 1210, **1219**, 1220, 1227
Gastropods **9:**1154, 1156, 1187, 1189, 1224, **1226**
Graptolites **9:**1154ff (*passim*), **1229**
Hominids **9:**1197, 1198, 1200, 1210, **1250**, 1266, 1271
Horses **9:**1197, 1247, 1248, 1270, 1271
Hyraces **9:**1246, 1247
Ichthyosaurs **9:**1181, 1189, 1205, 1211, **1237**, 1243
Insectivores **9:**1246
Insects **9:**1163, 1170, 1173, 1189, 1219, 1228, **1229**
Invertebrates **9:**1209, 1249
Jawless Fishes **9:**1163, **1230**
Labyrinthodonts **9:**1234, **1235**
Lagomorphs **9:1249**
Lampreys **9:**1231
Lemurs **9:**1249, 1250
Lepospondyls **9:1235**, 1236
Lizards **9:**1236, **1238**
Lungfish **9:**1164, **1232**, 1234
Mammal-like Reptiles **9:**1176, 1178, 1205, 1236, 1239, **1243**, 1245
Mammals **9:**1176ff (*passim*), 1209, 1210, 1236, 1242, 1244, **1245**
Man *see* Hominids
Marsupials **9:**1213, **1245**, 1246
Mollusks **8:**1084, **9:**1154, 1160, 1166, 1170, 1178, 1184, 1195, 1197, 1223, **1224**, 1226, 1227, 1237
Monkeys **9:**1249, 1250
Monotremes **9:1245**
Myomorphs **9:**1249
Nautiloids **9:**1156, 1164, 1224, **1225**, 1226
Nothosaurs *see* Plesiosaurs
Ornithiscians **9:1241**
Ostracods **9:**1160, 1162, 1185, 1207, **1228**
Pecora **9:**1248
Pelycosaurs **9:**1176, **1243**
Perissodactyls **9:**1195, **1247**
Pinnipeds **9:**1246
Placental Mammals **9:**1245, **1246**
Placoderms **9:**1163, **1232**
Placodonts **9:**1236, **1237**
Plesiosaurs **9:**1181, 1189, 1236, **1237**
Porifera *see* Sponges
Primates **9:**1192, **1249**
Primitive Mammals **9:1245**
Pterosaurs **9:**1181, 1189, 1236, **1239**
Radiolaria **8:**1007, 1061, **9:**1135, 1163, 1185ff (*passim*), 1219, **1220**
Reptiles **9:**1166ff (*passim*), 1205, 1206, 1209, 1235, **1236**
Rodents **9:**1195, 1198, 1245, **1249**
Saurischians **9:1241**
Sciuromorphs **9:**1249
Scleractinia *see* Corals
Seacows **9:**1246, 1247
Sharks **9:**1163, **1232**
Snakes **9:**1236, **1238**, 1239
Spiny Sharks **9:**1163, **1232**
Sponges **9:**1135, 1154, 1164, 1185, 1189, 1191, **1220**, 1227

Stromataporoids **9:**1163ff (*passim*), 1214, 1220, **1221**
Subungulates **9:**1195, **1246**
Suina **9:**1248
Thecodonts **9:**1181, 1211, 1236, **1239**, 1241, 1243
Therapsids **9:**1243
Tortoises *see* Turtles
Trace Fossils **9:**1154, 1186, 1211, 1224, 1228, **1230**
Trilobites **9:**1151ff (*passim*), 1223, 1227, **1228**, 1230
Turtles **9:**1181, 1187, 1189, **1236**, 1238
Tylopods **9:**1248
Vertebrates **9:**1176, 1205, **1230**
Whales **9:**1195, 1237, **1249**

12. ROCKS OF THE WORLD 9:1122

Amphibolites **8:**1092, **9:**1137, **1140**
Andesites **8:**1034, 1085, 1092, 1111, **9:**1127, 1155, 1162, 1180
Arenaceous Rocks **9:**1131
Argillaceous Rocks **9:**1130
Argillites **9:**1131
Arkoses **9:**1131, **1132**
Basalt **8:**1083, 1084, 1092, **9:**1124, 1125, 1126, **1127**, 1132
Bauxites **8:**1074, 1087, 1089, 1103, 1106, **9:**1135
Breccias **9:**1132
Boulder Clay *see* Tills
Calcareous Rocks **9:**1133
Carbonatite **8:**1087, **9:**1126
Cherts **8:**1087, 1097, **9:**1134, **1135**
Clays **8:**1070, 1088, **9:**1122, **1130**, 1131, 1136, 1138
Conglomerates **9:**1131, 1132, **1133**
Dacites **9:1126**, 1127
Diorite **8:**1085, 1086, 1092, **9:**1124, 1125, **1126**
Dolomite **8:**1088, 1089, 1090, 1104, **9:**1134, 1136
Eclogite **8:**1093, **9:**1129, 1137
Evaporites **8:**1074, 1083ff (*passim*), 1119, **9:**1130, 1133, 1134, **1135**
Gabbro **8:**1085, **9:**1124, **1127**
Gneisses **8:**1068, 1088, 1091, 1097, 1099, 1101, **9:**1139, 1140
Granite **8:**1083ff (*passim*), 1100, **9:**1125, 1126, 1127
Granodiorite **9:**1125, **1126**
Graywackes **9:**1131, **1132**
Hornfels **8:**1088, **9:**1138
Igneous Rocks **8:**1085ff (*passim*), **9:**1122
Ironstones **8:**1074, 1087, 1105, **9:**1134
Kimberlite **8:**1086, 1089, **9:**1128·
Laterites **8:**1074, 1087, 1106, **9:**1135, 1140
Limestones **8:**1066, 1070, 1087ff (*passim*), 1101, 1104, 1114, **9:**1133, 1134ff (*passim*)
Marls **9:**1131
Metamorphic Rocks **8:**1085, 1095, 1096, 1098, **9:**1136
Mudstones **9:**1130
Mylonites **9:**1139
Obsidian **8:**1081, 1089, **9:**1129
Oolites **9:**1134, 1135
Peridotite **9:**1128
Phonolite **8:**1095, **9:**1126
Phosphorites **9:**1135
Phyllites **9:**1138
Quartz Sandstones *see* Sandstones

1344 THEMATIC INDEX

Rhyodacites 9:1126
Rhyolite 8:1089, 9:1126, 1127
Rudaceous Rocks 9:1130, 1131, 1132
Sandstones 8:1097, 9:1129, 1131, 1136
Schists 8:1083ff (passim), 1099, 9:1137, 1138
Sedimentary Rocks 9:1129, 1136
Shales 8:1067, 1114, 9:1130, 1132, 1135
Siltstones 9:1131
Slates 8:1087, 9:1138, 1139
Syenites 8:1088, 1095, 1099, 9:1126
Tillites 9:1133
Tills 9:1133
Trachytes 9:1126

13. CHEMICAL ELEMENTS 8:1101

Aluminum 8:1074, 1089, **1103**, 1106, 9:1122, 1128
Antimony 8:1099, **1109**
Arsenic 8:1084, 1098, 1106, **1107**
Barium 8:1086, **1109**
Beryllium 8:1102
Bismuth 8:1111
Boron 8:1102
Bromine 8:1109, 1121
Cadmium 8:1099, **1108**
Caesium 8:1109
Calcium 8:1084, 1089, 1090, **1104**, 9:1123ff (passim)
Carbon 8:1084, 1089, 1091, **1102**, 1105, 1114, 1115, 9:1130, 1138
Cerium 8:1104
Chlorine 8:1109, 1121, 9:1126
Chromium 8:1074, 1088ff (passim), **1105**
Cobalt 8:1105
Copper 8:1073ff (passim), 1094, 1100, **1106**, 1110, 1121, 9:1126
Dysprosium 8:1105
Erbium 8:1105
Europium 8:1104
Fluorine 8:1084, 1100, 1109, 9:1126
Gadolinium 8:1104
Gallium 8:1099, **1106**, 1107
Germanium 8:1106
Gold 8:1073ff (passim), 1096, **1110**
Helium 8:1114
Holmium 8:1105
Iodine 8:1109
Iridium 8:1110
Iron 8:1081ff (passim), **1105**, 9:1123ff (passim), 1135, 1141
Lanthanum 8:1104, see also Rare Earth Elements
Lead 8:1075, 1083, 1090, 1106, **1111**, 1121
Lithium 8:1099, 1100, **1102**, 1109
Lutetium 8:1105
Magnesium 8:1086, 1089, 1100, **1103**, 9:1122ff (passim)
Manganese 8:1091, 1098, **1105**
Mercury 8:1088, **1110**
Molybdenum 8:1105, **1108**
Nickel 8:1105
Nitrogen 8:1114
Osmium 8:1110
Oxygen 8:1084, 1088, 1097, **1102**, 1104, 9:1135
Palladium 8:1110
Phosphorus 8:1084, 1088, **1104**, 1106, 9:1126, 1135
Platinum 8:1110
Potassium 8:1074, 1090, 1091, **1104**, 1109, 1121

Praseodymium 8:1104
Promethium 8:1104
Radium 8:1100, **1111**
Rare Earth Elements 8:**1104**, 1111, 1121, 9:1126
Rhodium 8:1110
Ruthenium 8:1110
Samarium 8:1104
Scandium 8:1104
Silicon 8:1084, 1097, **1104**, 1107, 9:1122
Silver 8:1075, 1078, 1090, **1108**, 1110
Sodium 8:1090, **1103**, 1121, 9:1128
Strontium 8:1074, 1087, **1108**
Sulfur 8:1079ff (passim), 1096, **1104**, 1114, 1121
Terbium 8:1105
Thorium 8:**1111**, 9:1126
Thulium 8:1105
Tin 8:1084, 1087, 1104, **1109**
Titanium 8:1092, 1096, **1105**
Tungsten 8:1084, 1101, **1110**
Uranium 8:1073, 1083, 1100, **1104**, 1111, 1114
Vanadium 8:1105
Ytterbium 8:1105
Yttrium 8:1104
Zinc 8:1075, 1083, 1090, 1099, **1106**, 1108, 1121
Zirconium 8:1101, **1108**, 1111

14. MINERALS 8:1081

Actinolite 8:**1083**, 1084, 1085, 1095, 1100
Agate 8:1083, 1087, 1097, 1101
Albite 8:1094, 1096, 1103, 9:1138
Amber 8:**1083**, 1102
Amethyst 8:**1083**, 1097
Amphiboles 8:1083, **1084**, 1086ff (passim), 9:1126, 1136ff (passim)
Andalusite 8:**1084**, 1093, 1099, 9:1135
Anhydrite 8:1083, **1084**, 1091, 1104, 9:1135
Apatite 8:1082, **1084**, 1088, 1104, 9:1135, 1140
Aquamarine 8:1080, **1084**, 1086
Aragonite 8:**1084**, 1102, 1104, 9:1134
Arsenopyrite 8:**1084**, 1087, 1107
Asbestos 8:1081, 1083, **1084**, 1087, 1098, 1099, 1100
Augite 8:1079, **1085**, 1089, 1092, 1097
Azurite 8:**1085**, 1089, 1094, 1106
Barite 8:1079, **1085**, 1087, 1100, 1101, 1104, 1109
Beryl 8:1084, **1086**, 1089, 1102
Biotite 8:1068, **1086**, 1094, 1095, 1101, 9:1124, 1126, 1138
Bornite 8:**1086**, 1106
Bronzite 8:**1086**, 1089, 1092, 1097
Calcite 8:1080ff (passim), **1086**, 1087ff (passim), 9:1129, 1131
Cassiterite 8:1079, **1087**, 1101, 1109
Celestine 8:1079, **1087**, 1100, 1108
Cerussite 8:**1087**, 1090, 1111
Chalcedony 8:1083, **1087**, 1093, 1097, 1101
Chalcopyrite 8:1078, **1087**, 1097, 1101
Chalybite see Siderite
Chamosite 8:**1087**, 9:1135
China Clay see Kaolinite
Chlorite 8:1079, **1087**, 1100, 9:1138, 1139
Chromite 8:1083, **1088**, 1099, 1105

Cinnabar 8:1088, 1110
Clay Minerals 8:1084, **1088**, 1092ff (passim), 9:1130, 1131, 1132
Coal 8:1102, 1105, **1115**, 9:1130, 1135
Cobaltite 8:1078, 1105
Collophane 8:1084, **1088**
Cordierite 8:**1088**, 9:1138
Corundum 8:1082, 1084, **1088**, 1098, 1103
Cristobalite 8:**1088**, 1095
Crocidolite 8:1085, **1089**, 1098
Cryolite 8:1089
Cuprite 8:**1089**, 1106
Diamond 8:1073, 1082, **1089**, 1091, 1098, 1102, 9:1128
Diopside 8:**1089**, 1097
Dolomite 8:1080, 1081, 1084, **1089**, 1103, 1104, 9:1135, 1136
Emerald 8:1080, 1081, 1084, 1086, **1089**
Enstatite 8:**1089**, 1097
Epidote 8:1079, **1089**, 9:1140
Feldspars 8:1086, 1088, **1090**, 1092ff (passim), 9:1124ff (passim)
Feldspathoids 8:**1090**, 1093ff (passim), 9:1124, 1126
Fluorite 8:1075, 1078, 1082, 1089, **1090**, 1104
Fool's Gold see Pyrite
Galena 8:1078, 1081, 1087, 1089, **1090**, 1099, 1104, 1111
Garnets 8:1078, **1090**, 9:1129, 1137, 1140
Gas see Natural Gas
Glauconite 8:1091, 9:1131
Glaucophane 8:1084, **1091**, 9:1138
Goethite 8:1087, **1091**, 1093, 1105, 9:1131
Graphite 8:1089, **1091**, 1102, 1108, 1117, 9:1138
Gypsum 8:1079, 1082, 1083, 1084, **1091**, 1104, 9:1135
Halite 8:1078, **1091**, 1100, 1103, **1119**, 9:1135, see also Salt
Halloysite 8:1088, **1092**
Hematite 8:1080, 1091, **1092**, 1093, 1105, 9:1131, 1138
Hornblende 8:1079, 1083, 1084, **1092**, 9:1124, 1125, 1126, 1137, 1138
Hypersthene 8:1085, 1089, **1092**, 1097
Ice 8:1011, 1019, **1092**
Idocrase 8:1079, **1092**
Illite 8:1088, **1092**
Ilmenite 8:**1092**, 1105, 1108
Jade 8:1083, 1084, 1092, 1095
Jadeite 8:**1092**, 1097
Jasper 8:1087, **1093**, 1097, 9:1135
Kaolinite 8:1087, 1088, 1092, **1093**, 9:1130
Kyanite 8:1080, 1083, 1084, **1093**, 1099
Lapis Lazuli/Lazurite 8:1090, **1093**, 1099
Leucite 8:1090, **1093**, 1104, 9:1124
Limonite see Goethite
Magnesite 8:**1093**, 1103
Magnetite 8:1078, 1083, 1088, 1091, **1094**, 1097, 1099, 1105
Malachite 8:1085, 1089, **1094**, 1106
Marcasite 8:**1094**, 1096
Micas 8:1086ff (passim), **1094**, 1095ff (passim), 9:1124ff (passim)
Microcline 8:1090, **1094**, 1095, 1096, 1098, 9:1124, 1125
Monazite 8:**1094**, 1104, 1108, 1111

Montmorillonite 8:1088, **1094**
Muscovite 8:1086, 1094, **1095**, 9:1136, 1138
Natural Gas 8:1091, 1102, **1114**, 9:1131
Nepheline 8:1080, 1088, 1090, **1095**, 1099
Nephrite 8:1083, 1084, **1095**, 1100
Oil see Petroleum
Olivine 8:1079, 1081, **1095**, 1096ff (passim), 9:1124, 1128, 1129, 1137
Opal 8:1081, 1089, **1095**, 1096, 9:1135
Orthoclase 8:1079ff (passim), **1096**, 1098, 9:1124, 1125, 1132
Peridot 8:1095, **1096**
Petroleum 8:1062, 1073, 1086, 1091, **1111**, 1118, 1119, 1121, 9:1130
Phlogopite 8:1086, 1094, 9:1129
Pitchblende see Uraninite
Plagioclase 8:1079, **1096**, 9:1124ff (passim), 1137, 1140
Polyhalite 8:1096
Pyrite 8:1078ff (passim), **1096**, 1099, 1104, 1105, 9:1131
Pyroxenes 8:1084ff (passim), **1097**, 1098ff (passim), 9:1124ff (passim)
Pyrrhotite 8:**1097**, 1105
Quartz 8:1082ff (passim), **1097**, 1098ff (passim), 9:1122ff (passim)
Realgar 8:1098, 1107
Rhodocrosite 8:**1098**, 1105
Rhodonite 8:1097, **1098**, 1105
Riebeckite 8:1084, 1085, 1089, **1098**
Rock Salt see Halite
Ruby 8:1081, 1088, **1098**, 1099
Rutile 8:1079, **1098**, 1105, 1108
Salt 8:1081, 1091, 1103, **1119**, see also Halite
Sanidine 8:1088ff (passim), **1098**, 9:1124
Sapphire 8:1088, **1098**, 1099
Scapolite 8:1090, 1098
Serpentines 8:1085, **1099**, 1100, 1105, 9:1129, 1137
Serpentinites 8:1099, 9:1128, 1137, 1138
Siderite 8:1084, 1087, 1089, **1099**, 1102, 1105, 9:1135
Sillimanite 8:1084, 1093, **1099**, 9:1137
Sodalite 8:1090, **1099**, 9:1124, 1126
Sphalerite 8:1078, 1090, **1099**, 1104, 1106
Sphene 8:**1099**, 1105, 9:1140
Spinels 8:1078, **1099**, 1103
Spodumene 8:1097, **1099**, 1102
Staurolite 8:1099
Stibnite 8:1079, 1098, **1099**, 1109
Strontianite 8:**1100**, 1108
Sylvite 8:**1100**, 1104
Talc 8:1082, **1100**
Titanite see Sphene
Topaz 8:1079, 1082, 1087, **1100**, 1109
Tourmaline 8:1080, 1087, 1089, **1100**, 1102, 1109
Tremolite 8:1083, 1084, 1085, 1095, **1100**
Turquoise 8:**1100**
Uraninite 8:1100, 1111
Vermiculite 8:1088, **1100**
Vesuvianite see Idocrase
Witherite 8:**1101**, 1109
Wolframite 8:1087, **1101**, 1110
Wollastonite 8:1097, **1101**
Zeolites 8:1083, **1101**
Zinc Blende see Sphalerite
Zircon 8:1079, **1101**, 1108

Glossary

This glossary explains to you the specialized vocabulary that is present in parts of the Encyclopedia. Cross-references to page numbers indicate where more detailed accounts related to the entries can be found in the main Encyclopedia; those page numbers in *italics* refer to relevant and helpful illustrations. Cross-references to other entries in the glossary are in SMALL CAPITALS.

Abaxial On the side facing away from the stem or axis.

Abiotic Devoid of life.

Ablation The loss of snow and ice from the surface of a GLACIER by melting, evaporation or *sublimation* (the direct passage from solid to vapor state).

Abundance Concerning the contribution (e.g. in numbers or BIOMASS of a SPECIES) made by a species, relative to others, in a community. (See pp. 715-6.)

Acaulescent Stemless or nearly so.

Accessory Adjective applied to minerals present in a rock in such small quantities that they are of negligible importance when considering the mineral composition of the rock.

Accessory fruits FRUITS derived from both tissues outside the OVARY and ovarian tissues.

Achene A small, dry, single-seeded FRUIT that does not split open.

Acid A substance that releases hydrogen (H⁺) IONS in solution and has a pH of less than 7. IGNEOUS ROCKS may be described as 'acid' if they contain more than 10% free quartz. (Acidity of soils, see pp. 805-6; acidity of water, see p. 944.)

Actinomorphic (Of flowers), having radial symmetry. Any longitudinal plane passing through the axis of the flower will divide it into essentially symmetrical halves (cf. ZYGOMORPHIC).

Acuminate (Of leaves), narrowing gradually by somewhat concave edges to a point.

Acute Having a sharp point.

Adaptability The ability to adjust to environmental conditions. (See p. 769.)

Adaptation The genetical or physiological process by which an organism becomes adjusted to its environment. (See pp. 766-75.)

Adaxial On the side facing the stem or axis.

Adnate Joined to or attached to; applied to unlike organs, e.g. STAMENS adnate to the PERIANTH (cf. CONNATE).

Adsorb See ADSORPTION.

Adsorption The process of holding molecules of gases or liquids onto a solid surface.

Adventitious Arising from an unusual position, e.g. roots from a stem or leaf.

Adventive A plant introduced by man into an area where it is not native.

Aeolian Literally, of the winds. The term is applied especially to sediments that have been eroded and transported by the wind.

Aeration Provision of air.

Aerenchyma A tissue composed of loosely packed, thin-walled cells with large air spaces between. It is found in stems, leaves and roots of plants that grow in oxygen-starved conditions, particularly in water or waterlogged soils. (See p. 770.)

Aerial root A root that originates above ground level. (See p. 891.)

Aerobic Term applied both to organisms that require oxygen for their survival, especially bacteria (see pp. 50-1), and to an environment in which oxygen is present in significant quantities.

Aestivation The arrangement of the parts of a flower within the bud, usually referring to SEPALS and PETALS.

Afforestation The planting of trees to produce a forest (see pp. 879-80, 938).

Agamospermy Reproduction by seed formed without sexual fusion of GAMETES. (See pp. 777-8.)

Agglomerate A rock made up of angular fragments of lava in a matrix of smaller, often ashy, particles. (See p. 1122.)

Albedo That amount of incident radiation which is reflected by a surface. (See pp. 835, 866.)

Algal bloom The turbid appearance of water due to the presence of large numbers of unicellular and filamentous algae. (See pp. 19, 945.)

Alginates Colloidal substances (see COLLOID) derived from members of the brown algae. (See p. 18.)

Alkaline Pertaining to substances that release hydroxyl (OH⁻) IONS in solution and have a pH of more than 7. IGNEOUS ROCKS may be described as alkaline if their FELDSPAR content primarily comprises sodium and potassium SILICATES. (Alkaline soils, see p. 809.)

Alkaloid A class of naturally occurring narcotic poisons, usually heterocyclic bases containing nitrogen. Alkaloids are found mainly in the flowering plants, but also in a few other plant groups and in some animals. They are important because they are poisonous, but they also have many medicinal uses. (See pp. 26, 226-7.)

Allele One of the alternative forms of a gene (see CHROMOSOME). (Alleles and genetic drift, see pp. 774-5.)

Allelopathy The negative effect of one plant on another by means of chemical products loosed into the environment. (See pp. 821-3; cf. AUTOTOXICITY.)

Allopatry (Of POPULATIONS, SPECIES and other TAXA), with distributions that do not overlap. (Spatial or allopatric isolation, see pp. 778-9.)

Allopolyploid A polyploid organism (see PLOIDY) in which one or more sets of CHROMOSOMES come from dissimilar populations, usually of different SPECIES. (Rapid speciation through polyploidy, see pp. 776-7.)

Alluvium Gravel, silt, sand and similar materials deposited by streams and rivers, mainly near their mouths. As alluvium is good agricultural soil, the earliest civilizations had their origins as farming communities centered on alluvial FLOOD PLAINS. (Alluvial soils, see p. 810.)

Alternate (Of leaves), one leaf at each NODE of the stem; (of STAMENS), between the PETALS.

Amorphous Adjective applied to structures or formations that have no apparent order, whether at an atomic, molecular, CRYSTALLINE or higher order.

Amphibious Able to live both on land and in the water. (Amphibians, see pp. 1235-6.)

Amphidiploid An ALLOPOLYPLOID.

Amphitropous (Of OVULES), attached near its middle, half-inverted.

Anaerobic Term applied both to organisms that do not require the presence of oxygen in order to survive, especially bacteria (see pp. 50-1), and to environments, such as the deep ocean floor (see pp. 1059-64), in which free oxygen is not present in any significant quantities.

Anatropous (Of OVULES), bent over through 180° to lie alongside its stalk (FUNICLE).

Androecium Male reproductive organs of a flower. See FLOWER.

Androgynophore A column on which STAMENS and CARPELS are borne.

Angiocarp A fungal fruiting body which is closed at least until the SPORES are ready for dispersal. (See Fungi, pp. 156-9.)

Angiosperm A plant producing seeds enclosed in an OVARY; a flowering plant. (See pp. 32-5, 367-675.)

Anion See ION.

Annual A plant that completes its life cycle from germination to death within one year. (See p. 724; cf. BIENNIAL, PERENNIAL.)

Annular Ring-like.

Anodyne A pain-killing or soothing medicine. (Medicinal and Narcotic Plants, see pp. 226-7.)

Anthelmintic A drug capable of destroying or expelling intestinal worms. (Medicinal and Narcotic Plants, see pp. 226-7.)

Anther (Of flowers), the terminal part of the male organs (STAMEN), usually borne on a stalk (filament) and developing to contain POLLEN.

Antheridium The male GAMETE-forming organ (sex organ) of many lower plants, such as mosses, ferns and fungi. Normally it produces motile SPERMS. (Mosses, see pp. 234-5; Ferns, see pp. 140-1; Fungi, see pp. 156-9.)

Anthesis The period of flowering; from the opening of the flower bud to the setting of the seed.

Anthocyanin The pigment usually responsible for pink, red, purple, violet and blue colors in flowering plants. (Dyes and Tannins from Plants, see p. 126.)

Anthropogenic Caused by man.

Anticline (In geology) see FOLD.

Antipetalous Occurring opposite the PETALS, on the same radius, as distinct from alternating with the petals.

Antiscorbutic An agent that prevents scurvy. (Medicinal and Narcotic Plants, see pp. 226-7.)

Antisepalous Occurring opposite the SEPALS, on the same radius, as distinct from alternating with the sepals.

Aperient A mild laxative. (Medicinal and Narcotic Plants, see pp. 226-7.)

Aperturate (Of POLLEN), having one or more apertures.

Apetalous Without PETALS.

Apex (adj. apical) The tip of an organ; the growing point.

Apical meristem A MERISTEM (q.v.) at the tip of an organ, such as a shoot, from which new growth is initiated.

Apocarpous With CARPELS free from each other.

Apomixis (adj. apomictic) Reproduction by seed formed without sexual fusion. (See pp. 777-8.)

Apoplast See CASPARIAN BAND.

Appressed Pressed closely to a surface and pointed to the APEX of the organ.

Aquatic Living in water.

Aqueous solution A solution of a substance in water.

Aquifer An underground rock formation through which GROUNDWATER can easily percolate. Sandstones, gravel beds and jointed limestones make good aquifers. (See p. 1070.)

Arborescent Tree-like in size and appearance.

Archesporium The layer of cells on the inside of a fern SPORANGIUM which normally gives rise to the SPORE mother cells. (Ferns, see pp. 140-1.)

Areole A group of hairs or spines, as found on the stems of cacti.

Aril A fleshy or sometimes hairy outgrowth from the HILUM or FUNICLE of a seed.

Ascocarp See PERITHECIUM.

Ascomycetes A class of fungi which reproduce by means of an ASCUS. (See Fungi, pp. 156-9.)

Ascospores See ASCUS.

Ascus A cylindrical, round, club-shaped or pear-shaped organ of certain fungi (ascomycetes) within which the spores (ascospores) are produced. (See Fungi, pp. 156-9.)

Asepalous Without SEPALS.

Aspectation The situation where SPECIES growing together have their main growth periods at different times of the year, thus reducing mutual interference.

Aufnahme Sampling unit in PHYTOSOCIOLOGICAL studies of vegetation—also called a *relevé*.

Aureole or **metamorphic aureole** The zone around an INTRUSION of IGNEOUS ROCK in which the heat of the intrusion has caused local thermal metamorphism (see METAMORPHIC ROCKS). The size of the aureole depends both on the nature of the intrusion and on the nature of the COUNTRY ROCK. (See p. 1139.)

Auricle (adj. auriculate) Small ear-like projections at the base of a leaf or leaf blade or BRACT.

Autochory Dispersal of DIASPORES (seeds, SPORES, etc.) by the plants' own mechanisms, as in explosive dehiscence of balsam (*Impatiens*) fruits. See also DEHISCENT.

Autopolyploid An organism that has more than the normal two sets (diploid, see PLOIDY) of CHROMOSOMES, all derived from the same parent SPECIES (cf. ALLOPOLYPLOID, AMPHIDIPLOID).

Autotoxicity Poisoning by substances produced by changes within the organism. (See p. 823; cf ALLELOPATHY.)

Autotrophic Able to synthesize food substances from inorganic materials (cf. HETEROTROPHIC).

Auxin A substance that controls plant growth.

Awn A stiff, bristle-like extension to an organ, usually at the tip.

Axil The upper angle formed by the union of a leaf with the stem.

Axile placentation A type of PLACENTATION in which the OVULES are borne on PLACENTAS on the central axis of an OVARY that has two or more LOCULES.

Axillary Pertaining to the organs in the AXIL, e.g. the buds, flowers, or INFLORESCENCE.

Axis The main or central stem of a herbaceous plant or of an INFLORESCENCE.

Axis of symmetry In crystallography, a line drawn through a crystal such that the crystal is symmetrical about it. See SYMMETRY.

Azoic That part of the Precambrian in which, it is thought, there was no life on Earth: it came immediately prior to the CRYPTOZOIC. The term is increasingly disused.

Baccate Berry-like.

Banded Term applied to formations and rocks in which there are recognizable bands of different chemical composition, physical nature, or both. The term is often used synonymously with LAMINAR, although the latter term implies that the bands are thin.

Basal Borne at or near the base (of a plant).

Basal placentation Having the PLACENTA at the base of the OVARY.

Basic rock An IGNEOUS ROCK which contains no (or very little) free quartz and whose FELDSPARS are dominantly SILICATES of calcium rather than of sodium or potassium.

Basidiomycete A class of fungi which reproduce by means of *basidiospores* (see BASIDIUM). It includes the mushrooms, toadstools and puffballs as well as microfungi such as rusts and smuts. (See Fungi, pp. 156-9.)

Basidiospore See BASIDIUM.

Basidium A specialized reproductive cell of BASIDIOMYCETE fungi, often club-shaped or cylindrical. Each cell produces usually four SPORES (basidiospores) on peg-like appendages (sterigmata). (See Fungi, pp. 156-9.)

Basifixed (Of ANTHERS), attached at the base to the filament, and therefore lacking independent movement (cf. DORSIFIXED).

Bast fiber Fibrous elements within the sugar-conducting tissues (PHLOEM) of thickened stems and roots.

Batholith A large subterranean INTRUSION of IGNEOUS ROCK, having an areal extent of upwards of 40mi² (100km²). (See pp. 1031, 1032, 1125.)

Benthic Pertaining to the bottom of the ocean or a lake.

Benthonic Adjective applied to organisms which live on, or very near to, the ocean floor.

Berry A fleshy FRUIT without a stony layer, and containing one or more SEEDS.

Betalains Red and yellow ALKALOID pigments present in members of the Caryophyllales. (See p. 417, 'Economic uses'.)

Bi- Prefix meaning two or twice.

Bicarpellate (Of OVARIES), derived from two CARPELS.

Biennial A plant that completes its life cycle in more than one, but less than two, years and which usually flowers in the second year (cf. ANNUAL, PERENNIAL).

Bifid Forked; having a deep fissure near the center.

Bilabiate Two-lipped.

Binomial The name of a SPECIES, consisting of two units, the GENUS title and a specific epithet. Both are italicized and only the initial letter of the genus part is capitalized, for example *Betula pendula*. (See pp. 698, 699-700.)

Biocide A substance that kills living organisms. (See pp. 946-7.)

Biofacies See FACIES.

Biogenic A term applied to materials (usually sediments or SEDIMENTARY ROCKS) which owe their origin to living organisms. For example, coal is of biogenic origin. (See e.g. pp. 1111-9.)

Biomass Quantitative estimate of the total amount of living matter (measured by dry weight) making up all or part of a specified unit such as a population; the total amount of living matter within a given area at a given time (see p. 709).

Biosystematics The study of the classification and relationships of organisms using the techniques and concepts of CYTOGENETICS.

Biotic Pertaining to life or living organisms.

Bipinnate (Of leaves), a PINNATE leaf with the primary leaflets themselves divided in a pinnate manner.

Bipinnatifid (Of leaves), a PINNATIFID leaf the segments of which are also pinnatifid.

Biseriate In two rows.

Bisexual (Of flowers), containing both male and female reproductive organs (cf. UNISEXUAL).

Blade The flattened part of a leaf, the LAMINA.

Boreal Relating to or growing in the northern latitudes dominated by coniferous forests. In some cases boreal is equated with 'cold'. (See pp. 750, 838-41, 898, 902-4. Conifers and their Allies, see pp. 100-3.)

Bostryx (Of INFLORESCENCES), a CYMOSE inflorescence with successive branches on one side only; normally coiled like a spring.

Bract A leaf, often modified or reduced, which subtends a flower or an INFLORESCENCE in its AXIL.

Bracteole A small leaf-like organ occurring along the length of a flower stalk, between a true subtending BRACT and the CALYX.

Breccia A type of rock composed of angular fragments cemented together by some material such as lime. (See pp. 979, 1132-3.)

Bryoid Pertaining to BRYOPHYTES (mosses, liverworts) and plants such as filmy ferns (e.g *Hymenophyllum*) resembling them (see pp. 234-5).

Bryophyte A moss or liverwort (see pp. 234-5).

Bulb An underground organ comprising a short, disk-like stem, bearing fleshy scale-leaves and buds and surrounded by protective scale-leaves; it acts as a PERENNATING organ and is a means of VEGETATIVE REPRODUCTION (cf. CORM, TUBER).

Bulbil A small BULB or bulb-like organ often produced on above-ground organs.

Caducous Falling off prematurely or easily.

Calc-alkaline rock An IGNEOUS ROCK in which the most prevalent FELDSPAR is rich in calcium.

Calcareous Containing or rich in lime. (See pp. 1130, 1131, 1133-4, 1187, 1190.)

Calcicole A plant that favors soil containing lime.

Calcinomorphic (Of soils), developed over CALCAREOUS rocks which largely control their characteristics.

Calcrete The lime-crust found over limestones in arid areas when any water with its calcium carbonate moves upward by evaporation.

Caldera An extremely large crater of volcanic origin, resulting from repeated or massive explosion, collapse, or the amalgamation of a number of smaller craters. (See p. 1058.)

Calyculus A group of leaf-like appendages below the CALYX.

Calyx Collective term for all the SEPALS of a flower.

Cambium A layer of cells that occurs within the stem and roots which divides to form secondary permanent tissues.

Campanulate Bell-shaped.

Campylotropous (Of OVULES), bent over through 90° so that the stalk (*funicle*) appears to be attached to the side of the ovule.

Canyon A steep-sided valley formed where a river has eroded down through horizontal strata of hard rock. The most famous is the Grand Canyon, Ariz., which is about 220mi (350km) long and has a greatest depth of about 1.1mi (1.75km).

Capitate Head-like.

Capitulum (adj. capitulate) An INFLORESCENCE consisting of a head of closely packed stalkless flowers.

Capsule A dry FRUIT which normally splits open to release its SEEDS; the SPORANGIUM of BRYOPHYTES.

Carbonates Minerals which contain the carbonate ION $CO_3{}^{2-}$. Among the more important minerals are calcite ($CaCO_3$), aragonite ($CaCO_3$), dolomite ($CaMg(CO_3)_2$), magnesite ($MgCO_3$) and malachite ($CuCO_3.Cu(OH)_2$).

Carcinogen An agent that causes or creates a predisposition to cancer. (Medicinal and Narcotic Plants, see pp. 226-7.)

Cardiac glycoside A class of drug that increases the force of contraction of the heart without increasing its oxygen consumption. (Medicinal and Narcotic Plants, see pp. 226-7.)

Carminative An agent that relieves flatulence. (Medicinal and Narcotic Plants, see pp. 226-7.)

Carnivorous plant One that is capable of catching and digesting small animals such as insects. (See pp. 121 (*Dionaea*), 125, *125*, 273, 392-3, 404-5, 496, 772, *772*, *878*.)

Carotenoids Fat-soluble pigments including carotenes (yellow and orange) and xanthophylls (yellow); they are found in CHROMOPLASTS and CHLOROPLASTS of plants. (See p. 794.)

Carpel One of the flower's female reproductive organs, comprising an OVARY and a STIGMA, and containing one or more OVULES.

Caruncle (adj. carunculate) A fleshy, sometimes colored, outgrowth near the HILUM of some seeds.

Caryopsis A dry fruit (ACHENE) typical of grasses.

Casparian band A layer of thickening, mainly SUBERIN, in the cell walls of a sheath of cells known as the *endodermis*, which is located between the outer or *cortical* layer and the inner *stele* (water- and nutrient-conducting layer) in all roots and many stems of higher plants. The Casparian band prevents the direct passage of water and solutes through the *apoplast* (i.e., between the cell walls and through the intercellular spaces), which must in consequence enter the cells to allow passage from the cortex to the stele.

Catastrophic selection The elimination of ecologically marginal populations, except for one or more exceptionally adapted individuals, by an environmental extreme.

Cation See ION.

Catkin A pendulous INFLORESCENCE of simple, usually UNISEXUAL, flowers.

Cerrado Brazilian term for savanna-woodland (see p. 856).

Chert A form of quartz resembling flint. (See pp. *1074*, 1135.)

Chlorenchyma Parenchymatous cells (see PARENCHYMA) that contain CHLOROPLASTS.

Chloridoid Resembling or pertaining to the grass genus *Chloris*.

Chlorophyll The green pigment of plant cells necessary for PHOTOSYNTHESIS (see pp. 794-5).

Chloroplast A PLASTID containing CHLOROPHYLL; found in algal and green plant cells.

Chlorosis (Of green parts of a plant), turning yellowish or whitish.

Chromophore See CHROMOPROTEIN.

Chromoplast A colored PLASTID. It usually contains red or yellow pigment.

Chromoprotein A light-absorbing substance comprising an absorbing *chromophore* attached to a protein which modifies the wavelength.

Chromosomes Thread-like strands of DNA and proteins which occur in the nucleus of living cells and carry the units of heredity, the *genes*. (See pp. 762-3.)

Chronistics A discipline concerned with attempts to determine relationships between TAXA with reference to an assumed evolutionary timescale. (See p. 696.)

Chytrid A member of an order of fungi (Chytridales) which are microscopic, water- or soil-inhabiting SPECIES often parasitic on algae or higher plants. (See Fungi, pp. 156-9.)

Cilium (adj. ciliate) A small hair-like structure on the surface of certain cells which, by waving movements, brings about locomotion.

Cincinnus A monochasial (see MONOCHASIUM), CYMOSE INFLORESCENCE with branches alternating from one side of the vertical axis to the other; normally curved to one side.

Circumboreal Growing throughout the BOREAL regions of all northern hemisphere continents.

Circumscissile Opening all round by a transverse split.

Cirque A steep-sided hollow eroded by a GLACIER. Where the glacier has retreated, cirques are commonly occupied by lakes: where it is still present, they are generally occupied by *névé*, compacted snow. Cirques are also known as *corries* or *cwms*. (See pp. *1012*, 1019.)

Cladode A flattened stem which has assumed the form and function of a leaf.

Cladogram A branching diagram representing the phylogenetic relationship (see PHYLOGENY) between TAXA (the branches) in which the vertical scale is considered to indicate time or evolutionary advancement. (See pp. 696-7.)

Clastic rock A rock composed of weathered or eroded particles of other rocks (see EROSION and WEATHERING). In general, these particles have been transported to their present position from the areas in which the erosion or weathering took place.

Claw The narrow basal part of some PETALS and SEPALS.

Cleavage Of a mineral, the tendency to split along a definite plane parallel to an actual or possible CRYSTAL face: for example, galena, whose crystals are cubic, cleaves along three mutually perpendicular planes. Such cleavage is useful in identifying minerals: for example aragonite and calcite have the same chemical composition ($CaCO_3$) but quite different cleavages. (See pp. *1082, 1086*.)
  Rock cleavage most commonly takes place between roughly parallel beds whose resistances under deformation to internal shearing differ. (See p. *1138*.)

Cleistogamic (cleistogamous) (Of flowers), self-pollinating, without the flower ever opening.

Climax A state of equilibrium between a plant community and the prevailing environment, representing the final stage of an ecological SUCCESSION (see pp. 711-4).

Cline A gradual change in any measurable character with populations, SPECIES etc. (See p. 706.)

Clone A group of plants which have arisen by VEGETATIVE REPRODUCTION from a single parent and which are therefore all genetically identical. (See pp. 932, 933.)

Co-dominant One of two or more SPECIES that together dominate a vegetation type.

Coenocytic Not having cross-walls, so that many individual nuclei occupy the same area of CYTOPLASM; non-cellular.

Colloid or colloidal solution A system in which two (or more) substances are uniformly mixed such that one is extremely finely dispersed throughout the other. A colloid may be viewed intuitively as a halfway stage between a suspension and a solution, the size of the dispersed particles being larger than simple molecules but still too small to be viewed through an optical microscope. A typical example of a colloid is fog (water in air).

Colpate (Of POLLEN), having one or more *colpi* (oblong-elliptic apertures in the pollen-wall).

Colpus (pl. colpi) See COLPATE.

Column (of a flower) The combined STYLE and STIGMA, typically of orchids.

Columnar Column-shaped or with column-shaped constituents.

Compaction The 'pressing together' of the individual grains of a sediment, usually resulting from the weight of overlying sediment, to form a SEDIMENTARY ROCK.

Compound Consisting of several parts; e.g., a LEAF with several leaflets or an INFLORESCENCE with more than one group of flowers.

Conidia See CONIDIOPHORE.

Conidiophore The stalk (HYPHA) on which one or more asexual SPORES (*conidia*) are borne.

Conifer A cone-bearing tree, e.g. pine, larch, fir etc. (See *Families of Conifers* in Thematic Index. Conifers and their Allies, see pp. 100-3.)

Connate Joined or attached to; applied to similar organs fused during development, e.g. STAMENS fused into a tube (cf. ADNATE).

Connective (Of STAMENS), the tissue connecting the POLLEN SACS of an ANTHER.

Consociation A part of an association dominated by one SPECIES.

Consolidation In geology, any process whereby a soft, loose material is transformed into a harder, denser one. A typical process is COMPACTION.

Constancy The occurrence of essentially the same association of SPECIES in different localities.

Contorted (Of SEPALS and PETALS), twisted in the bud so that they overlap on one side only; spirally twisted.

Convergent evolution The process by which similar structures are developed independently in unrelated organisms; often shown by organisms inhabiting similar environments. (See pp. 769-70, 853-5.)

Convolute Rolled together.

Cordate (Of leaves), heart-shaped.

Cordillera An extended mountain system, often comprising a number of parallel ranges, associated with a GEOSYNCLINE. In many cases, a cordillera appears as a string of islands.

Core The innermost sphere of the Earth, with a diameter of about 4350mi (7000km). It is thought to be subdivided into an inner core, which is solid, and an outer core, which is predominantly liquid. The main constituents of the core are thought to be iron and nickel. (See pp. 974, 996.)

Coriaceous Leathery.

Corm (adj. cormous) A bulbous, swollen, underground stem-base bearing scale-leaves and ADVENTITIOUS roots; it acts as a PERENNATING or storage organ and is a means of VEGETATIVE REPRODUCTION.

Corolla All the PETALS of a flower; it is normally colored.

Corona A series of PETAL-like structures in a flower, either outgrowths from the petals, or modified from the STAMENS, e.g. a daffodil 'trumpet'.

Corrie See CIRQUE.

Cortical layer (In plants) see CASPARIAN BAND.

Corymb (adj. corymbose) A rounded or flat-topped INFLORESCENCE like a RACEME, though the flower stalks are longer on the outside so that all the flowers are at about the same level.

Cotyledon The first leaf, or pair of leaves, of an EMBRYO within the seed. See DICOTYLEDON, MONOCOTYLEDON.

Country rock The local rock surrounding a particular rock body, most commonly an INTRUSION of IGNEOUS ROCK or an ORE deposit.

Craton See KRATON.

Crenate (Of leaf margins), shallowly round-toothed with indentations no further than one-eighth of the distance to the midrib.

Crenulate Finely CRENATE.

Cross-bedding In sedimentary structures, LAMINAR records of usually short-lived changes in the velocity of the current in which the sediment was laid down. The angles of such laminae to the main bedding plane give an indication of the direction of current flow. (See pp. *1017*, 1129.)

Cross-fertilization See FERTILIZATION.

Cross-pollination See POLLINATION.

Crust The outermost layer of the Earth, having a typical depth of around 22mi (35km). (See p. 973.)

Cryopedogenesis Development of soils under cold conditions.

Cryptogam A general term applied to plants that do not produce seeds, e.g. mosses and ferns. (See pp. 724, 725. Mosses, see pp. 234-5; Ferns, see pp. 140-1.)

Cryptophyte Plants with their dormant buds and other surviving organs situated below the soil or water surface (see p. 725).

Cryptozoic The aeon of geological time in which life first appeared and in which the rocks of the Precambrian were formed. The rocks do not contain any FOSSILS that can be used for dating—hence the name Cryptozoic, which means 'hidden life'. The aeon of visible life is called, in contrast, the PHANEROZOIC.

Crystals Homogeneous solid objects having naturally formed plane faces. This order in their external appearance reflects the regularity of their internal structure, an internal regularity which is the keynote of the crystalline state. The study of crystals and the crystalline state is the province of *crystallography*. (See pp. 1075-80.)

Culm The stem of a grass or sedge.

Cultivar (abbreviation cv) Cultivated VARIETY. A TAXONOMIC rank used to denote a variety that is known only in horticultural cultivation. Cultivar names are nonlatinized and in living languages; typographically they are distinguished by a non-italic typeface, with a capital initial letter and enclosed in single quotation marks, for example *Betula pendula* 'Fastigiata'. (See pp. 956-8.)

Cupule (adj. cupulate) A cup-shaped sheath, surrounding some FRUITS.

Cuticle The waxy or fatty layer on the outer surface of epidermal cells (cf. EPIDERMIS).

cv Abbreviation for CULTIVAR.

Cwm See CIRQUE.

Cycadophyte Member of the phylum Cycadophyta, the cycads; they belong to the general group known as GYMNOSPERMS. (See pp. 100, 112.)

Cyme An INFLORESCENCE in which each terminal growing point produces a flower. Subsequent growth is therefore from a lateral growing point, the oldest flowers being at the APEX, or center, if flat.

Cymose Arranged in a CYME; cyme-like.

Cypsela A single-seeded FRUIT derived from a UNILOCULAR, INFERIOR OVARY.

Cystolith A CRYSTAL or deposit of lime, within a cell.

Cytogenetics The study of the mechanisms of CHROMOSOMES, their behavior, and the effect they have on inheritance and evolution (see pp. 914-5, 927, 933-4, 958).

Cytology The study of cells and their internal structure.

Cytoplasm The PROTOPLASMIC content of a cell (excluding the nucleus).

Deciduous (Of plants), shedding their leaves seasonally.

Declinate (Of STAMENS), curving downwards.

Decoction An extract obtained by boiling.

Decumbent Prostrate; lying flat, but with the growing tip extended upwards.

Decussate (Of leaves), arranged in opposite pairs on the stem, with each pair at 90° to the preceding pair.

Deflation The TRANSPORTATION of loose surface debris by the wind. See also AEOLIAN.

Degradation The lowering of the level of the land by any or all of the processes that together comprise DENUDATION: EROSION, WEATHERING and TRANSPORTATION.

Dehiscent Splitting open to discharge the contents (cf. INDEHISCENT).

Demulcent A MUCILAGINOUS or oily substance capable of soothing damaged mucous membranes. (Medicinal and Narcotic Plants, see pp. 226-7.)

Dendritic Adjective applied to any form reminiscent of a tree—with branches, subsidiary branches, etc. A typical application is to a drainage system. A *dendrite* is a branched CRYSTAL form, common in ice (especially in the form of frost) and certain minerals, and of prime importance in metals, which often consist of dendrites embedded in a matrix of the same or (for alloys) different composition.

Dendrochronology The dating of past events by the study of annual rings in trees. A hollow tube is inserted into the tree trunk and a core from bark to center removed. The rings are counted, examined and compared with rings from dead trees so that the chronology may be extended further back in time. Through such studies important corrections have been made to the system of radiocarbon dating; though of course, in geological terms, the timespan covered is extremely short. (See p. 735.) See also RADIOMETRIC DATING.

Dentate Having a toothed margin.

Denticulate Having a finely toothed margin.

Denudation Those processes that contribute to the DEGRADATION of the land, namely EROSION, WEATHERING and TRANSPORTATION.

Deposition The end result of TRANSPORTATION.

Derived Originating from an earlier form or group.

Desmids A group of freshwater green algae in which the cell-wall is in two halves, united by a narrow connection. (Algae, see pp. 18-21.)

Detrital Adjective describing particles of rocks or more usually minerals derived by EROSION or WEATHERING from pre-existing rocks. Rocks made up of detrital particles are known as CLASTIC ROCKS.

Di- Prefix meaning two.

Diagenesis An envelope term for the processes occurring close to the Earth's surface and affecting a particular sediment. Deeper within the Earth, where temperatures and pressures are higher, metamorphism takes place (see METAMORPHIC ROCK), and there is no sharp borderline between the two processes. The end-result of diagenesis is the formation of a coherent SEDIMENTARY ROCK.

Diaphoretic An agent that increases perspiration. (Medicinal and Narcotic Plants, see pp. 226-7.)

Diaspore A dispersal propagule, e.g. a SEED, FRUIT, SPORE etc.

Diastrophism The large-scale deformation of the Earth's CRUST to produce such features as continents, oceans, mountains and rift valleys. Typical processes are faulting, folding and PLATE TECTONICS.

Diatoms A class of unicellular marine or freshwater algae with the brown pigment isofucoxanthin, as well as CHLOROPHYLL, in the CHLOROPLASTS. The cell-wall is in two halves, one overlapping the other. It is made of pectic materials impregnated with silica and is finely sculptured. (Algae, see pp. 18-21.)

Dichasium (Of INFLORESCENCES), a form of CYMOSE inflorescence with each branch giving rise to two other branches (cf. MONOCHASIUM).

Dichotomous Branching into two equal forks.

Dicotyledon A member of one of two subclasses of ANGIOSPERMS (see pp. 32-5); a plant whose EMBRYO has two COTYLEDONS (cf. MONO-COTYLEDON). (See pp. 377-618.)

Didymous In pairs.

Didynamous Having two STAMENS longer than others.

Differentiation In a MAGMA, the separation (usually through CRYSTALLIZATION at different times) of the various constituents to produce different varieties of IGNEOUS ROCK. The term is used analogously for the concentration of the constituents of a rock during metamorphism (see METAMORPHIC ROCKS), resulting in, for example, the banding of a GNEISS.

Dimorphism (adj. dimorphic) Having two distinct forms.

Dinoflagellate A member of the algal order Dinophyta—single-celled aquatic algae which move by the action of two flagella. (See pp. 1215-6. Algae, see pp. 18-21.)

Dinophyta See DINOFLAGELLATE.

Dioecious Having male and female flowers borne on separate plants.

Dip The angle between an inclined plane and the horizontal plane. The dip of a FAULT is the angle between the fault plane and the horizontal (its complement is the *hade*, the angle between the fault plane and the vertical). The dip of a slope is regarded as perpendicular to the *strike*, the direction in which a horizontal straight line may be drawn on the slope.

Diploid See PLOIDY.

Discontinuity A layer within the Earth where the speed of transmission of seismic waves changes. Best known, though not most important, is the MOHOROVICIC DISCONTINUITY.

Disk The fleshy outgrowth developed from the receptacle at the base of the OVARY or from the STAMENS surrounding the ovary; it often secretes NECTAR.

Distichous Arranged in two vertical rows.

Diuretic An agent that tends to increase the flow of urine.

Division A major TAXONOMIC subdivision of the plant kingdom (cf. PHYLUM).

Dormancy The condition of being inactive, usually during unfavorable conditions.

Dorsal Term used to describe the back parts of an animal (e.g., the dorsal fins of a fish), or those parts that are generally uppermost. In botany, the dorsal part of, say, a leaf is that side turned away from the stem.

Dorsifixed (Of ANTHERS), attached at the back to the filament (cf. BASIFIXED).

Drepanium (Of INFLORESCENCES), a CYMOSE inflorescence with successive branches on one side only; normally flattened in one plane and curved to one side.

Drift The material left behind when a GLACIER retreats. The unstratified material deposited directly onto the land is called *till*. *Fluvioglacial drift*, material which has been transported by melted waters of the glacier, is in contrast well stratified. Drift may be up to 330ft (100m) deep, composed of particles that vary from fine sand up to huge boulders.

Drupe A fleshy FRUIT containing one or more SEEDS, each of which is surrounded by a stony layer.

Ecological niche The environment most favorable for a particular organism which is better adapted to that environment than any other organism.

Ecosystem An entire community of plants and animals interacting with its particular environment, consisting of 'producers' (mostly green plants), 'consumers' (animals) and 'decomposers' (bacteria and fungi). (See pp. 689-90, 708-15, 784.)

Edaphic Pertaining to the soil.

Elaiosome A fleshy outgrowth on a seed with oily substances attractive to ants.

Elliptic (Of leaves), oval-shaped, with narrowed ends.

Eluviation Removal of fractions of the clay-HUMUS complex in soils by PODZOLIZATION or LATERIZATION.

Embryo The rudimentary plant within the seed.

Embryo sac The central portion of the OVULE; a thin-walled sac within the NUCELLUS containing the egg nucleus.

Emetic An agent that induces vomiting. (Medicinal and Narcotic Plants, see pp. 226-7.)

Emplacement The development of an IGNEOUS ROCK body surrounded by another rock, most usually through INTRUSION.

Endemic A population, SPECIES, GENUS, or family which is of a more restricted distribution than is expected for that rank.

Endocarp The innermost layer of the OVARY wall (PERICARP) of a FRUIT. In some fruits it becomes hard and stony (cf. DRUPE).

Endodermis See CASPARIAN BAND.

Endosperm Fleshy tissue, containing stored nutritive material, found in some seeds.

Endozoochory The dispersal of DIASPORES (seeds etc.) that pass through the digestive systems of animals (e.g. when fruit-eating birds eat the soft pulp but excrete the hard seeds). (See p. 816; cf. EPIZOOCHORY, SYNZOOCHORY.)

Entire (Of leaves), with an undivided margin.

Envelope The rock surrounding an INTRUSION of IGNEOUS ROCK, usually comprising a metamorphic AUREOLE surrounded by COUNTRY ROCK.

Enzyme A protein which mediates (catalyzes) a specific biochemical reaction.

Epeirogeny Large-scale upward or downward movement of a landmass; not to be confused with the more dynamic processes that comprise OROGENY.

Epharmony Concerned with unrelated SPECIES.

Epibionty The phenomenon of being an 'old' ENDEMIC with a restricted distribution resulting from contraction of a former wider area.

Epicalyx A whorl of SEPAL-like appendages resembling the CALYX but outside the true calyx.

Epicontinental Adjective describing, for example, a sea situated within a continental mass or covering the continental shelf.

Epidermis The outer protective, usually single-celled, layer of many plant organs, particularly leaves and herbaceous stems.

Epigynous (Of flowers), with the SEPALS, PETALS and STAMENS inserted near the top of the OVARY.

Epipetalous Attached to the PETALS or COROLLA.

Epiphyte (adj. epiphytic) A plant that grows on the surface of another, without being dependent on it for nutrition. (See p. 721.)

Epizoochory The carrying of DIASPORES (fruits, seeds etc.) on the outside of an animal (e.g. by hooks attaching them to fur or wool). (See p. 816; cf. ENDOZOOCHORY, SYNZOOCHORY.)

Erect (Of an OVULE), upright, with its stalk at the base.

Ericoid Like *Erica*—a dwarf shrub with small, inrolled leaves.

Erosion The wearing away of the Earth's surface by natural agents. Running water constitutes the most effective eroding agent, the process being accelerated by the TRANSPORTATION of particles eroded or weathered further upstream. Other important agents of erosion include groundwater, ocean waves and GLACIERS. Rocks exposed to the atmosphere undergo the closely related process of WEATHERING. (See pp. 1010-4.)

Essential oil A vegetable oil made up of complex mixtures of volatile organic compounds that impart the characteristic fragrance or taste to plants. They are often extracted for use in perfumes and flavorings. (See p. 136.)

Etiolated (Of plants), pale in color and straggling in appearance—caused by exclusion of light.

Eugeosyncline (In geology) see GEOSYNCLINE.

Eukaryote (adj. eukaryotic) Any organism that has a membrane-bound nucleus, which includes all fungi, green plants and algae (except the blue-green algae—cf. PROKARYOTE). (See pp. 753, 757.)

Eulittoral Referring to the zone and its inhabitants lying between upper and lower tide limits (cf. LITTORAL).

Eusporangium (adj. eusporangiate) One of the two main types of SPORANGIA found in ferns. They are stalked and have walls at least two cells thick (cf. LEPTOSPORANGIUM). (Ferns, see pp. 140-1.)

Eustatic Adjective describing worldwide, rather than local, sea-level changes.

Eutrophic (Of lakes, etc.), rich in nutrients (cf. OLIGOTROPHIC).

Evaporites Sedimentary deposits of salts that have fallen out of solution owing to the evaporation (and thus concentration) of a body of water. Evaporite deposits have the least soluble salts at the bottom, followed by progressively more soluble salts.

Evapotranspiration The loss of water from an area, both via the vegetation and the ground surface.

Evergreen Having leaves all the year round.

Exine The outer layer of the wall of a POLLEN grain.

Exocarp The outermost layer of the FRUIT wall.

Expectorant An agent that tends to promote discharge of mucus from the respiratory tract. (Medicinal and Narcotic Plants, see pp. 226-7.)

Exserted Protruding.

Exstipulate Without STIPULES.

Extrorse (of ANTHERS) Opening away from the axis of growth towards the COROLLA.

Extrusion The consolidation of MAGMA on the surface of the Earth to form volcanic IGNEOUS ROCKS. See also INTRUSION.

Facies (pl. facies) Appearance or aspect. In geology, of a sediment, the total of those of its characteristics that uniquely indicate the conditions of its deposition. *Biofacies* or fossil facies are sediments characterized by the type of FOSSIL organisms which they contain.

Fasciation The coalescing of stems, branches etc. into bundles.

Fascicle A cluster or bundle.

Fault A fracture in the Earth's CRUST on either side of which there has been relative movement. Faults seldom occur in a single plane: usually a vast number of roughly parallel faults take place in a belt (*fault zone*) a few hundred yards across. Faults may be large enough to be responsible for such features as rift valleys, or, in contrast, microscopically small. (See pp. 1022-3.)

Fauna The animals occurring in a particular region and/or, to the paleontologist, period of time. See also FLORA.

Febrifuge An agent that reduces the temperature of the body. (Medicinal and Narcotic Plants, see pp. 226-7.)

Feldspars The most abundant minerals in the Earth's crust, widely distributed in IGNEOUS, METAMORPHIC, and SEDIMENTARY rocks. They are aluminosilicates containing potassium, sodium and calcium, and are divided into *alkali feldspars*, in which potassium is dominant, and *plagioclase feldspars*, which vary continuously in composition from pure sodium feldspar to pure calcium feldspar (see p. 1091).

Fell-field See FJELDMARK.

Female flower A flower containing functional CARPELS, but not STAMENS.

Fertilization The fusion of male and female reproductive cells (*gametes*). *Cross-fertilization* occurs between gametes from separate plants; *self-fertilization* occurs between gametes from the same plant.

Festucoid Resembling fescue-grass (*Festuca*).

Filament The ANTHER-bearing stalk of a STAMEN.

Filiform Threadlike.

Fimbriate (of margins) Fringed, usually with hairs.

Fissure vein See VEIN.

Fjeldmark Areas of rock-debris and open, mineral soil with sparse plant-cover, usually at high elevations with cold conditions. (See pp. 855, 902.)

Flood plain A plain bordering usually the lower reaches of a river, initially formed by the downstream migration of meanders, widening the river valley. When the river floods, sediment is carried over its banks and deposited over the flood plain, so that the level of the plain gradually rises, especially near to the channel, to form raised banks called *levees*. Further deposition of sediment may raise both the levees and the river channel itself. (See pp. 1039-40.) See also ALLUVIUM.

Flora The plants occurring in a particular region and/or, to the paleontologist, period of time. See also FAUNA.

Flower The structure concerned with sexual reproduction in ANGIOSPERMS. Essentially it consists of the male organs (*androecium*), comprising the STAMENS, and female organs (*gynoecium*), comprising the OVARY, STYLE(S), and STIGMA(S), usually surrounded by a WHORL of PETALS (the COROLLA) and a whorl of SEPALS (the CALYX). Male and female flowers may be in the same flower (bisexual) or in separate flowers (unisexual). (See pp. 32-5, 367-73.)

Fluorapatite A rock-forming SILICATE in which fluorine is an important constituent. (See pp. 1084, 1104.)

Fluvioglacial drift See DRIFT.

Fold A buckling in rock strata occurring as a result of horizontal pressures in the Earth's CRUST. Folds convex upwards are called *anticlines*; those that are convex downwards, *synclines*. Folds may be tiny or up to hundreds of miles across. (See pp. 1028-9.)

Foliose Bearing leaves.

Follicle A dry FRUIT which is derived from a single CARPEL and which splits open along one side only.

Foraminifera Minute marine organisms with perforated shells. (See p. 1219.)

Forb A non-grasslike herb.

Forma (form) A TAXONOMIC division ranking below variety and used to distinguish plants with trivial differences.

Fossils The remains, traces or impressions of living organisms that inhabited the Earth during past ages. There are a number of mechanisms whereby fossil remains may be preserved. *Trace fossils* may take the form of, for example, footprints, burrows or preserved droppings. (See pp. 730-5, 1206-10.)

Fracture A breakage of a rock or mineral in a direction other than the CLEAVAGE direction. (See p. 1082.)

Free (Of PETALS, SEPALS etc.), not joined to each other or to any other organ.

Free central placentation A type of PLACENTATION in which the OVULES are borne on PLACENTAS on a free, central column within an OVARY that has only one LOCULE.

Fruit Strictly the ripened OVARY or group of ovaries of a seed plant and its contents. Loosely, the whole structure containing ripe SEEDS, which may include more than the ovary. (See pp. 34, 151-3; cf. ACHENE, BERRY, CAPSULE, DRUPE, FOLLICLE, NUT, SAMARA.)

Fruticose Resembling a SHRUB.

Funicle The stalk of an OVULE.

Gamete The haploid reproductive cell (male or female) that is produced during sexual reproduction. At FERTILIZATION the nucleus of the gamete fuses with another gamete of the opposite sex to form a diploid ZYGOTE that develops into a new individual. (See also PLOIDY.)

Gametophyte See PROTHALLUS.

Gamopetalous With PETALS fused, at least at the base.

Gamosepalous With SEPALS fused, at least at the base.

Gangue See ORE.

Gemma A cell or group of vegetative cells produced by some algae, fungi and bryophytes which are dispersed and may grow into new individuals—a form of asexual reproduction. (Algae, see pp. 18-21.)

Gene See CHROMOSOMES.

Genotype The genetic constitution of an organism.

Genus A TAXONOMIC rank grouping together more or less closely related plants. The genus title is the first word of the species binomial (see SPECIES). A genus may be divided into *subgenera*, *sections* and *series*, in descending order of hierarchy. (See pp. 695-6.)

Geomorphology The study of the physical features of the Earth's surface in relation to the underlying geological structure.

Geosyncline An elongate depression in the Earth's crust that fills with great thicknesses of sediment, beneath which the floor of the geosyncline progressively subsides. A *eugeosyncline* has a depth of sediment of the order of 16,500ft (5000m) and contains a large amount of volcanic rocks. A *miogeosyncline* has a smaller depth of sediment (of the order of 6500ft or 2000m) and an almost complete absence of volcanic rocks. (See pp. 1034, 1036, 1091, 1132, 1151, 1158, 1166, 1179-80, 1269.)

Geotropic Pertaining to plant-growth in relation to gravity.

Ginkgophyte Member of the phylum Ginkgophyta, now including only the maidenhair tree (*Ginkgo biloba*), but with many FOSSIL representatives; included in the general group called GYMNOSPERMS. (See p. 216.)

Glabrous Without hairs or projections.

Glacier A mass of ice that survives for several years. There are three recognized types of glacier: *ice sheets* and *caps*; *mountain* or *valley glaciers*; and *piedmont glaciers*. They form wherever conditions are such that annual precipitation of snow, sleet and hail is greater than the amount that can be lost through evaporation or otherwise. Mountain glaciers usually result from the coalescing of bodies of snow that have accumulated in CIRQUES; and a piedmont glacier occurs when a mountain glacier spreads out of its valley into a contiguous lowland area. Glaciers account for about 75% of the world's fresh water. (See pp. 748-50, 903-4, 905, 1011-2, 1018-20, 1048-50.)

Gland (adj. glandular) Secreting organ producing oil, resin, nectar, water etc. (cf. HYDATHODE, NECTARY).

Glaucous With a waxy, grayish-blue bloom.

Globose Spherical, rounded.

Glycoside A class of compound found in many plants, yielding a sugar on hydrolysis along with other substances.

Gneiss A general term to describe any of a number of highly regionally metamorphosed, usually coarse-grained rocks (see METAMORPHIC ROCKS) with a banded, laminated structure. (See p. 1139.) See also SCHIST.

Gondwanaland The southern-hemisphere continent that was formed as PANGAEA split up. Stratigraphic and other evidence suggest it comprised what are now Antarctica, Australia, India, South America and other, smaller units. (See pp. 740-3, 1173, 1181.)

Graminoid Resembling a grass.

Graptolite An extinct marine animal found as a FOSSIL in rocks of PALEOZOIC age. (See pp. 1229-30.)

Groundwater Water that accumulates beneath the Earth's surface. It may be *meteoric*, where rainwater has percolated down from above, or *juvenile*, where water has risen from beneath. (See p. 1070.)

Gymnosperm A seed plant in which the seeds are not enclosed in an OVARY; conifers are the most familiar examples. (See pp. 100-3, see also *Families of Conifers* in Thematic Index.)

Gynobasic style A STYLE that arises near the base of a deeply-lobed OVARY.

Gynoecium The female reproductive organs of a flower; see PISTIL.

Gynophore Stalk of a CARPEL or GYNOECIUM.

Gyttja Lake sediments, usually black, containing much organic matter. (See pp. 826, 881.)

Habit The characteristic mode of growth or occurrence of plants; the form and shape of a plant.

Hade See DIP.

Halophyte A plant adapted to growth under highly saline conditions. (See pp. 772, 885-91.)

Haploid See PLOIDY.

Hardy Able to withstand extreme conditions, usually of cold.

Haustorium (pl. haustoria) Organ of various parasitic or symbiotic plants used to draw nutrients from the host plants. (See also PARASITE, SYMBIOSIS.)

Head A dense INFLORESCENCE of small, crowded, often stalkless flowers—a CAPITULUM.

Helicoid (Of CYMOSE INFLORESCENCES) coiled like a spring.

Hematite Iron ORE in the form of ferric oxide. (See p. 1092.)

Herb (adj. herbaceous) A plant that does not develop persistent woody tissue above ground and either dies at the end of the growing season or overwinters by means of underground organs such as BULBS, CORMS or RHIZOMES. (See pp. 174-5.)

Heterocyst (Of blue-green algae), a thick-walled transparent cell in which fixation of nitrogen takes place. (Bacteria and Blue-green Algae, see pp. 50-1.)

Heteromorphy Occurrence in different forms (cf. HOMEOMORPHY).

Heterophylly (adj. heterophyllous) Having leaves of more than one type on the same plant.

Heterospory The condition of having SPORES of two kinds, usually termed *microspores* and *megaspores*.

Heterostyly Having STYLES (and usually STAMENS) of two or more lengths in different flowers within a SPECIES.

Heterotrophic Unable to synthesize food from simple inorganic substances and thus requiring a source of organic food, as in the fungi. (See Fungi, pp. 156-9.)

Heterozygous Having different forms (ALLELES) of a gene at the same locus on HOMOLOGOUS CHROMOSOMES (cf. HOMOZYGOUS).

Hexaploid See PLOIDY.

Hilum The scar left on a seed marking the point of attachment to the stalk of the OVULE.

Hirsute Covered in rough, coarse hairs.

Homeomorphy Similarities of MORPHOLOGY between members of different genera within the same PHYLUM. It is distinct from *homomorphy*, similarities of morphology (usually only superficial) between members of different phyla.

Homologous Structures, traits or properties which share a common ancestry but may differ in structure, function, or behavior; (of CHROMOSOMES), pairing during nuclear division of structurally similar chromosomes that have identical genetic loci in the same sequence.

Homomorphy See HOMEOMORPHY.

Homozygous Having identical ALLELES at the same locus on HOMOLOGOUS CHROMOSOMES (cf. HETEROZYGOUS).

Honey guide Markings (e.g. lines or dots) on the PERIANTH which direct insects to the NECTAR.

Horizon Any horizontal stratum that can be distinguished within a sediment or a geological series. (Of soils), one of a series of layers forming the *soil profile*. Four horizons (A, B, C and D) are usually distinguished, of which the D horizon is the bedrock. (See p. 1140.)

Hornblende A blackish to dark green mineral composed principally of SILICATES of calcium, iron and magnesium; a constituent of granite and other rocks. (See p. 1092.)

Humus The organic constituent of a soil, formed by the partial decomposition of plant and animal remains. (See pp. 803-4, 1140-1.)

Hybrid The offspring of two plants of different TAXA, most often SPECIES. (See pp. 781, 932, 934, 935.)

Hydathode A specialized gland, usually found in leaves that exude water.

Hydromorphic (Of plants), with features related to and developed under conditions of abundant water.

Hydrophyte An aquatic plant (see p. 725).

Hydrosere A SUCCESSION of plant communities that accompanies the silting up of a body of fresh water. (See p. 823; see also LITHOSERE, PLAGIOSERE, PRISERE, PSAMMOSERE, SUBSERE, XEROSERE.)

Hydrosphere See LITHOSPHERE.

Hydrothermal Adjective describing processes, and their products, that involve the action of heated or superheated water. Hydrothermal ORE deposits occur around INTRUSIONS of IGNEOUS ROCK.

Hygrochastic (Of organs), opening in moist air and closing in dry air, e.g. CAPSULES.

Hygromorphic = HYDROMORPHIC.

Hygrophyte = HYDROPHYTE.

Hypanthium A cup-shaped enlargement of the floral receptacle or the bases of the floral parts, which often enlarges and surrounds the fruits, e.g. the fleshy tissue in rose-hips. (See p. 492 diagram 6.)

Hypha The tubular filamentous units of construction of fungi which together make up the MYCELIUM. (See Fungi, pp. 156-9.)

Hypocotyl The part of an embryo or seedling that lies between the seed leaves (*cotyledons*) and the primary root (*radicle*).

Hypogynous (Of flowers), with the SEPALS, PETALS and STAMENS attached to the receptacle or axis, below and free from the OVARY.

Igneous rocks Those rocks which form directly from a molten silicate melt, comprising one of the three main types of the rocks of the Earth. They CRYSTALLIZE from the MAGMA either at the Earth's surface (EXTRUSION) or beneath it (INTRUSION), resulting in the two principal classes, VOLCANIC ROCKS and PLUTONIC ROCKS. (See pp. 1122-9.)

Illite A clay mineral, similar to MICA; the dominant mineral in shales and mudstones. (See p. 1092.)

Illuviation Redeposition of leached colloidal

materials in different soil HORIZONS. (See also LEACHING, COLLOID.)

Imbricate (Of SEPALS, PETALS, leaves), overlapping, as in a tiled roof.

Imparipinnate (Of leaves), a PINNATE leaf with an unpaired terminal leaflet occurring centrally.

Inaperturate (Of POLLEN grains), without an aperture; without any pores or furrows.

Incised (Of leaves), sharply and deeply cut.

Inclusion A foreign body enclosed within a rock or mineral: the foreign body may be solid, liquid or gaseous.

Incompatible Of plants between which HYBRIDS cannot be formed.

Indefinite (Of flower parts), of a number large enough to make a precise count difficult.

Indehiscent Not opening to discharge the contents (cf. DEHISCENT).

Indumentum A covering, usually of hairs.

Indurate Hardened.

Indusium (adj. indusiate) A flap of tissue that covers the SPORANGIUM cluster (SORUS) of some ferns. (Ferns, see pp. 140-1.)

Inferior (Of OVARIES), an ovary with the SEPALS, PETALS and STAMENS attached to its APEX.

Inflorescence Any arrangement of more than one flower, e.g. BOSTRYX, CAPITULUM, CORYMB, CYME, DICHASIUM, FASCICLE, PANICLE, RACEME, RHIPIDIUM, SPADIX, SPIKE, THYRSE and UMBEL.

Infructescence A cluster of FRUITS, derived from an INFLORESCENCE.

Inserted Growing out of another organ.

Insolation The amount of radiant heat and light received from the sun by a particular place at a particular time.

Integument (Of OVULES), the outer protective covering of the ovule; usually two are found in ANGIOSPERMS.

Intensity, Mercalli A measure of the extent of the effects of an earthquake on a particular area. Clearly the Mercalli intensity depends both on the MAGNITUDE of the earthquake and on the position (especially distance) of the observer. The scale runs from I, where the shocks can be detected only by seismograph, to XII, 'catastrophic'. (See p. 1026.)

Intergeneric hybrid A hybrid with parents belonging to different genera.

Interglacial Period between glaciations in which temperatures rise sufficiently to support warmth-loving plants and closed forest (cf. INTERSTADIAL).

Internode The length of stem that lies between two leaf-joints (*nodes*).

Interspecific Occurring between members of different SPECIES (cf. INTRASPECIFIC).

Interstadial Period between glaciations in which temperatures do not rise sufficiently to

support warmth-loving plants and closed forest (cf. INTERGLACIAL; see pp. 749-51).

Intraspecific Occurring between members of the same SPECIES (cf. INTERSPECIFIC).

Introrse Directed and opening inwards toward the center of the flower (cf. EXTRORSE).

Intrusion The forcing of MAGMA into preexisting rocks beneath the surface of the Earth to form a body of IGNEOUS ROCK, itself termed an intrusion. See also EXTRUSION. (See pp. 1030-2.)

Involucel A whorl of BRACTEOLES.

Involucre A whorl of BRACTS beneath or surrounding an INFLORESCENCE.

Ion An atom or group of atoms that has become electrically charged by gain or loss of negatively charged electrons. An *anion* has a negative charge, a *cation* a positive charge. (See pp. 806, 820, 890.)

Irradiance Density of light radiation falling on a given surface.

Irregular (Of flowers), not regular; not divisible into halves by an indefinite number of longitudinal planes; ZYGOMORPHIC.

Island arc A curving chain of islands found associated with an ocean trench, earthquake activity and volcanism: an example is Japan. The arcs and their associated features are manifestations of plate underthrusting (see PLATE TECTONICS). (See pp. 1062-3.)

Isomer A chemical compound containing atoms of the same elements in the same numbers as another compound but differing in structural arrangement.

Isopleth Lines on a map connecting places with the same values for rainfall, temperature, height and other such features.

Isostasy The theoretical tendency of the Earth's CRUST to maintain equilibrium as it floats on the mantle, assumed to result from flows of the dense plastic SIMA in the lower crust in response to local changes in the pressure on it of the lighter SIAL above. Local differences in the proportion of sima to sial thus maintain an equal weight of crust all round the Earth. The mechanism of isostasy is nowadays being increasingly questioned. (See pp. 909, 1020, 1023.)

Isotope One of two or more forms of an element differing in atomic weight.

Joint A fracture in a rock distinct from a FAULT in that there has been no lateral displacement between the two sides. Best known are *shrinkage joints*, which can occur in extrusive IGNEOUS ROCKS to form distinctive columnar structures: as the surface of the lava cools, there are surface contractions towards discrete centers giving rise to a pattern of polygonal, generally hexagonal, cracks which, with further cooling, develop in depth to produce the columns. (See p. 1023.)

Kaolinite Clay with a low exchange capacity—the ADSORPTION of calcium IONS is not much greater than that of potassium ions. (See p. 1093.)

Karyotype The characteristic size, shape and number of the set of CHROMOSOMES of a *somatic* (non-reproductive) cell.

Kernel A general term applied to the abundant nutritive tissue of a large SEED, as with the seed inside the stone of a peach.

Kraton, craton or **shield** A large mass of IGNEOUS and METAMORPHIC rock, generally of Precambrian age and covered with at most a very superficial layer of sediment, which comprises a major crustal unit. Usage of all three terms varies widely. (See p. 1156.)

Krummholz A term applied to trees at the TIMBERLINE on mountains, which have their trunks almost horizontal and branches almost vertical to form a dense scrub. (See p. 868.)

Labellum Either of the two parts, usually upper and lower lip, into which the COROLLA of orchids is divided.

Lacerate (Of leaves), irregularly cut.

Ladder vein See VEIN.

Lamina (Of flowers), the thin, flat blade of a leaf or petal; (of rocks), a thin sheet or plate.

Laminar Made up of or resembling *laminae*, thin sheets or plates, usually parallel.

Lanceolate Narrow with tapering ends, as a lance.

Land bridge A short-lived land connection between continents, of primary importance in that it permits migration of fauna between the continents concerned. The status of land bridges in the history of life on Earth—and even their very existence—has recently been questioned. (See pp. 908-9.)

Lateral Arising from the side of the parent axis or attached to the side of another organ.

Laterite Red or yellowish iron-containing tropical clay soil. (See p. 1135.)

Laterization A process of soil formation occurring in tropical regions. The minerals are converted to clay, while pronounced leaching causes hydroxides of aluminum and iron to accumulate in the deeper layers. (See p. 1010.)

Latex A milky and usually whitish fluid that is produced by the cells of various plants and is the source of e.g. rubber, gutta percha, chicle and balata. (See pp. 197-8.)

Laticiferous Producing a milky juice (LATEX).

Laurasia The northern-hemisphere continent that was formed as PANGAEA split up. Stratigraphic and other evidence suggests it comprised what are now Europe, North America and northern Asia. (See pp. 741-4, 1170-3, 1180-1.)

Leaching The action of percolating rainwater on rocks and soils. Rainwater dissolves various substances during its descent through the atmosphere (most important of which is carbon dioxide, CO_2): the resulting solution is usually acidic, and can selectively dissolve various substances as it percolates down through the soil or rock, carrying them down to a lower level. (See p. 1140.) See also WEATHERING.

Leaf An aerial and lateral outgrowth from a stem which makes up the foliage of a plant. Its prime function is the manufacture of food by PHOTOSYNTHESIS. It typically consists of a stalk (*petiole*) and a flattened blade (*lamina*).

Leaflet Each separate LAMINA of a compound leaf.

Leaf-succulent See SUCCULENT.

Lenticel A PORE through the bark which allows gaseous exchange.

Lepidodendroid Resembling *Lepidodendron*, a giant FOSSIL horsetail. (Horsetails, see pp. 180-1.)

Leptophyll (Of leaves), up to 0.04in² (25mm²) in area. (Cf. MACRO-, MEGA-, MESO-, MICRO-, NANO-, NOTHOPHYLL; see p. 725.)

Leptosporangium (adj. leptosporangiate) One of the two main types of SPORANGIA found in ferns. They have little or no stalk and walls that are only one cell thick (cf. EUSPORANGIUM). (Ferns, see pp. 140-1.)

Levee See FLOOD PLAIN.

Liana A woody climbing vine.

Lignified Converted into wood or woody tissue (see also SCLERENCHYMA).

Lignin One of the most important constituents of the cell-wall in secondary tissues.

Lignotuber See XYLOPODIUM.

Ligulate Strap-shaped or tongue-shaped.

Ligule (Of leaves), a scale-like membrane on the surface of a leaf; (of flowers), the strap-shaped COROLLA in some Compositae.

Limb The upper, expanded portion of a CALYX or COROLLA with fused parts (cf. TUBE).

Linear (Of leaves), elongated, and with parallel sides.

Lithophyte A plant which grows on stones and not in the soil.

Lithosere A type of XEROSERE; a SUCCESSION of plant communities that begins on a bare rock surface. (See pp. 823, 825; see also HYDROSERE, PLAGIOSERE, PRISERE, PSAMMOSERE, SUBSERE, XEROSERE.)

Lithosol A young soil developed over solid rock (cf. REGOSOL).

Lithosphere A term used either for the rocks of the Earth—as contrasted with the atmosphere and *hydrosphere* (waters of the Earth)—or for the upper part of the Earth's CRUST.

Littoral The region of the shore covered at the highest spring tide but uncovered at the lowest spring tide. The term is also used adjectivally to describe organisms, deposits, etc., characteristic of this region.

Load Of a stream, the solid material carried along by the water, either in solution or suspension or dragged along the bed. See also TRANSPORTATION.

Lobe (Of leaves or PERIANTHS), a curved or rounded part.

Lobed (Of leaves), with curved or rounded edges.

Locule The chamber or cavity of an OVARY which contains the OVULES, or of an ANTHER which contains the POLLEN.

Loculicidal Splitting open longitudinally along the dorsal suture (midrib) of each segment of the wall.

Lode See VEIN.

Loess Wind-deposited silt found in deposits up to 160ft (50m) thick. Extremely porous, it forms a highly fertile topsoil.

Long profile Of a stream, a plot from source to mouth of the vertical height of the bed.

Macromolecule A molecule containing large numbers of atoms.

Macrophyll (Of leaves), between 28.25 and 254.25in² (18,225 and 164,025mm²) in area. (Cf. LEPTO-, MEGA-, MESO-, MICRO-, NANO-, NOTHOPHYLL; see p. 725.)

Magma Molten material formed in the upper MANTLE or CRUST of the Earth, composed of a mixture of various complex SILICATES in which are dissolved various VOLATILES, including notably water. In suitable circumstances magma CRYSTALLIZES to form IGNEOUS ROCKS, the gaseous materials being lost during the solidifying process. The term magma is also, though rarely, applied to other fluid substances, such as molten salt, in the Earth's crust. (See pp. 1030, 1033, 1057, 1074, 1122, 1124, 1128, 1136.)

Magnitude, Richter A measure of the size of an earthquake event. The Richter scale was originally devised by C. F. Richter (1900-), and runs from 0 to 10, about one quake a year registering 8 or over. The magnitude M is calculated from

$$M = \log_{10}\frac{A}{T} + B;$$

where A and T are respectively the amplitude and period of either the P pulse or the portion of the surface-wave packet with greatest amplitude, and B is a correction factor that takes account of the distance of the recording station from the event. (See p. 1026.)

Malacophyllous With soft leaves.

Male flower A flower containing functional STAMENS but no CARPELS.

Mantle The layer of the Earth between the internal CORE and the external CRUST; its internal radius is about 2200mi (3500km) and its outer radius around 3940mi (6345km), the latter corresponding to a depth of about 22mi (35km) beneath the surface of the Earth. (See pp. 973-4, 996.)

Maquis A term used in some Mediterranean areas (e.g. Corsica) for SCLEROPHYLLOUS scrub. (See pp. 836, 843.)

Marginal placentation A type of PLACENTATION in which the OVULES are borne along the fused margins of a single CARPEL, e.g. pea seeds in a pod.

Materia medica Substances used as remedies in medicine, and their study. (See pp. 226-7.)

Matorral Scrub. (See p. 843.)

Megaphanerophyte Plants with at least some dormant buds borne on twigs up to more than 98ft (30m) above the ground. (Cf. MESO-, MICRO-, and NANOPHANEROPHYTES; see p. 725.)

Megaphyll (Of leaves), over 254.25in² (164,025mm²) in area. (Cf. LEPTO-, MACRO-, MESO-, MICRO-, NANO-, NOTHOPHYLL; see p. 725.)

Megaspore See HETEROSPORY.

Meiosis Two successive nuclear divisions of a diploid cell in the course of which the CHROMOSOME number is reduced from diploid to haploid (see PLOIDY); the haploid cells often subsequently develop into GAMETES (cf. MITOSIS). (See pp. 762-3.)

Membranous Resembling a membrane; thin, dry and semi-transparent.

Mericarp A one-seeded portion of a FRUIT which splits up when the fruit is mature, e.g. the fruits of the Umbelliferae (see pp. 569-71).

Meristem A group of cells capable of dividing indefinitely.

Mesic With adequate or high moisture availability or needs.

Mesocarp The middle layer of the fruit wall (PERICARP). It is usually fleshy, as in a berry.

Mesomorphic (Of plants), with features related to adequate moisture availability.

Mesophanerophyte Plants with at least some dormant buds borne on twigs 26–98ft (8–30m) above the ground (cf. MEGA-, MICRO-, and NANOPHANEROPHYTES; see p. 725).

Mesophyll The internal tissues of a leaf which are concerned with PHOTOSYNTHESIS. Also, a term used to describe leaves of size between 3.14 and 28.25in² (2,025–18,225mm²)—the size range for most leaves from broad-leaved trees of temperate climates. (Cf. LEPTO-, MACRO-, MEGA-, MICRO-, NANO-, NOTHOPHYLL; see p. 725.)

Mesophyte A plant having moderate moisture requirements

Mesotrophic Adapted to living in MESIC (non-extreme) conditions.

Metamorphic rocks Rocks that have undergone change through the agencies of heat, pressure or chemical action, and comprising one of the three main types of the rocks of the Earth. SEDIMENTARY ROCKS undergo *prograde metamorphism*, by which they lose VOLATILES such as water and carbon dioxide, under conditions of heat and pressure beneath the Earth's surface. IGNEOUS ROCKS, and rocks that have already been metamorphosed once, undergo *retrograde metamorphism*, absorbing volatiles, usually from sediments that are being metamorphosed nearby. (See pp. 1136-40.)

Metazoa A subkingdom containing multicellular animals with differentiated tissues. (Origins, see p. 757.)

Meteorite The part of a *meteoroid* that has survived the passage through the atmosphere to reach the Earth's surface. Meteoroids are small particles of interplanetary matter believed to consist of asteroidal and cometary debris. Most burn up due to friction in the Earth's atmosphere, showing a trail of fire, known as a meteor, in the night sky. Parts of the larger meteoroids survive this fiery passage to impact with the surface of the Earth, sometimes producing large craters like that in Arizona. Meteorites are of two types: 'stones', whose composition is not unlike that of the Earth's CRUST; and 'irons', which contain about 80-95% iron, 5-20% nickel and traces of other elements. Intermediate types also exist. (See pp. 986-9.)

Meteoroid See METEORITE.

Mica A shiny mineral composed principally of aluminum silicate (see p. 1094).

Microclimate Local climatic conditions (see pp. 787, 789).

Microhabitat The localized environmental conditions of a population or even an individual.

Micronutrients Inorganic elements required in minute amounts for plant growth, e.g. boron, chlorine, copper, iron, manganese and zinc. (See p. 807.)

Microphanerophyte Plants with at least some dormant buds borne on twigs up to 6.5–26ft (2–8m) above the ground (cf. MEGA-, MESO-, and NANOPHANEROPHYTES; see p. 725).

Microphyll (Of leaves), between 0.35 and 3.14in² (225–2,025mm²) in area. (Cf. LEPTO-, MACRO-, MEGA-, MESO-, NANO-, NOTHOPHYLL; see p. 725.)

Micropyle The opening through the INTEGUMENTS of an OVULE, through which the pollen-tube grows after pollination.

Microspore See HETEROSPORY.

Microtopography The detailed structure of the surface of a body including a very small part of the Earth's surface.

Midrib The central or largest vein of a leaf or CARPEL.

Miogeosyncline (In geology) see GEOSYNCLINE.

Mitochondrion An ORGANELLE, surrounded by a double membrane, found in eukaryotic cells; contains enzymes vital to cellular metabolism. (See also EUKARYOTE.)

Mitosis A form of nuclear division in which the CHROMOSOME complement is duplicated exactly and the daughter nuclei remain haploid, diploid or polyploid (see PLOIDY). The form of division that occurs during normal vegetative growth (cf. MEIOSIS).

Mohorovicic discontinuity or **Moho** A layer of the Earth once regarded as marking the boundary between CRUST and MANTLE, evidenced by a change in the velocity of seismic waves. Its physical significance is uncertain. Perhaps more important are the discontinuities between CORE and mantle (Gutenberg or Oldham Discontinuity), with a radius of about 2200mi (3500km); and that between inner and outer core, with a radius of about 750–1050mi (1200–1650km). (See p. 973.)

Mono- Prefix meaning single, one or once.

Monocarpic Fruiting only once and then dying.

Monochasium A CYMOSE INFLORESCENCE in which there is a single terminal flower with below it a single branch bearing flower(s).

Monoclimax A CLIMAX vegetation in which only one SPECIES dominates.

Monocolpate (Of POLLEN), having a single *colpus* (an oblong-elliptic aperture).

Monocotyledon One of two subclasses of ANGIOSPERMS; a plant whose embryo has one COTYLEDON (cf. DICOTYLEDON). (See pp. 32-5, 619-75.)

Monoculture Cultivation of a single crop. (Cereals, see p. 83.)

Monoecious Having separate male and female flowers on the same plant (cf. DIOECIOUS).

Monogeneric (Of a family), containing only one GENUS.

Monopodial (Of stems or RHIZOMES), with a single main axis from which branches or appendages arise (cf. SYMPODIAL). (See also RACEME.)

Monotypic Having only one member (SPECIES, GENUS etc.).

Montmorillonite A form of clay with a high exchange-capacity, i.e. it ADSORBS calcium more than potassium IONS. (See p. 1094.)

Mor HUMUS formed under acid conditions (cf. MULL). (See pp. 803, 807.)

Morph Form.

Morphology The study of the form and structure of animals and plants.

Motile Able to move.

Mucilage (adj. mucilaginous) A slimy secretion which swells on contact with water.

Mull HUMUS formed under alkaline conditions (cf. MOR). (See p. 803.)

Multiseriate (Of flower parts), borne in many series or WHORLS.

Mutation An inherited change in the structure of a gene from one allelic form to another. (See also ALLELE.)

Mycelium The mass of HYPHAE which constitutes the body of a fungus. (See Fungi, pp. 156-9.)

Mycorrhiza The symbiotic association (see SYMBIOSIS) of the roots of some VASCULAR plants with fungal HYPHAE.

Naked (Of flowers), lacking a PERIANTH.

Nanophanerophyte Plants with at least some dormant buds borne on twigs up to 10in–6.5ft (25cm–2m) above the ground (cf. MEGA-, MESO-, and MICROPHANEROPHYTE; see p. 725).

Nanophyll (Of leaves), with an area not exceeding 0.35in² (225mm²). (Cf. LEPTO-, MACRO-, MEGA-, MESO-, NANO-, NOTHOPHYLL; see p. 725.)

Nectar A sugary liquid secreted by some plants; it forms the principle raw material of honey.

Nectary The gland in which NECTAR is produced.

Neoteny In an organism, the retention of larval characteristics at and beyond sexual maturity, especially in those organisms whose larvae never completely metamorphose into the adult form. It has been suggested that neoteny may be a powerful evolutionary agent, sessile adult forms being gradually excluded from the lifecycle; but evidence is lacking.

Névé Compacted snow.

Node The point on a stem where one or more leaves are borne.

Nothophyll (Of leaves), between 3.14 and 7in² (2,025–4,500mm²) in area. (Cf. LEPTO-, MACRO-, MEGA-, MESO-, MICRO-, NANOPHYLL; see p. 725.)

Nucellus The central nutritive tissue of the OVULE, containing the EMBRYO SAC and surrounded by, in ANGIOSPERMS, two INTEGUMENTS.

Numerous (Of floral parts), usually meaning more than ten (cf. INDEFINITE).

Nunatak Isolated areas of rock projecting through land-ice or snow (see p. 911).

Nut A dry, single-seeded and non-opening (INDEHISCENT) fruit with a woody PERICARP. (See pp. 244-5.)

Obligate PARASITE unable to grow on its own; entirely dependent on a host for nutrition.

Obovate (Of leaves), having the outline of an egg, with the broadest part above the middle and attached at the narrow end.

Obovoid (Of solid objects), inversely egg-shaped, with the widest point above the middle.

Ochrea A cup-shaped structure formed by the joining of STIPULES or leaf bases around a stem.

Old Red Sandstone The continental FACIES of the British Devonian. (See pp. 1162-3, 1165, 1166.)

Oligotrophic (Of lakes, etc.), poor in nutrients (cf. EUTROPHIC).

Oogonium The unicellular female sex organ of certain fungi and algae. (Fungi, see pp. 156-9. Algae, see pp. 18-21.)

Oolite A limestone made up of OOLITHS. (See pp. 1134, 1135.)

Oolith A more or less spherical particle of rock which has developed by the accretion of material about an initial nucleus. The accretion may be concentric (so that in cross-section circular bands of material may be seen) or radial, and combinations are known. Larger ooliths are termed *pisoliths*. Concentration of ooliths can form, for example, oolitic limestones, often called OOLITES. (See pp. 1134, 1135.)

Opposite (Of leaves), occurring in pairs on opposite sides of the stem; (of STAMENS), inserted in front of the PETALS.

Orbicular More or less circular.

Ore An aggregate of minerals and rocks from which it is commercially worth while to extract minerals—usually metals. An ore has three parts: the COUNTRY ROCK in which the deposit is found; the *gangue*, the unwanted rocks and minerals of the deposit; and the desired mineral itself. (See pp. 1071-5.)

Organelle A specialized cellular part analogous to an organ (e.g a MITOCHONDRION).

Orogeny Any process which results in the formation of mountains; i.e. relative changes of level within a landmass. Overall changes in the level of a landmass constitute EPEIROGENY. A period of mountain-building in a particular area may be described as an orogeny. (See p. 1036.)

Orthoclase A form of FELDSPAR in which the CRYSTALS have two lines of CLEAVAGE at right angles. (See p. 1096.)

Orthogenesis Gradual evolution of related groups of organisms in the same direction due to inherited 'tendencies'. (See p. 764.)

Orthotrophous (Of OVULES), borne on a straight stalk (FUNICLE); not bent over.

Ovary The hollow basal region of a CARPEL, containing one or more OVULES and surrounded by the STYLE(S) and STIGMA(S). It is made up of one or more carpels which may fuse together in different ways to form one or more chambers (*locules*). The ovary is generally above the PERIANTH parts (*superior*) or below them (*inferior*).

Ovate (Of leaves), having the outline of an egg with the narrow end above the middle.

Ovoid (Of solid objects), egg-shaped.

Ovule The structure in the chamber (*locule*) of an OVARY containing the egg cell within the EMBRYO SAC which is surrounded by the NUCELLUS. The ovule develops into the SEED after fertilization.

Paleo- A prefix meaning 'ancient'. Thus *paleogeography* is the geography of the Earth in past ages; *paleoclimatology* the study of climates in past ages; *paleontology* the study of FOSSIL life; and *paleobotany* the study of fossil plants. Special cases are: *Paleozoic*, the era of ancient life; and *paleomagnetism*, the study of the information within certain rocks relating to the magnetic field of the Earth in past ages. This latter area of study has been of paramount importance in many of the Earth sciences, not least in validating the theory of PLATE TECTONICS.

Palmate (Of leaves), with more than three segments or leaflets arising from a single point, as in the fingers of a hand (cf. PINNATE).

Palynology A branch of paleontology embracing the study of FOSSIL SPORES, especially of POLLEN. Its importance as an aid to correlation is rapidly increasing. (See p. 734.)

Pampas Argentinian grasslands (prairies). (See pp. 832, 859.)

Pan A hard layer in soil (see p. 805).

Pangaea The primeval supercontinent which split up to give LAURASIA to the north and GONDWANALAND to the south. Pangaea formed in the Permian, gradually disintegrating during the succeeding periods. (See pp. 741, 742-3, 1001, 1174, 1179, 1181.)

Pangenesis A theory of inheritance in which the cells of an organism were thought to contain particles that circulate freely within it and are transmitted from parent to offspring.

Panicle (adj. paniculate) (Of INFLORESCENCES), strictly a branched RACEME, with each branch bearing a further raceme of flowers. More loosely, it applies to any complex, branched inflorescence.

Papilla (adj. papillate) A small blunt hair or projection.

Pappus A ring of fine hairs (often feathery, sometimes scale-like) developed from the CALYX, and crowning fruits of members of the Compositae (see pp. 613-8) and some other flowering-plant families.

Páramo Upland treeless plateau in tropical South America. (See p. 861.)

Parasite A plant that obtains its food from another living plant to which it is attached.

Parenchyma (adj. parenchymatous) A tissue made up of thin-walled, living, photosynthetic or storage cells, which is capable of division even when mature. The commonest type of plant tissue.

Parietal placentation A type of PLACENTATION in which the OVULES are borne on PLACENTAS on the inner surface of the outer wall of the OVARY.

Paripinnate A PINNATE leaf with all leaflets in pairs (cf. IMPARIPINNATE).

Pathogen An agent that causes disease.

Peat An accumulation of plant material incompletely decomposed due to lack of oxygen, usually as a result of waterlogged conditions. (See pp. 810, 875-82.)

Pedate (of leaves) A PALMATELY divided compound leaf, having three main divisions, and having the outer division one or more times. There may be a free central leaflet.

Pedicel The stalk of a single flower.

Peduncle The stalk of an INFLORESCENCE.

Pegmatite A term to describe a coarse-grained IGNEOUS ROCK, usually applied to those having a granitic composition. (See p. 1031.)

Pelagic An adjective applied to marine creatures that are not BENTHONIC; i.e., that are free-swimming or PLANKTONIC.

Peltate (Of leaves), more or less circular and flat with the stalk inserted in the middle.

Pendulous Hanging down.

Perennate To live over from season to season.

Perennial A plant that persists for more than two years and normally flowers annually (cf. ANNUAL, BIENNIAL).

Perfect flower A flower with functional male and female organs.

Perianth The floral envelope whose segments are usually divisible into an outer WHORL (*calyx*) of SEPALS, and an inner whorl (*corolla*) of PETALS. The segments of either or both whorls may fuse to form a tube.

Pericarp The wall of a FRUIT that encloses the SEEDS and which develops from the OVARY wall.

Periglacial Of conditions in areas under the strong influence of, but beyond the margins of, a GLACIER.

Perigynous (Of flowers), having the STAMENS, COROLLA and CALYX inserted around the OVARY, their bases often forming a DISK.

Perisperm The nutritive storage tissue in some seeds, derived from the NUCELLUS.

Peristome The fringe of teeth that occurs at the tip of the CAPSULE of mosses. (Mosses, see pp. 234-5.)

Perithecium A closed, spherical or flask-shaped fruiting body (*ascocarp*) of certain ASCOMYCETE fungi; each has a small PORE at the top to allow release of the ascospores. (See Fungi, pp. 156-9.)

Permafrost Permanently frozen ground, typical of the treeless tundra of Siberia and common throughout polar regions. The permafrost layer may attain depths of up to 2000ft (600m). (See pp. 851, 936-7, 1050-1.)

Permeability A measure of the ease with which water may pass through or into a rock. (See p. 1070.)

Persistent Remaining attached, not falling off.

Petal A non-reproductive (sterile) part of the flower, usually conspicuously colored; one of the units of the COROLLA.

Petaloid Petal-like.

Petiole The stalk of a leaf.

Petrogenesis An envelope term embracing all aspects and features of the formation of rocks.

Petrology The study of rocks in all aspects.

pH A logarithmic measure of hydrogen-ION concentration which gives an indication of the acidity or alkalinity of a solution. (See p. 805; see also ACID, ALKALINE.)

Phanerophyte Plants with dormant buds exposed on twigs high above the ground (cf. MEGA-, MESO-, MICRO-, and NANOPHANEROPHYTES; see p. 725).

Phanerozoic The aeon of visible life, the period of time represented by rock strata in which FOSSILS appear, running from about 600 million years ago through to the present and containing the Paleozoic, Mesozoic and Cenozoic eras. It is contrasted with the AZOIC ('no life') and CRYPTOZOIC ('hidden life').

Phenecotype A population adapted to its local environment by a physiological modification not involving permanent, heritable change.

Phenetic Relating to all the features of an organism.

Phenology The study of periodical phenomena of plants, e.g. the flowering and fruiting times in response to climate.

Phenotype The characteristics of an individual or a population as determined by the GENOTYPE interacting with the environment.

Phloem That part of the tissue of a plant which is concerned with conducting food material. In woody stems it is the innermost layer of the bark (cf. XYLEM).

Photoperiodism A mechanism whereby organisms respond to duration and timing of light and dark periods. (See pp. 794-5.)

Photosynthesis The process by which green plants manufacture sugars from water and carbon dioxide by converting the energy from light into chemical energy with the aid of the green pigment CHLOROPHYLL. (See p. 794.)

Phototropism Movement and orientation of plants in response to light. (See p. 794.)

Phyllode A flattened leaf stalk (PETIOLE), which has assumed the form and function of a leaf blade.

Phyllosphere or **phyllophane** The environment produced for microorganisms on the external surfaces of living leaves. It is the result of an interaction of nutrients and surface structures of the leaf with gases and water, especially dew, from the atmosphere. (See p. 789.)

Phylogeny The study of the evolutionary history of groups of organisms. (See pp. 696-7.)

Phylum (pl. phyla) A major TAXONOMIC subdivision of either the plant or the animal kingdom (for plants, the term *division* is commonly used in its place), e.g. Bryophyta, Pterophyta, Anthophyta (flowering plants).

Physiognomy The overall appearance of a community. (See pp. 717-27.)

Phytochorion A floristic division of the world. (See pp. 894-8.)

Phytochrome A pigment in green plants that is associated with the absorption of light—a photoreceptor. (See p. 794.)

Phytocoenology The description and delimitation of plant communities. (See pp. 727-8.)

Phytocoenon A PHYTOSOCIOLOGICAL unit of vegetation derived by comparing samples of vegetation—an abstract community (cf. PHYTOCOENOSE). (See pp. 709, 727-8.)

Phytocoenose A plant assemblage occupying a particular piece of vegetation—a 'real' community (cf. PHYTOCOENON). (See p. 709.)

Phytogeography The study of the geographical distribution of plants.

Phytosociology The study of plants as gregarious organisms, concerned with the 'sociological' interactions between plants of the same and of different SPECIES, and the way in which they grow together to form plant communities. (See pp. 727-30.)

Phytotoxin A substance poisonous to plants. (See p. 944.)

Phytotron A building in which plants can be grown under a series of carefully controlled environmental conditions. (See p. 691.)

Pinna Each segment of a fern leaf. (Ferns, see pp. 140-1.)

Pinnate (Of leaves), compound, with leaflets in pairs on opposite sides of the midrib (cf. IMPARIPINNATE, PARIPINNATE, PALMATE).

Pinnatifid (Of leaves), pinnately divided at least as far as the midrib.

Pinnatisect (Of leaves), pinnately divided, but not as far as the midrib.

Pinnule Each segment of a pinnate leaf.

Pisolith (In geology) see OOLITH.

Pistil The female reproductive organ (*gynoecium*) consisting of one or more CARPELS, comprising OVARY, STYLE, and STIGMA.

Pistillate A flower that has only female organs.

Pistillode A sterile, often reduced, PISTIL.

Placenta Part of the OVARY wall to which the OVULES are attached.

Placentation The arrangement and distribution of the OVULE-bearing PLACENTAS within the OVARY (cf. AXILE, BASAL, FREE CENTRAL, MARGINAL and PARIETAL PLACENTATION).

Placer An ORE deposit which owes its origin to the action of water. In general the water has both transported the mineral to its present position and removed extraneous matter about it. (See p. 1074.)

Plagiosere A SUCCESSION of plant communities differing from that which would normally occur under completely natural circumstances as a result of human activities such as felling, burning, or animal activities such as grazing. (See p. 823; see also HYDROSERE, LITHOSERE, PRISERE, PSAMMOSERE, SUBSERE, XEROSERE.)

Plankton (adj. planktonic) Organisms that float (usually at the surface) in marine or other waters, generally possessing at best weak locomotive abilities. (See p. 274.)

Planosol Continental soil formed on a flat surface and subject to periodic heavy waterlogging so that a hard PAN forms by compaction of the clay washed down from the upper, A, HORIZON. (See p. 805.)

Plasmodia Naked multinucleate masses of moving PROTOPLASM which feed in amoeboid fashion, as in some stages of the life history of certain slime fungi. (See Fungi, pp. 156-9.)

Plasmolysis Shrinkage and breaking up of the cell contents of plants undergoing water shortage. (See p. 799.) Cf. TURGOR.

Plastid Any of various ORGANELLES found in the CYTOPLASM of photosynthetic plant cells. These may contain chlorophyll (e.g. chloroplasts), other pigments (e.g. CHROMOPLASTS), or they may be unpigmented (e.g. leucoplasts).

Plate tectonics, theory of Fundamental theory of modern geology, arising from studies of continental drift, earthquake and volcano distributions, and sea-floor spreading—which phenomena it largely explains. The Earth's CRUST is viewed as consisting of a number of semi-rigid plates in motion relative to each other. Where plates meet, one edge is subducted beneath the other: in mid-ocean, this results in ocean trenches, deep seismic activity and arcs of volcanic islands; at continental margins, similar subduction of the oceanic plate results also in OROGENIES. Where lighter continental blocks are forced together, neither edge is subducted and more complex orogeny results. Belts of shallow earthquakes define the mid-ocean ridges where new material is emerging. (See pp. 741-5, 1003-8, 1025-6, 1032-3.)

Ploidy Referring to the number of full CHROMOSOME sets in a nucleus, i.e. *haploid* = one set, *diploid* = two sets, *triploid* = three sets, *tetraploid* = four sets, *hexaploid* = six sets, *polyploid* = more than two sets. (See pp. 776-7.)

Plumule The rudimentary shoot in an EMBRYO.

Pluton See PLUTONIC ROCK.

Plutonic rock An IGNEOUS ROCK formed, usually as a large INTRUSION or *pluton*, at depth beneath the surface of the Earth. (See pp. 1122-3.)

Pneumatophores Extensions of the roots of plants of swampy habitats, such as mangroves, which grow up out of the water to ensure adequate AERATION. (See p. 891.)

Podzolization A process of soil formation occurring in wet climates where internal soil drainage is good and levels of calcium carbonate are low. Leaching of minerals takes place in the A HORIZON, and the minerals (chiefly iron and aluminum sesquioxides) accumulate in the B horizon. (See pp. 807, 1140.)

Pollen Collective name for the pollen grains, i.e. the minute SPORES (microspores) produced in the ANTHERS.

Pollen sac The chamber (locule) in an ANTHER where the POLLEN is formed.

Pollination The transfer of POLLEN grains from STAMEN to STIGMA. *Cross-pollination* occurs between flowers of different plants of the same SPECIES; *self-pollination* occurs between flowers of the same plant, or within one flower.

Pollinium A mass of POLLEN grains produced by one ANTHER-lobe, cohering together and transported as a single unit during POLLINATION, as in the orchids.

Polyclimax The occurrence of several apparently stable vegetation types in an area, due to EDAPHIC and other factors apart from climate. (See p. 714.)

Polygamodioecious Having male and bisexual flowers on one individual plant and female and bisexual flowers on another.

Polygamous Having separate male, female and bisexual flowers on the same plant.

Polygene One of a number of genes determining the same character.

Polypetalous With PETALS free from each other.

Polyploid See PLOIDY.

Polytopy Term applied to distributions consisting of several disconnected areas. (See pp. 907-8.)

Pome A fleshy false FRUIT, the main flesh comprising the swollen receptacle and floral parts surrounding the OVARY, as in the apple and other members of the family Rosaceae. (See pp. 491-4.)

Pore A small hole.

Porosity A measure of the amount of empty space within a given volume or rock, and hence of the amount of water that that rock body can absorb. Since certain porous rocks will not permit the transmission of water, porosity cannot be considered a synonym of PERMEABILITY. (See p. 1070.)

Porphyry Adjective describing a rock in which large isolated CRYSTALS are set in a rather fine matrix.

Prisere A SUCCESSION of plant communities developed on an originally bare, non-vegetated surface. (See p. 823; see also HYDROSERE, LITHOSERE, PLAGIOSERE, PSAMMOSERE, SUBSERE, XEROSERE.)

Profile (Of soil) see HORIZON.

Progymnosperm An early or presumed ancestor of the GYMNOSPERMS.

Prokaryote (adj. prokaryotic) Any organism lacking a membrane around its nuclei, PLASTIDS and other cell ORGANELLES, as in bacteria and blue-green algae (cf. EUKARYOTE). (See p. 753. Bacteria and Blue-green Algae, see pp. 50-1.)

Prophase An early stage in nuclear division when the CHROMOSOMES become visible and distinct from each other.

Protandrous (Of flowers), the maturing of STAMENS and the consequent release of their POLLEN before the STIGMAS of the same flower become receptive.

Proteolytic enzyme A substance that aids the breakdown of proteins.

Prothallus The more or less independent sexual phase (*gametophyte*) of certain primitive plants such as ferns and club mosses. (See pp. 94, 140. Ferns, see pp. 140-1; Club Mosses, see pp. 94-5.)

Protogynous (Of flowers), the receptiveness of the STIGMAS before the STAMENS of the same flower mature and release their POLLEN.

Protoplasm Organized COLLOIDAL complex of organic and inorganic substances (e.g. proteins and water) that forms the living nucleus, CYTOPLASM, PLASTIDS, and MITOCHONDRIA of a cell.

Province (faunal or floral) At a particular time, a distinct ecological region. (See p. 898.)

Proximal Near to.

Psammosere A type of XEROSERE; a SUCCESSION of plant communities developed during the colonization of sandy areas. (See p. 825; see

also HYDROSERE, LITHOSERE, PLAGIOSERE, PRISERE, SUBSERE, XEROSERE.)

Pseudobulb (adj. pseudobulbous) A swollen, bulb-like part of the stem of orchids.

Pseudocopulation The attempted copulation by male insect visitors with a part of a flower which resembles the female of the insect SPECIES, as in the orchids. (See pp. *767, 773, 780.*)

Pseudo-whorled (Of leaves), arising close together and so appearing to arise at the same level, although not in fact doing so.

Psilophyte Any member of the phylum Psilophyta; notably the whisk ferns (*Psilotum, Tmesipteris*), which are the only VASCULAR plants to lack roots and true leaves. (See p. 95.)

Psychoactive drug A drug capable of affecting mental activity. (Medicinal and Narcotic Plants, see pp. 226-7.)

Psychotomimetic drug A drug capable of inducing psychotic symptoms (mental disturbances involving distortion of contact with reality). (Medicinal and Narcotic Plants, see pp. 226-7.)

Pteridophyte A unit of classification of plants that encompasses the lower VASCULAR plants, i.e. ferns, club mosses and their allies, and horsetails. (Ferns, see pp. 140-1; Club Mosses, see pp. 94-5; Horsetails, see pp. 180-1.)

Pteridosperm Any member of the 'seed-ferns' (Pteridospermales), gymnospermous seed plants dominant in the Carboniferous period, but now extinct. See also GYMNOSPERM.

Pubescent Covered in soft, short hairs.

Punctate Shallowly pitted or dotted, often with glands.

Purgative An agent that causes evacuation of the bowels. (Medicinal and Narcotic Plants, see pp. 226-7.)

Pycnidium A minute, hollow, GLOBOSE or flask-shaped asexual fruiting body of some fungi containing conidiospores. (See Fungi, pp. 156-9.)

Pyrenoid A starch-rich body found in some algae and liverworts. (Algae, see pp. 18-21. Liverworts, see pp. 234-5)

Pyritic sand A form of sand rich in iron sulfide. (See Pyrite, p. 1096.)

Pyroclastic rock A rock made up of particles thrown into the air by volcanic eruption. (See pp. *1034*, 1122.)

Racemate An optically inactive form of a chemical compound that also exists in optically active forms.

Raceme (adj. racemose) An INFLORESCENCE consisting of a main axis, bearing single flowers alternately or spirally on stalks (*pedicels*) of approximately equal length. The apical growing point continues to be active so there is usually no terminal flower and the youngest branches or flowers are nearest the apex. This mode of growth is known as *monopodial.*

Radiation An increase (through time) in diversity and abundance of a type of organism. (See pp. 773-4.)

Radical (Of leaves), arising from the base of a stem or from a RHIZOME; basal.

Radicle The rudimentary root in an EMBRYO.

Radiometric dating Any technique whereby the age of a rock or artifact may be determined by comparison of the amount of a particular radioactive substance (of known half-life), present there, and the amount of one or more of its decay products. Best known is the carbon-14 technique, though, as C^{14} has a half-life of only about 5730 years, it is of interest primarily to the archeologist rather than to the geologist. (See pp. 735, 1142-3, *1146.*)

Raphe A ridge or tissue visible on the TESTA of seeds developed from OVULES which are bent over through 180° (*anatropous*). It results from the fusion of the stalk (*funicle*) with the rest of the bent-over ovules.

Ray (Of wood), radial strands of living cells concerned with the transport of water and food.

Receptacle Flat, concave or convex part of the stem from which all parts of a flower arise; the floral axis.

Recombination The production of combinations of allelic forms of genes (see ALLELE) in GAMETES different from those in the plant producing them, as a result of the independent segregation of CHROMOSOMES and the exchange of chromosome segments during MEIOSIS.

Recurved Curved or bent backwards.

Red beds An assemblage of SEDIMENTARY ROCKS characterized by a red color resulting from formation in a highly oxidizing environment, the redness being due to the presence of iron in a ferric, rather than ferrous, state. (See p. 1131.)

Reflexed Bent sharply backwards at an angle.

Refugia Habitats that have escaped drastic changes in climate, enabling SPECIES and populations to survive, often in isolation.

Regolith A collective term for the unconsolidated material of the Earth's surface lying upon the bedrock. The most important component of the regolith is soil.

Regosol A young soil developed over unconsolidated material, e.g. rock fragments (see LITHOSOL). (See p. 810.)

Regression A withdrawal of the sea from the land; the converse of TRANSGRESSION.

Regular (Of flowers), radially symmetrical, with more than one plane of symmetry; ACTINOMORPHIC.

Rejuvenation The effect of an uplift of the land or a fall in the sea level on a drainage system: the stream initially reaches the sea by way of frequent waterfalls, which migrate upstream as a result of rapid downcutting.

Replacement In FOSSILS, any process whereby the

original skeletal material of the organism is replaced by another mineral, often such that all the details of the skeleton are preserved.

Restitution nucleus A single nucleus instead of two resulting from a failure in MEIOSIS.

Reticulate Marked with a network pattern, usually of veins.

Retting The breaking down of fibrous material into separate fibers by soaking in water and allowing microbial activity to take place. (See Fibers from Plants, pp. 144-5.)

Rhachis The major axis of an INFLORESCENCE or of a fern-frond. (Ferns, see pp. 140-1.)

Rhipidium (Of INFLORESCENCES), a CYMOSE inflorescence with branches alternating from one side of the vertical axis to the other; normally flattened in one plane and fan-shaped.

Rhizoid Root-like or roothair-like structures found in most lower plants, which help to anchor the plants and absorb water and nutrients. Not true roots.

Rhizome (adj. rhizomatous) A horizontally creeping underground stem which lives over from season to season (*perennates*) and which bears ROOTS and leafy shoots.

Rhizomorph A thick strand of fungal HYPHAE. (See Fungi, pp. 156-9.)

Root The lower, usually underground part of a plant. It anchors the plant in the soil and absorbs water and mineral nutrients by means of the root hairs.

Rosette A group of leaves arising closely together from a short stem, forming a radiating cluster on or near the ground.

Rotate (Of COROLLAS), wheel-shaped; with the PETALS or lobes spreading out from the axis of a flower.

Ruderal (Of plants), occurring on disturbed ground and, particularly, rubbish dumps.

Ruminate (Of ENDOSPERM in seeds), irregularly grooved and ridged; having a 'chewed' appearance.

Saddle vein See VEIN.

Sagittate (Of leaves), shaped like an arrowhead with two backward-directed barbs.

Salverform Trumpet-shaped.

Samara A dry FRUIT that does not split open and has part of the fruit wall extended to form a flattened membrane or wing.

Saponins A toxic soap-like group of compounds which is present in many plants.

Saprophyte A plant that cannot live on its own, but which needs decaying (non-living) organic material as a source of nutrition.

Scale A small, often membranous, reduced leaf frequently found covering buds and BULBS.

Scaled Covered by scale leaves.

Scandent Climbing.

Scape A leafless flower-stalk.

Scapose With a solitary flower on a SCAPE.

Scarious Dry and membranous, with a dried-up appearance.

Schist A METAMORPHIC ROCK in which the tendency to split into layers along perfect CLEAVAGE planes is pronounced. (See pp. 1138-9.)

Schizocarp A FRUIT derived from a simple or compound OVARY in which the LOCULES separate at maturity to form single-seeded units.

Sclerenchyma A tissue composed of cells with thickened cell-walls, often woody (*lignified*), and which give mechanical strength and support.

Sclerophyllous With leathery leaves.

Sclerotium A hardened resting body produced by some fungi as a means of surviving harsh environmental conditions. (See Fungi, pp. 156-9.)

Scorpioid (Of CYMOSE INFLORESCENCES), curved to one side like a scorpion's tail.

Scrambler A plant with a spreading, creeping HABIT usually anchoring by hooks, thorns or tendrils.

Scree Mountain slope covered with loose stones.

Sedimentary rocks Rocks which consist of weathered particles of IGNEOUS, METAMORPHIC or even former sedimentary rock transported, usually by water, and deposited in distinct strata. They may also be of organic origin, as is chalk, or of volcanic origin, as are PYROCLASTIC ROCKS. Sedimentary rocks are important as they contain FOSSILS as well as most of the Earth's mineral resources: the order of their strata is clearly of importance to the stratigrapher. They comprise one of the three main types of rocks of the Earth's CRUST. (See pp. 1129-35.)

Seed A unit of sexual reproduction developed from a fertilized OVULE; an EMBRYO enclosed in the TESTA which is derived from the INTEGUMENT(S). It either lies naked on the ovuliferous-scale as in GYMNOSPERMS (including CONIFERS) or is enclosed in the fruit as in ANGIOSPERMS (flowering plants).

Seedling The young plant that develops from a germinating seed.

Segregation Any process which results in a concentration of a particular mineral (or group of minerals) in a rock of different composition. In IGNEOUS and METAMORPHIC rocks, an example of segregation is DIFFERENTIATION.

Self-fertilization See FERTILIZATION.

Self-incompatible Incapable of SELF-FERTILIZATION, usually because the pollen-tube cannot germinate or grows very slowly.

Self-pollination See POLLINATION.

Semi-parasite A plant which, although able to grow independently, is much more vigorous if it establishes a parasitic relationship on another plant. See also PARASITE.

Sepal A floral leaf or individual segment of the CALYX of a flower; usually green.

Septicidal (Of fruits), splitting open longitudinally through the septa so that the CARPELS are separated.

Septum (adj. septate) A cross-wall dividing cells or compartments; (of OVARIES), the wall between two chambers (*locules*) of an ovary made up of two or more fused CARPELS (*syncarpous ovary*).

Sere A type of plant SUCCESSION. (See p. 823; see also HYDROSERE, LITHOSERE, PLAGIOSERE, PRISERE, PSAMMOSERE, SUBSERE, XEROSERE.)

Seriate Arranged in a row.

Serrate (Of margins), toothed, like a saw.

Serrulate (Of margins), finely toothed, like a saw.

Sessile Without a stalk, e.g. leaves without PETIOLES or a STIGMA without a STYLE.

Seta The stalk of the CAPSULE in mosses and liverworts. (Mosses, see pp. 234-5.)

Sheath (Of leaves), the base of a leaf or leaf-stalk (*petiole*) which encases the stem.

Sheathing (Of leaves), with a sheath that encases the stem.

Shield See KRATON.

Shoot The above-ground portions of a VASCULAR plant, such as the stems and leaves; the part of a plant which develops from the PLUMULE of the EMBRYO.

Shrub A PERENNIAL woody plant with well developed side-branches that appear near the base, so that there is no trunk. They are less than 30ft (10m) high.

Sial (*silica-aluminum*) A collective term for those rocks, lighter and more rigid than those of the SIMA and composed to a great extent of silica and aluminum, that form the upper portion of the Earth's CRUST.

Sierozem Gray soils of arid deserts which have a high calcium content and feebly differentiated HORIZONS. (See p. 808.)

Silicates Minerals containing the silicate SiO_4^{4-} ION and including also silica (SiO_2) itself. The silicates, together with the aluminosilicates, are the most important class of minerals and comprise about 90% of the rocks of the Earth's CRUST. (See also Silicon. p. 1104.)

Silicule or **Silicula** A dry fruit that opens along two lines and has a central PERSISTENT partition, as in the Cruciferae (see p. 469); it is as broad as, or broader than, it is long.

Silique or **Siliqua** A SILICULE-type of fruit that is longer than it is broad.

Sima (*silica-magnesium*) Collective term for those rocks, denser and more plastic than the SIAL and composed to a great extent of silica and magnesium, that form the lower portion of the Earth's CRUST.

Simple (of leaves) Not divided or lobed in any way.

Simple umbel (of INFLORESCENCES) An UMBEL in which the stalks (*pedicels*) arise directly from the top of the main stalk.

Sinuate (Of margins), divided into wide irregular teeth or lobes which are separated by shallow notches.

Soil profile See HORIZON.

Solifluction Movement of wet soil down a slope.

Solitary (Of flowers), occurring singly in each AXIL.

Solum A collective term for the A and B HORIZONS of a soil profile, i.e. those between the litter on the surface and the partly weathered base rock or *substrate* beneath.

Somatic (Of cells) non-reproductive. See also KARYOTYPE.

Sorus A cluster of SPORANGIA, as in ferns. (Ferns, see pp. 140-1.)

sp. Abbreviation for SPECIES (singular).

Spadix A spike of flowers on a swollen fleshy axis.

Spathe (adj. spathaceous) A large BRACT subtending and often ensheathing an INFLORESCENCE. Applied only in the MONOCOTYLEDONS.

Spatulate or **Spathulate** (Of leaves), shaped like a spoon.

Species The basic unit of classification. Species are grouped into *genera* (see GENUS) and variations may be categorized into SUBSPECIES, VARIETY and FORMA (form) in descending order of hierarchy. A species name consists of two units (*binomial*): the genus title and a specific epithet. Both are italicized and only the initial letter of the genus part is capitalized, for example *Betula pendula*. (See pp. 695-6.)

Sperm Male GAMETE.

Spicate Spike-like.

Spike An INFLORESCENCE of simple RACEMOSE type in which the flowers are stalkless.

Spikelet A small SPIKE, as in the grasses.

Spine The hard and sharply-pointed tip of a branch or leaf, usually round in cross-section.

Spinose Spiny.

Sporangium A hollow structure in which SPORES are formed.

Spore Reproductive cell of a plant that is capable of developing into a new individual, either directly or after it has fused with another SPORE.

Sporophyll A fertile leaf or leaf-like organ.

spp. Abbreviation for SPECIES (plural).

Spur A hollow, usually rather conical, projection from the base of a SEPAL, PETAL, or fused COROLLA.

Stamen The male reproductive organ of a

flower. It consists of a usually bilobed ANTHER borne on a stalk (filament).

Staminate Having stamens (male organs) but no carpels (female organs) (cf. PISTILLATE).

Staminode A sterile, often reduced or modified STAMEN.

Stand A uniform group of plants growing in a continuous area.

Stele (In plants) see CASPARIAN BAND.

Stellate Star-shaped.

Stem The main supporting axis of a plant. It bears leaves with buds in their AXILS. Usually aerial, it can however be subterranean.

Stem-succulent See SUCCULENT.

Steppe Strictly, the natural grasslands of Eurasia. (See pp. 859-60.)

Sterigmata See BASIDIUM.

Sterile Not involved in reproduction; not bearing sex organs; unable to reproduce sexually.

Stigma The receptive part of the female reproductive organs of flowering plants on which the POLLEN grains germinate: the APEX of a CARPEL.

Stipe A stalk, as in the stalk of large fungi or the stalk of a fern leaf.

Stipitate Having a stalk or STIPE.

Stipulate Having STIPULES.

Stipule (adj. stipular) A leafy appendage, often paired, and usually at the base of the leaf-stalk.

Stolon A shoot that roots at the tip and produces new plants.

Stomata PORES that occur in large numbers in the EPIDERMIS of plants, particularly leaves, and through which gaseous exchange takes place.

Stooling (Of plants), having several stems arising together at the base.

Strain (In geology) deformation produced by STRESS.

Stratigraphy Concerned with the relative positions and sequence of geological strata.

Stress (In geology) the internal forces within a body resulting from the external forces acting upon it. The four main types of stress are: shearing; bending; tension and compression; and torsion. The deformations resulting from stress are described as *strain*.

Strike See DIP.

Strobilus A cone; a shortened section of a stem bearing modified leaves or scales (appendages) on which SPORANGIA are produced.

Stroma (pl. stromata) A dense mat of HYPHAE from which fungal fruiting bodies are produced. (See Fungi, pp. 156-9.)

Stromatolite Precambrian FOSSILS formed in

dolomite or limestone and interpreted as blue-green algae formed at the advent of life on Earth. (See p. 757. Bacteria and Blue-green Algae, see pp. 50-1.)

Style (adj. stylar) The elongated apical part of a CARPEL or OVARY bearing the STIGMA at its tip.

Sub-Antarctic Strictly, refers to the area between about 50°S and 60°S latitude, but may be extended further northwards in discussions of PHYTOGEOGRAPHICAL affinities.

Subapical Below the APEX.

Subduction The forcing of one plate under another (see PLATE TECTONICS).

Suberin A complex fatty substance that occurs in the walls of certain types of cells, e.g. cork and those in the CASPARIAN BAND, rendering them impervious to water.

Subglobose Almost round or spherical.

Subjacent Literally, 'lying under'. The term is also used in geology to mean 'bottomless': a BATHOLITH can be termed subjacent if its base cannot be detected.

Sublimation See ABLATION.

Sublittoral Growing near the sea but not within the tidal limits (cf. LITTORAL).

Subsere A secondary SUCCESSION of plant communities on land which has been cleared or abandoned by man. (See p. 823; see also HYDROSERE, LITHOSERE, PLAGIOSERE, PRISERE, PSAMMOSERE, XEROSERE.)

Subshrub A SHRUB which has tender new growth that dies back seasonally.

Subspecies A TAXONOMIC division ranking between SPECIES and VARIETY. It is often used to denote a geographical variation of a species. Abbreviation ssp. (See also pp. 695-6.)

Substrate Partly weathered base rock (see also SOLUM).

Succession The sequence of changes in the vegetation of an area from the initial colonization to the development of the CLIMAX communities (see pp. 823-8).

Succulent With fleshy or juicy organs containing reserves of water—hence *stem-succulents, leaf-succulents.*

Sudd Water plants with floating stems from which tall leafy shoots grow.

Suffrutescent (Of herbaceous plants), having a PERSISTENT woody stem base.

Superior (Of OVARIES), occurring above the level at which the SEPALS, PETALS and STAMENS are borne (cf. INFERIOR).

Suture A line of union; the line along which DEHISCENCE often takes place in fruits.

Symbiont An organism that lives in a SYMBIOTIC relationship with another.

Symbiosis (adj. symbiotic) The non-parasitic relationship between living organisms to their mutual benefit.

Symmetry If a plane can be drawn through a CRYSTAL such that the halves of the crystal on either side are exact mirror images of each other, the plane is a plane of symmetry, denoted *m*. If a straight line (axis) can be drawn through the crystal such that, when the crystal is rotated through an angle of 60°, 90°, 120°, 180° or 360° about the axis, it fills exactly the same space as it did originally, then the axis is a (rotation) axis of symmetry, denoted 6, 4, 3, 2 or 1 (called hexad, tetrad, triad, diad or identity axes respectively) depending on how many times the 'symmetry operation' must be performed to bring the crystal back to its original orientation (i.e. a rotation of 360°). All crystals have an infinite number of identity axes.

The crystal may also have an inversion axis of symmetry about which, after inversion, the crystal may be rotated through a certain angle to occupy exactly its original space. Inversion axes are denoted $\bar{6}$, $\bar{4}$, $\bar{3}$ and $\bar{2}$ (a $\bar{2}$ axis is equivalent to a plane of symmetry and so the description is rarely used). A $\bar{1}$ axis implies that the crystal has a center of symmetry, which lies at the center of any line through it joining opposite faces.

Crystals are usually classified according to the symmetry they display. (See pp. 1075-81.)

Sympatric Of populations and SPECIES that occur together in the same area. (See e.g. p. 776.)

Sympetalous With the PETALS united along their margins, at least at the base.

Sympodial (Of stems or RHIZOMES), with the apparent main stem consisting of a series of usually short AXILLARY branches (cf. CYME, MONOPODIAL).

Syncarpous (Of OVARIES), made up of two or more fused CARPELS.

Syncline (In geology) see FOLD.

Syntaxon Any level of the hierarchical classification of vegetation determined by PHYTOSOCIOLOGICAL methods.

Synusia A group of plants occupying a specific habitat within an ECOSYSTEM and having a similar role, though TAXONOMICALLY unrelated. (See p. 729.)

Synzoochory The deliberate carrying of DIASPORES (seeds etc.) in the mouths or on the limbs of animals, e.g. ants and birds. (See p. 816; cf ENDOZOOCHORY, EPIZOOCHORY.)

Taiga Northernmost coniferous forest, with open boggy and rocky areas between (see p. 841).

Taxon (pl. taxa) Any taxonomic group, such as a SPECIES, GENUS, family etc.

Taxonomy (adj. taxonomic) The science of classification of living organisms. (See pp. 694-7.)

Tectonic Adjective pertaining to deformation of the Earth's CRUST and the processes whose effect is such deformation. (See also PLATE TECTONICS, THEORY OF.)

Tendril Part or all of a stem, leaf or PETIOLE modified to form a delicate, thread-like appendage; a climbing organ with the ability to coil around objects.

Tepal A PERIANTH-segment that is not clearly distinguishable as being either a SEPAL or a PETAL.

Teratogen A substance that can cause malformation of the fetus.

Terminal Situated at the tip.

Ternate (Of leaves), compound, divided into three parts more or less equally. Each part may itself be further subdivided.

Terpene A large group of hydrocarbons found in ESSENTIAL OILS. (See p. 136.)

Terra rossa Red, often acid and clay, soils developed over hard Paleozoic limestone in the Mediterranean basin. (See pp. 810, *811*.)

Terrestrial Only living on the land.

Terrigenous An adjective applied to sediments derived from the land, whether mixed in with marine material or deposited on the land.

Tessellated (Of leaves), marked with a fine chequered pattern, like a mosaic.

Testa The outer protective covering of a seed.

Tethys The sea that lay between the supercontinents of LAURASIA and GONDWANALAND. As the continents evolved towards their present form, Tethys was closed off, though the Mediterranean is regarded as a remnant. The sediments of the Tethys GEOSYNCLINE are to be found in folded mountain chains such as the Himalayas. (See pp. 741-2, 745, 1179-81.)

Tetraploid See PLOIDY.

Thallus (adj. thalloid, thallose) A type of plant body not distinctly divided into root, stem and leaves.

Theca One half of an ANTHER containing two POLLEN SACS.

Therophyte An ANNUAL plant (see p. 725).

Throat The site in a CALYX or COROLLA of united parts where the tube and limbs meet.

Thyrse (Of INFLORESCENCES), densely branched, broadest in the middle, and in which the mode of branching is CYMOSE.

Till (In geology) see DRIFT.

Tiller A shoot produced from the base of the original stalk(s).

Timberline The upper limit of tree growth on mountains. (See p. 868.)

Tomentose Densely covered in short hairs.

Topiary The practice or art of trimming trees and shrubs into unusual shapes.

Topocline A gradual change in the characteristics of plant populations in relation to a topographical gradient. (See p. 706.)

Transgression The advance by the sea over the surface of the land, for EUSTATIC or other reasons. Transgression is the converse of REGRESSION.

Transpiration Movement of water vapor out from plant leaves or stems. (See p. 843.)

Transportation The conveyance of eroded or other material from one place to another by one of the following agencies (or a combination thereof): running water, the sea, the wind, GLACIERS or gravity. The end result of transportation is *deposition*, the depositing of the material in a new locale. (See pp. 1010-20.)

Tree A large PERENNIAL plant with a single branched and woody trunk and with few or no branches arising from the base (cf. SHRUB).

Tri- Prefix meaning three.

Trichome A hair-like outgrowth.

Tricolpate (Of POLLEN), having three *colpi* (oblong-elliptic apertures; see COLPATE).

Trifoliolate (Of leaves), having three leaflets.

Trilobites Paleozoic marine arthropods (see p. 1229).

Triploid See PLOIDY.

Trophic Pertaining to nutrition.

Tube The united, usually cylindrical part of the CALYX or COROLLA made up of united parts (cf. LIMB).

Tuber An underground stem or root that lives over from season to season and which is swollen with food reserves (cf. BULB, CORM, RHIZOME).

Tubercle A rounded swelling or protuberance.

Turbidite The sedimentary deposit formed by the action of a turbidity current. Such currents, moving mixtures of fine particles and water, are extremely fluid and so can run for long distances down submarine slopes, spreading sediment over a wide area. (See p. 1016.)

Turgor The rigidity of cells resulting from their uptake of water. (See p. 845, cf. p. 799, plasmolysis.)

Turion A short, scaly branch produced from a RHIZOME.

Ultrabasic rock Usually PLUTONIC though sometimes volcanic IGNEOUS ROCK containing little or no quartz, FELDSPARS or feldspathoids but rich in the SILICATES of iron and magnesium. (See p. 1122.)

Ultraviolet radiation Radiation of wavelengths below 300nm, just beyond the visible spectrum.

Umbel An umbrella-shaped INFLORESCENCE with all the stalks (*pedicels*) arising from the top of the main stem. Umbels are sometimes compound, with all the stalks (*peduncles*) arising from the same point and giving rise to several terminal flower stalks.

Undershrub A PERENNIAL plant with lower woody parts, but herbaceous upper parts that die back seasonally.

Understory Lower layer of ARBORESCENT vegetation in a community, such as SHRUBS in a forest.

Undulate (Of leaves), with wavy margins.

Unifoliate With a single leaflet that has a stalk distinct from the stalk of the whole leaf.

Unilocular (Of OVARIES), containing one chamber (*locule*) in which the OVULES or seeds occur.

Uniseriate Arranged in a single row, series or layer, e.g. PERIANTH-segments.

Unisexual (Of flowers), of one sex.

Utricle A small, bladder-like single-seeded dry fruit.

Vacuole The cavity in the PROTOPLASM of a cell, containing gases or fluid.

Valvate (Of PERIANTH-segments), with the margins adjacent without overlapping (cf. IMBRICATE).

Valve One of the distinct pieces, usually articulated, of which a shell is made up. Many shells have only a single valve, while members of the class Bivalvia and many other creatures have shells with two.

var Abbreviation for VARIETY.

Variety A TAXONOMIC division ranking between SUBSPECIES and FORMA, although in the past often used as the main subdivision of a SPECIES. Such taxa are named by adding the italicized variety name, for example *Pinus ponderosa* var *arizonica*. It was once used to designate variants of horticultural origin or importance, but the rank of CULTIVAR should now be used for this category, although many names of horticultural origin still reflect the historical use of the variety rank. (See p. 697.)

Varve A layer of sediment deposited in the course of a single year, specifically in a lake formed of glacial meltwater. Characteristically, a varve has a silt layer overlying a sand layer. Study of varves is of considerable importance in geological dating. (See p. 735.)

Vascular Possessing vessels; able to conduct water and nutrients.

Vascular bundle A strand of tissue involved in water and food transport.

Vasoactive drug A drug that acts on blood vessels. (Medicinal and Narcotic Plants, see pp. 226-7.)

Vegetative reproduction (or propagation) Production of offspring without sexual reproduction or use of sexual apparatus. (See pp. 777-8.)

Vein (in botany) Any of the visible strands of conducting and strengthening tissues running through a leaf.

Vein (in geology) A mineral formation that is of far greater extent in two dimensions than in the third. Sheetlike *fissure veins* occur where fissures formed in the rock become filled with minerals. *Ladder veins* form in series of fractures in, for example, dikes. *Saddle veins* are lens-shaped, concave below and convex above. Veins containing economically important ORES are termed *lodes*. (See p. 1023.)

Venation The arrangement of the veins of a leaf.

Ventral Term used to describe the front parts of an animal, or those parts generally turned towards the ground. In botany, the ventral side of, say, a leaf is that side turned towards the stem. See also DORSAL.

Vernalization The process of exposing seedlings to low temperatures which is necessary if subsequent flowering and fruiting is to be effective. (See p. *123*.)

Vernation (Of leaves), the manner and pattern of arrangement within the bud.

Verticillaster (Of INFLORESCENCES), with groups of flowers arranged in whorls at the NODES of an elongated stalk.

Verticillate Arranged in WHORLS.

Vessels Tube-like cells arranged end to end in the wood of flowering plants and which form the principal pathway in the transport of water and mineral salts.

Vicariance A term applied to the occupation of discontinuous areas by closely related TAXA.

Viviparous (Of seeds), germinating before becoming detached from the parent.

Volatile Adjective used of substances that readily vaporize.

Volatiles Substances present in the MAGMA that would in normal circumstances be gaseous at the temperature of the magma: they are inhibited from vaporizing both because of the high pressure and because of their tendency to be dissolved in the melt. Most common are carbon dioxide and water.

Volcanic rock An extrusive IGNEOUS ROCK (see EXTRUSION), though the term is sometimes taken to include certain associated intrusive rocks (see INTRUSION). (See pp. 1122-3.)

Water table The uppermost level of GROUNDWATER saturation.

Weathering The breaking down of rocks through contact with the atmosphere (e.g., by wind, by rain). There are two types of weathering: chemical, including processes such as LEACHING; and physical, usually related to temperature changes though other factors may play a part. Unlike EROSION, weathering does not imply TRANSPORTATION. (See pp. 1008-14.)

Weed A plant growing in cultivated ground where it is not wanted.

Whorl The arrangement of organs, such as leaves, PETALS, SEPALS and STAMENS, so that they arise at the same level on the axis in an encircling ring.

Xeromorphic Possessing characteristics such as reduced leaves, succulence (see SUCCULENT), dense hairiness or a thick CUTICLE, which are adaptations to conserve water and so withstand extremely dry conditions. (See e.g. Xerophytes, p. 770.)

Xerophyte A plant which is adapted to withstand extremely dry conditions. (See p. 770.)

Xerosere A SUCCESSION of plant communities that occurs on bare rock surfaces, cliff faces, lava flows, scree, blown sand etc. (See pp. 824-5; see also HYDROSERE, LITHOSERE, PLAGIOSERE, PRISERE, PSAMMOSERE, SUBSERE.)

Xylem The woody fluid-conveying (VASCULAR) tissue concerned with the transport of water about a plant (cf. PHLOEM).

Xylopod(ium) A distended woody stem-base or rootstock used for water storage in some TREES and SHRUBS of arid regions—also known as a *lignotuber*.

Zygomorphic (Of flowers), having bilateral symmetry. There is only one longitudinal plane passing through the axis that will divide the flower into essentially symmetrical halves (cf. ACTINOMORPHIC).

Zygote A fertilized GAMETE; a DIPLOID cell formed when two HAPLOID gametes fuse.

Bibliography

The following is a guide to the other authoritative works that you can consult for more detailed information on specific topics. For convenience, it has been divided into a number of helpful categories:

Cultivated and Useful Plants
Ecology and Biogeography
Flora and General Botanical Works
Flowering Plants
Trees and Shrubs
The Solar System
Earth Sciences

Cultivated and Useful Plants

Bailey, L. H. (1949). *Manual of Cultivated Plants* (revised edition). The Macmillan Company, New York.

Bailey, L. H. & Bailey, E. Z. et al. (1977). *Hortus Third*. Macmillan Publishing Co. Inc., New York; Collier Macmillan, London.

Baker, H. G. (1970). *Plants and Civilization* (2nd edn). Wadsworth Publishing Company Inc., Belmont.

Brooklyn Botanic Garden (1964). *Dye Plants and Dyeing—a Handbook. Plants and Gardens* (vol. 2, no. 3), Brooklyn Botanic Garden, New York.

Brouk, B. (1975). *Plants Consumed by Man*. Academic Press, London, New York, San Francisco.

Calabrese, F. (1978), *Frutticoltura Tropicale e Subtropicale*. Cooperativa Libraria Universitaria Editrice, Bologna.

Chittenden, F. J. (ed.) (1956-69). *Dictionary of Gardening* (2nd edn). Clarendon Press, Oxford.

Cobley, L. S. & Steele, W. M. (1976). *An Introduction to the Botany of Tropical Crops*. Longman, London, New York.

Emboden, W. A. (1972). *Narcotic Plants*. Macmillan, New York.

Harrison, S. G., Masefield, G. B. & Wallis, M. (1969). *The Oxford Book of Food Plants*. Oxford University Press, Oxford.

Hay, R. & Synge, P. M. (1969). *The Dictionary of Garden Plants in Colour in the House and Greenhouse Plants*. Ebury Press and Michael Joseph, London.

Hill, A. F. (1952). *Economic Botany* (2nd edn). New York, Toronto & London.

Howes, F. N. (1974). *A Dictionary of Useful and Everyday Plants and their Common Names*. Cambridge University Press, London, New York.

Irvine, F. R. (1969). *West African Crops*. Oxford University Press, Oxford.

Lewis, W. & Elvin-Lewis, P. F. (1977). *Medical Botany*. John Wiley, London, Sydney, Toronto.

National Research Council (1979). *Tropical Legumes: Resources for the Future*. National Academy of Sciences, Washington, D.C.

Nicholson, B. E., Wallis, M., Anderson, E., Balfour, A. P., Fish, M. & Finnis, V. (1963). *The Oxford Book of Garden Flowers*. Oxford University Press, Oxford.

Purseglove, J. W. (1968). *Tropical Crops. Dicotyledons*. Longman, London.

Purseglove, J. W. (1972). *Tropical Crops. Monocotyledons*. Longman, London.

Rizzini, C. T. (1971). *Arvores e Madeirias Uteis do Brasil. Manual de Dendrologia Brasileira*. Editora Edgard Blücher Ltda, São Paulo.

Rizzini, C. T. & Mors, W. B. (1976). *Botânica*

Econômica Brasileira. EPU, Editora da Universidade de São Paulo, São Paulo.

Schery, R. W. (1972). *Plants for Man* (2nd edn). Prentice-Hall, Englewood Cliffs, N.J.

Schultes, R. F. & Hofmann, A. (1980). *Plants of the Gods*. Hutchinson, London, Melbourne, Sydney, Auckland, Johannesburg.

Simmonds, N. W. (ed.) (1976). *Evolution of Crop Plants*. Longman, London, New York.

Stobart, T. (1970). *Herbs, Spices and Flavourings*. The International Wine and Food Publishing Company, London.

Synge, P. M. (ed.) (1956). *Supplement to the Dictionary of Gardening*. Clarendon Press, Oxford.

Synge, P. M. (ed.) (1969). *Supplement to the Dictionary of Gardening* (2nd edn). Clarendon Press, Oxford.

Tanaka, T. (1976). *Tanaka's Cyclopedia of Edible Plants of the World* (5th edn, Nakao). Keigaku Publishing Co., Tokyo.

Uphof, J. S. (1968). *Dictionary of Economic Plants* (2nd edn). Steckert-Hafner, New York.

Vickery, M. L. & B. (1979). *Plant Products of Tropical Africa*. Macmillan, London, Basingstoke.

Ecology and Biogeography

Anderson, J. B. (1981). *Ecology for Environmental Sciences*. Arnold, London.

Bannister, P. (1976). *Introduction to Physiological Plant Ecology*. Blackwell, Oxford.

Barbour, M. G., Birk, J. H. & Pitts, W. D. (1980). *Terrestrial Plant Ecology*. Addison-Wesley, London.

Birks, H. J. B. & Birks, H. H. (1980). *Quaternary Palaeoecology*. Arnold, London

Cain, S. A. (1944). *Foundations of Plant Geography*. Harper and Row, New York.

Cox, C. B., Healey, I. N. & Moore, P. D. (1973). *Biogeography, an ecological and evolutionary approach*. Blackwell, London.

Dajoz, R. (1977). *Introduction to Ecology*. Hodder and Stoughton, London.

Daubenmire, R. (1968). *Plant Communities. A textbook of plant synecology*. Harper and Row, New York.

Daubenmire, R. (1978). *Plant Geography, with special reference to North America*. Academic Press, London.

Etherington, J. R. (1975). *Environment and Plant Ecology*. Wiley, New York.

Greig-Smith, P. (1982). *Quantitative Plant Ecology* (3rd edn). Blackwell, London.

Jones, G. (1979). *Vegetation Productivity*. Longman, London

Kellman, M. C. (1975). *Plant Geography*. Methuen, London.

May, R.M. (1976). *Theoretical Ecology. Principles and Applications*. Blackwell, London.

Miles, J. (1979). *Vegetation Dynamics*. Wiley, New York.

Mueller-Dombois, D. & Ellenberg, H. (1974). *Aims and Methods of Vegetation Ecology*. Wiley, New York.

Odum, E. P. (1971). *Fundamental Ecology* (3rd edn). Saunders, Philadelphia.

Pielou, E. C. (1979). *Biogeography*. Wiley, New York.

Poole, R. W. (1974). *An Introduction to Quantitative Ecology*. McGraw-Hill, New York.

Ricklefs, R. E. (1976). *The Economy of Nature*. Chiron, Portland.

Seddon, B. (1971). *Introduction to Biogeography*. Duckworth, London.

Stott, P. (1981). *Historical Plant Geography*. Allen and Unwin, London.

Walter, H. (1973). *Vegetation of the Earth, in relation to climate and the eco-physiological conditions*. Springer-Verlag, New York.

Watts, D. (1971). *Principles of Biogeography. An Introduction to the functional mechanisms of ecosystems*. McGraw-Hill, London.

Wettstein, R. (1933-35). *Handbuch der Systematischen Botanik* (4th edn). Leipzig-Wien.

Whittaker, R. H. (1975). *Communities and Ecosystems* (2nd edn). MacMillan, New York.

Flora and General Botanical Works

Annals of the Royal Botanic Garden, Calcutta (1887-). Calcutta.

Baillon, H. E. (1886-95). *Histoire de Plantes*. Paris.

Bentham, G. & Hooker, J. D. (1862-83). *Genera Plantarum* (vols 1-3). London.

Botanical Magazine, The (1793-). London.

Botanical Register (1863-1942). London.

Collinson, A. S. (1977). *Introduction to World Vegetation*. Allen and Unwin, London.

Dalla Torre, C. G. de & Harms, H. (1900-07). *Genera Siphonogamarum*. Leipzig.

Dyer, R. A. (1975). *The Genera of South African Plants*. Praetoria. (A new edn of E. P. Phillips' work of the same title.)

Engler, H. G. A. (ed.) (1900-53). *Das Pflanzenreich. Regni vegetabilis Conspectus*, nos 1-107. Berlin.

Engler, H. G. A. (1964). *Syllabus der Pflanzenfamilien* (12th edn, by H. Melchior *et al*). Bros Borntraeger, Berlin.

Engler, H. G. A. & Prantl, K. A. E. (1887-1915). *Die natürlichen Pflanzenfamilien* (1st edn). Leipzig.

Engler, H. G. A. & Prantl, K. A. E. (eds). *Die natürlichen Pflanzenfamilien* (2nd edn 1926). Wilhelm Engelmann, Leipzig.

Exell, A. W. et al. (1960-78) *Flora Zambesiaca.* Crown Agents for Overseas Governments & Administration, London.

Eyre, S. R. (1968). *Vegetation and Soils, a world picture* (2nd edn). Arnold, London.

Graf, A. B. (1963). *Exotica 3.* Roehrs Company, Rutherford, N.J.

Hegi, G. (1906-31). *Illustrierte Flora von Mittel-Europa* (1st edn, vols 1-7). München.

Hegi, G. (1936-). *Illustrierte Flora von Mittel-Europa* (2nd edn, vols 1-). München.

Hegi, G. (1966-). *Illustrierte Flora von Mittel-Europa* (3rd edn, vols 1-). München.

Hooker, W. J. (1836-54). *Icones Plantarum.* London.

Janick, J. et al. (1974). *Plant Science* (2nd edn). San Francisco.

Journal of Botany, British and Foreign (1863-1942). London.

Komarov, V. L. (ed) *Flora of the USSR* (vol. 9, 1939, vol. 10, 1941). Moskva-Leningrad. English translation by Israel Program for Scientific Translation.

Lawrence, G. H. M. (1951). *Taxonomy of Vascular Plants.* New York.

Marloth, R. (1913-32). *The Flora of South Africa.* Cape Town.

Martius, C. F. P. von (1840-1906). *Flora Brasiliensis.* München, Wien, Leipzig.

Mathew, B. (1973). *Dwarf Bulbs.* B. T. Batsford, London.

Mathew, B. (1978). *The Larger Bulbs.* B. T. Batsford, London.

McClean, R. C. & Ivimey-Cook, W. R. (1973). *Textbook of Theoretical Botany* (vol. 4). Longman, London.

Ohuri, J. (1965). *Flora of Japan.* Smithsonian Institute, Washington, D.C.

Radford, A. E., Dickison, W. C., Massey, J. R. & Bell, C. R. (1974). *Vascular Plant Systematics.* New York.

Swift, L. H. (1974). *Botanical Classifications.* Connecticut.

Transactions of the Linnean Society of London (1791-1875). London.

Transactions of the Linnean Society of London (Botany) (1875-). London.

Tutin, T. G., et al. (eds) (1964-80). *Flora Europaea* (vols 1-5). Cambridge University Press, Cambridge, London, New York, New Rochelle, Melbourne, Sydney.

Urania Pflanzenreich. Höhere Pflanzen. (Vol. 1 (1971), vol. 2 (1973)). Leipzig, Jena and Berlin.

Flowering Plants

Albertson, Alice O. (1973). *Nantucket Wild Flowers.* Theophrastus, Little Compton, Rhode Island.

Amberger, Leslie P. (1974). *Flowers of the Southwest Mountains* (6th edn). S.W. Parks and Monuments Association, Globe, Arizona.

Audubon Society (1979). *The Audubon Society Field Guide to North American Wildflowers a) Eastern Region* (by William A. Nuring and Nancy Olmstead) *b) Western Region* (by Richard Spellenberg). Alfred A. Knopf, Inc., New York.

Bare, Janet E. (1979). *Wildflowers and Weeds of Kansas.* University press of Kansas, Lawrence, Kansas.

Batson, Wade T. (1980). *Wild Flowers in South Carolina.* University of South Carolina Press, Columbia, South Carolina.

Bell, C. Ritchie & Taylor, Bryan J. (1982). *Florida Wild Flowers and Roadside Plants.* Laurel Hill Press, Chapel Hill, North Carolina.

Blackall, W. E. (revised and edited R. J. Grieve, 1954, 1956). *How to know Western Australian Wild Flowers.* The University of Western Australia Press, Nedlands, Western Australia.

Broughton, Jacqueline (1976). *A Sketchbook of Santa Barbara's Native Wildflowers.* Santa Barbara Botanic Garden, Santa Barbara, California.

Brown, Clair A. (1972). *Wildflowers of Louisiana and Adjoining States.* Louisiana State University Press, Baton Rouge, Louisiana.

Brown, Vinson & Yocum, Chas. (1971). *Wildlife and Plants of the Cascades.* Naturegraph Publishing Inc., Happy Camp, California.

Cabat, Erni & Engard, Rodney G. (1985). *Arizona Wildflowers and the Southwest.* Cabat Studio Publications, Tucson, Arizona.

Campbell, Carlos C. et al. (1977). *Great Smoky Mountains Wildflowers* (4th edn). University of Tennessee Press, Knoxville, Tennessee.

Clark, Lewis J. (1974). *Wild Flowers of Marsh and Waterway.* Superior Publications, Superior, Wisconsin.

Clark, Lewis J. (1975). *Wild Flowers of the Arid Flatlands.* Superior Publications, Superior, Wisconsin.

Clark, Lewis J. (1976). *Wild Flowers of the Pacific Northwest.* Superior Publications, Superior, Wisconsin.

Clements, F. E. & Clements, E. S. (1963). *Rocky Mountain Flowers (An Illustrated Guide for Plant-Lovers & Plant Users).* Hafner imprint of Macmillan Publishing Co., New York.

Common Wildflowers of the Grand Canyon. (n.d.). Nature & Scenic Books, Wheelwright Press Ltd., Salt Lake City, Utah.

Craighead, John J. et al. (1974). *A Field Guide to Rocky Mountain Wildflowers.* Houghton Mifflin Co., Boston, Massachusetts.

Cronquist, A. (1968). *The Evolution and Classification of Flowering Plants.* London.

Dannen, Kent & Dannen, Donna (1981). *Rocky Mountain Wildflowers.* Tundra Books, New York.

Davis, P. H. & Cullen, J. C. (1979) *The Identification of Flowering Plant Families* (2nd edn). Cambridge University Press, London, New York, Melbourne.

De Bray, Lys (1978). *The Wild Garden.* W. H. Smith Publishers Inc., New York.

Dodge, Natt N. & Janish, Jeanne R. (1976). *Flowers of the Southwest Deserts* (revised Priets, T.J. and Dodson, Carolyn (eds)). S. W. Parks and Monuments Association, Globe, Arizona.

Dormon, Caroline (1958). *Flowers Native to the Deep South.* Claitors Publishing Division, Baton Rouge, Louisiana.

Duncan, Wilbur H. & Foote, Leonard E. (1975). *Wildflowers of the Southeastern United States.* University of Georgia Press, Athens, Georgia.

Dunes of Dare Garden Club (1980). *Wildflowers of the Outer Banks: Kitty Hawk to Hatteras.* University of North Carolina Press, Chapel Hill, North Carolina.

Ferris, Roxana S. (1970). *Flowers of the Point Reyes National Seashore.* University of California Press, Berkeley, California.

Fichter, George S. (1982). *Wildflowers of North America.* Random House Inc., New York.

Fielder, John (1985). *Colorado Wildflowers.* Littlebooks, Westcliffe Publications Inc., Englewood, Colorado.

Fleming, Glenn et al. (1976). *Wildflowers of Florida.* Banyan Books Inc., Miami, Florida.

Good, R. (1974). *The Geography of the Flowering Plants* (4th edn). Longman, London

Greene, Wilhelmina F. & Blomquist, Hugo L. (1953). *Flowers of the South: Native and Exotic.* University of North Carolina Press, Chapel Hill, North Carolina.

Gupton, Oscar V. & Swope, Fred C. (1979). *Wildflowers of the Shenandoah Valley and Blue Ridge Mountains.* University Press of Virginia, Charlottesville, Virginia.

Harris, Stuart K. et al. (1979). *AMC Field Guide to Mountain Flowers of New England.* Appalachian Mountain Club Books, Boston, Massachusetts.

Haskins, Leslie L. (1979). *Wild Flowers of the Pacific Coast.* Dover Publications Inc., Mineda, New York.

Headstrom, Richard (1984). *Suburban Wildlfowers: An Introduction to the Common Wildflowers of your Backyard and Local Park.* Prentice-Hall, Englewood Cliffs, New Jersey.

Heiser, C. B. (1969). *Nightshades—the Paradoxical Plants.* W. H. Freeman, San Francisco.

Heywood, V. H. (ed.) (1978). *Flowering Plants of the World.* Oxford University Press, Oxford, London, Melbourne.

Heywood, V. H., Harborne J. B. & Turner B. L. (1977). *The Biology and Chemistry of the Compositae* (2 vols). Academic Press, London, New York, San Francisco.

Horn, Elizabeth L. (1976). *Wildflowers Three, the Sierra Nevada.* Touchstone Press, Oregon.

House, Millie B. (1986). *The Joy of Wildflowers: A Fieldbook of Familiar Flowers of Rural and Urban Habitats in the Eastern United States.* Prentice-Hall, Englewood Cliffs, New Jersey.

Hunter, Carl G. (1984). *Wildflowers of Arkansas.* Ozark Society, Hot Springs, Arizona.

Hutchinson, J. (1926, 1934). *The Families of Flowering Plants* (vols 1-2). Oxford University Press, Oxford.

Hutchinson, J. (1959). *The Families of Flowering Plants* (2nd edn, vols 1-2). Oxford University Press, Oxford.

Hutchinson, J. (1964, 1967). *The Genera of Flowering Plants (Angiospermae),* (vol. 1 (1964), vol. 2 (1967)). London.

Jaeger, Edmund C. (1941). *Desert Wild Flowers.* Stanford University Press, Stanford, California.

Justice, William S. and Bell, C. Ritchie (1968). *Wild Flowers of North Carolina.* University of North Carolina Press, Chapel Hill, North Carolina.

Keaster, Glenn (1980). *Sierra Flower Finder: A Guide to Sierra Nevada Wildflowers.* Nature Study Guild. (Distributed by Wilderness Press, Berkeley, California.)

Klimas, John E. Jr (1984). *A Pocket Guide to the Common Wildflowers of Connecticut.* Walker & Co., New York.

Larrison, Earl J. et al. (1977). *Washington Wildflowers.* Seattle Audubon Society. (Distributed by Pacific Search Press, Seattle, Washington.)

Laurence, Jeanne (1974). *An Album of Alaskan Wildflowers.* Superior Publications.

Lommasson, Robert C. (1973). *Nebraska Wild Flowers.* University of Nebraska Press, Lincoln, Nebraska.

Loughmiller, Campbell & Loughmiller, Lynn (1984). *Texas Wildflowers.* University of Texas Press, Austin, Texas.

McGrath, Anne (1981). *Wildflowers of the Adirondacks.* North Country Books Inc., Sylvan Beach, New York.

McHoul, Lilian (1979). *Wildflowers of Marin: A Layman's Handbook.* Tamal Land Press, Fairfax, California.

McKenzie, Katherine (1976). *Wildflowers of the Midwest.* Tundra Books of Northern New York, Plattsburgh, New York.

McKenzie, Katherine (1976). *Wildflowers of the Northeast.* Tundra Books of Northern New York, Plattsburgh, New York.

McKenzie, Katherine (1977). *Wildflowers of the South.* Tundra Books of Northern New York, Plattsburgh, New York.

Martin, William C. & Hutchins, Charles R. (1984). *Spring Wildflowers of New Mexico.* University of New Mexico Press, Albuquerque, New Mexico.

Martin, William C. & Hutchins, Charles R. (1986). *Summer Wildflowers of New Mexico.* University of New Mexico Press, Albuquerque, New Mexico.

Monserud, Wilma & Ownbey, Gerald B. (1971). *Common Wild Flowers of Minnesota.* University of Minnesota Press, Minneapolis, Minnesota.

Morganson, Dana (1975). *Yosemite Wildflower Trails.* Yosemite Natural History Association, Yosemite National Park, California.

Moyle, John B. & Moyle, Evelyn W. (1977). *Northland Wildflowers.* University of Minnesota Press, Minneapolis, Minnesota.

Munz, Philip A. (1962). *California Desert Wildflowers.* University of California Press, Berkeley, California.

Munz, Philip A. (1962). *California Mountain Wildflowers.* University of California Press, Berkeley, California.

Munz, Philip A. (1962). *California Spring Wildflowers: from the base of the Sierra Nevada & Southern Mountains to the Sea.* University of California Press, Berkeley, California.

Munz, Philip A. (1962). *Shore Wildflowers of California, Oregon & Washington.* University of California Press, Berkeley, California.

Newcomb, Lawrence (1979). *Newcomb's Wildflower Guide: An Ingenious New Key System for Quick Positive Field Identification of the Wildflowers, Flowering Shrubs and Vines of Northeastern and North-Central North America.* The Little House Press Inc., Chicago, Illinois.

Nichaus, Theodore F. (1974). *Sierra Wildflowers: Mt Lassen to Kern Canyon.* University of California Press, Berkeley, California.

Owenby, Clinton B. (1980). *Kansas Prairie Wildflowers.* University of Iowa Press, Iowa City, Iowa.

Parker, Lucile (1981). *Mississippi Wildflowers.* Pelican, Gretna, Los Angeles.

Perry, Frances & Hay, Roy (1982). *A Field Guide to Tropical and Sub-Tropical Plants.* Van Nostrand Reinhold Co. Inc., New York.

Peterson, Roger T. & McKenny, Margaret (1974). *A Field Guide to Wildflowers of Northeastern and North Central North America.* Houghton Mifflin Co., Boston, Massachusetts.

Petrides, George A. (1973). *A Field Guide to Trees and Shrubs.* Houghton Mifflin Co., Boston, Massachusetts.

Porsild, A. E. (1974). *Rocky Mountain Wild Flowers.* University of Chicago Press, Chicago, Illinois.

Porter, C. L. (1967). *Taxonomy of Flowering Plants.* San Francisco and London.

Prentice, T. Merrill & Sargent, Elizabeth O. (1973). *Weeds and Wildflowers of Eastern North America.* Peabody Museum Publications, Cambridge, Massachusetts.

Rendle, A. B. (1904, 1938). *The Classification of Flowering Plants* (1st edn, vols 1-2). Cambridge University Press, Cambridge.

Rendle, A. B. (1930). *The Classification of Flowering Plants* (2nd edn, vol. 1). Cambridge University Press, Cambridge.

Rickett, Harold (1966). *Wildflowers of the United States* (6 vols). New York Botanical Garden, New York.

Ross-Craig, S. (1948-73). *Drawings of British Plants.* London.

Rowley, G. D. (1978). *The Illustrated Encyclopaedia of Succulents and Cacti.* Salamander Books, London.

Sharples, Ada W. (1983). *Alaska Wild Flowers.* Stanford University Press, Stanford, California.

Sharsmith, Helen K. (1965). *Spring Wildflowers of the San Francisco Bay Region.* University of California Press, Berkeley, California.

Simonds, Roberta L. & Tweedie, Henrietta (1984). *Wild Flowers of the Great Lakes Region.* Chicago Review Press Inc., Chicago, Illinois.

Smith, Arlo I. (1980). *A Guide to the Wildflowers of the Mid-South.* Memphis State University Press, Memphis, Tennessee.

Smith, Helen V. (1966). *Michigan Wildflowers.* Cranbrook Publishing, Ann Arbor, Michigan.

Soó, R. von (1963). *Fejlödéstörténeti Növényrendszertan.* Budapest.

Stebbins, G. L. (1974). *Flowering Plants. Evolution above the Species Level.* London.

Stokes, Donald & Lillian (n.d.). *A Guide to Enjoying Wildflowers.* Little, Brown & Co. Inc., Boston, Massachusetts.

Takhtajan, A. (1959). *Die Evolution der Angiospermen.* Jena.

Takhtajan, A. (1969). *Flowering Plants. Origin and Dispersal.* Translated by C. Jeffrey. Edinburgh.

Taylor, Ronald & Valum, Rolf (n.d.). *Wildflowers Two: Sagebrush Country.* Toucheston Press, Oregon. (Distributed by Gem Guides Book Co., Pico Rivera, California.)

Taylor, Ronald J. (1983). *Rocky Mountain Wildflowers.* Peter Smith Publisher Inc., Magnolia, Massachusetts.

Thorne, R. F. (1974). The 'Amentiferae' or Hamamelidae as an artificial group: a summary statement. *Brittonia,* 25: 395-405.

Thorne, R. F. (1974). A Phylogenetic Classification of the Annoniflorae. *Aliso,* 8: 147-209.

Thorne, R. F. (1976). A Phylogenetic Classification of the Angiospermae. *Evolutionary Biology,* 9: 35-106.

Venning, Frank D. (1984). *Wildflowers of North America.* Western Publishing Co. Inc., Racine, Wisconsin.

Watts, May T. (1985). *Flower Finder: A Manual for Identifying Spring Wildflowers and Flower Families East of the Rockies.* Nature Study Guild. (Distributed by Wilderness Press, Berkeley, California.)

Welsh, Stanley L. (1986). *Flowers of the Canyon Country.* Canyon Publishing Co., Conoga Park, California.

Wharton, Mary E. & Barbour, Roger W. (1971). *A Guide to the Wildflowers and Ferns of Kentucky.* University Press of Kentucky, Lexington, Kentucky.

Wiley, Leonard (1966). *Rare Wild Flowers of North America.* Wiley, New York.

Willis, J. C. (8th edn by H. K. Airy Shaw 1973). *A Dictionary of Flowering Plants and Ferns.* Cambridge University Press, Cambridge, New York, Melbourne.

Young, Dorothy K. (1976). *Wildflowers of the Redwood Empire.* Naturegraph Publishers Inc., Happy Camp, California.

Trees and Shrubs

Bean, W. J. (1970-76). *Trees and Shrubs Hardy in the British Isles* (8th edn, ed. G. Taylor and D. L. Clarke) (vols 1-3). John Murray, London.

Brockman, C. (1968). *Trees of North America.* Western Publishing Co. Inc., Racine, Wisconsin.

Carr, J. D. (1976). *The South African Acacias.* Conservation Press (Pty) Ltd., Johannesburg, London, Manzini.

Dallimore, W. & Jackson, A. B. (1966). *A Handbook of Coniferae & Ginkgoaceae* (4th edn revised R. G. Harrison). Edward Arnold, London.

Elias, T. S. (1980). *The Complete Trees of North America: Field Guide and Natural History.* Van Nostrand Reinhold Co. Inc., New York.

Gaussen, H. (1943-68). *Les Gymnosperms, Actuelles et Fossiles.* Toulouse.

Hillier's Manual of Trees & Shrubs (1977) (4th edn). David & Charles, Newton Abbot.

Krüssman, G. (1960). *Die Nadelgehölze* (2nd edn). Paul Parey, Berlin & Hamburg.

Menninger, E. A. (1962). *Flowering Trees of the World for Tropics and Warm Climates.* Hearthside Press Inc., New York.

Mitchell, A. F. (1972). *Conifers in the British Isles.* HMSO, London.

Mitchell, A. F. (1974). *A Field Guide to the Trees of Britain & Northern Europe.* Collins, London.

Palmer, E. (1977). *A Field Guide to the Trees of Southern Africa.* Collins, London, Johannesburg.

Petrides, George A. (1973). *A Field Guide to Trees and Shrubs.* Houghton & Mifflin Co., Boston, Massachusetts.

Polunin, O. & Everard, B. (1976). *Trees & Bushes of Europe.* Oxford University Press, London, New York, Toronto.

Rehder, A. (1940). *Manual of Cultivated Trees and Shrubs Hardy in North America* (2nd edn—reprint 1956). Macmillan Publishing Company Inc, New York.

Santapau, H. (1966). *Common Trees.* National Book Trust, India, New Delhi.

Schneider, C. K. (1904-12). *Illustriertes Handbuch der Laubholzkunde.* Gustav Fischer, Jena.

The Solar System

Baker, V. R. (1982). *The Channels of Mars.* Adam Hilger.

Beatty, J. K., O'Leary, B. & Chaikin, A. (1981). *The New Solar System.* Cambridge University Press.

Brandt, J. C. & Chapman, R. D. (1983). *Introduction to Comets.* Cambridge University Press.

Carr, M. H. (1984). *The Surface of Mars.* Yale University Press.

Gehrels, T. (1982). *Jupiter.* University of Arizona Press.

Gehrels, T. & Matthews, M. (1984). *Saturn.* University of Arizona Press.

Hunten, D. (Editor) (1983). *Venus.* University of Arizona Press.

Moore, P. (1977). *Guide to the Planets.* Lutterworth Press.

Moore, P. & Hunt, G. (1983). *The Atlas of the Solar System.* Mitchell Beazley.

Moore, P. & Mason, J. (1985). *The Return of Halley's Comet.* Patrick Stephens, London; W. W. Norton, New York.

Noyes, R. W. (1982). *The Sun Our Star.* Harvard.

Tombaugh, C. (1980). *Out of the Darkness; the Planet Pluto.* Stackpole Books.

Earth Sciences

Ager, D. V. (1973). *The Nature of the Stratigraphical Record* (2nd edn). Macmillan, London.

Berry, L. G., Mason, B., & Dietrich, R. V. (1959). *Mineralogy* (2nd edn). Freeman, San Francisco.

Bolt, B. A. (1978). *Earthquakes: A Primer.* Freeman, San Francisco.

Brownlow, A. H. (1979). *Geochemistry.* Prentice-Hall, Englewood Cliffs, New Jersey

Bullard, F. M. (1976). *Volcanoes of the Earth.* University of Texas Press, Texas.

Carey, S. W. (1976). *The Expanding Earth.* University of Tasmania, Tasmania.

Charig, A. L. (1979). *A New Look at the Dinosaurs.* Heinemann, London.

Clarkson, E. N. K. (1979). *Invertebrate Palaeontology and Evolution,* Allen and Unwin, London.

Dent, D. & Young, A. (1981). *Soil Survey and Land Evaluation.* Allen and Unwin, London.

Eicher, D. L., McAlester, A. L. & Rottman, M. L. (1984). *The History of the Earth's Crust.* Prentice-Hall, Englewood Cliffs, New Jersey.

Elder, J. (1978). *The Bowels of the Earth.* Oxford University Press, Oxford.

Eldredge, N. & Cracraft, T. (1980). *Phylogenetic Patterns and the Evolutionary Process.* Columbia University Press, New York.

Fortey, R. A. (1982). *Fossils: the Key to the Past.* Heinemann, London.

Francis, P. (1979). *Volcanoes.* Penguin Books, London.

Glaessner, M. F. (1984). *The Dawn of Animal Life.* Cambridge University Press, Cambridge.

Goudie, A. (1982). *The Human Impact.* Basil Blackwell, Oxford.

Gribbin, J. (1978). *Climatic Change.* Cambridge University Press, Cambridge.

Hallam, A. (ed) (1977). *Patterns of Evolution as Illustrated by the Fossil Record.* Elsevier, Amsterdam.

Harland, W. B. et al. (1983). *A Geologic Time Scale.* Cambridge University Press, Cambridge.

Kemp, T. S. (1982). *Mammal-like Reptiles and the Origin of Mammals.* Academic Press, London.

Knill, J. (1979). *Industrial Geology.* Oxford University Press, Oxford.

Lane, N. G. (1978). *Life of the Past.* Merrill, Westerville.

McElhinny, M. W. (1973). *Palaeomagnetism and Plate Tectonics.* Cambridge University Press, Cambridge.

Menard, H. W. (1977). *Ocean Science.* Freeman, San Francisco.

Paul, C. (1980). *The Natural History of Fossils.* Weidenfeld and Nicolson, London.

Press, F. & Siever, R. (1982). *Earth* (3rd edn). Freeman, San Francisco.

Raup, D. M. & Jablonski, D. (eds) (1986). *Pattern and Process in the History of Life.* Springer-Verlag, Berlin.

Raup, D. M. & Stanley, S. M. (1978). *Principles of Palaeontology* (2nd edn). Freeman, San Francisco.

Savage, D. E. & Russell, D. E. (1983). *Mammalian Palaeofaunas of the World.* Addison-Wesley, Reading, Massachusetts.

Skinner, B. J. (1969). *Earth Resources.* Prentice-Hall, Englewood Cliffs, New Jersey.

Smith, D. G. (ed) (1981). *The Cambridge Encyclopedia of Earth Sciences.* Cambridge University Press, Cambridge.

Smith, P. J. (ed) (1986). *The Earth.* Macmillan, New York.

Stanley, S. M. (1986). *Earth and Life through Time.* Freeman, San Francisco.

Taylor, T. N. (1981). *Palaeobotany: An Introduction to Fossil Plant Biology.* McGraw-Hill, London.

van Andel, T. H. (1981). *Science at Sea – Tales of an Old Ocean.* Freeman, San Francisco.

Walker, J. G. C. (1978). *Evolution of the Atmosphere.* Macmillan, London.